"The PsychoSystems team at the University of Amsterdam has sparked a conceptual and methodological revolution in psychology. Their network approach to mental disorders is galvanizing our field, producing an urgent need for an accessible, user-friendly text for novices as well as for experienced researchers. Network Psychometrics with R is a splendid book that fulfills this need admirably. Importantly, the authors are seasoned teachers of network analysis, accustomed to introducing the approach to beginners in the field."

—Professor Richard McNally, Harvard University, USA

"This thorough introduction into all important details of network psychometrics, by a group of authors including many of the leading scientists in the field, fills an important lacuna in the literature. It is highly recommended for widespread use in teaching and applied research."

—Professor Peter Molenaar, Pennsylvania State University, USA

Network Psychometrics with R

A systematic, innovative introduction to the field of network analysis, *Network Psychometrics with R: A Guide for Behavioral and Social Scientists* provides a comprehensive overview of and guide to both the theoretical foundations of network psychometrics as well as modeling techniques developed from this perspective.

Written by pioneers in the field, this textbook showcases cutting-edge methods in an easily accessible format, accompanied by problem sets and code. After working through this book, readers will be able to understand the theoretical foundations behind network modeling, infer network topology, and estimate network parameters from different sources of data. This book features an introduction on the statistical programming language R that guides readers on how to analyze network structures and their stability using R. While *Network Psychometrics with R* is written in the context of social and behavioral science, the methods introduced in this book are widely applicable to data sets from related fields of study. Additionally, while the text is written in a non-technical manner, technical content is highlighted in textboxes for the interested reader.

Network Psychometrics with R is ideal for instructors and students of undergraduate and graduate level courses and workshops in the field of network psychometrics as well as established researchers looking to master new methods.

Adela-Maria Isvoranu is postdoctoral researcher of psychology at the University of Amsterdam.

Sacha Epskamp is assistant professor of psychology at the University of Amsterdam.

Lourens J. Waldorp is associate professor of psychology at the University of Amsterdam.

Denny Borsboom is professor of psychology at the University of Amsterdam.

Network Psychometrics with R

A Guide for Behavioral and Social Scientists

First Edition

Edited by:

Adela-Maria Isvoranu

Sacha Epskamp

Lourens J. Waldorp

Denny Borsboom

Cover image: alphacreative.des
First published 2022
by Routledge
2 Park Square, Milton Park, Abingdon, Oxon OX14 4RN

and by Routledge
605 Third Avenue, New York, NY 10158

Routledge is an imprint of the Taylor & Francis Group, an informa business

© 2022 selection and editorial matter, Adela-Maria Isvoranu, Sacha Epskamp, Lourens J. Waldorp, Denny Borsboom; individual chapters, the contributors

British Library Cataloguing-in-Publication Data
A catalogue record for this book is available from the British Library

Library of Congress Cataloging-in-Publication Data
A catalog record has been requested for this book

ISBN: 978-0-367-62876-5 (hbk)
ISBN: 978-0-367-61294-8 (pbk)
ISBN: 978-1-003-11123-8 (ebk)

DOI: 10.4324/9781003111238

Typeset in LaTeX
by Sacha Epskamp & Adela-Maria Isvoranu

Access the companion website:
http://www.routledge.com/cw/Isvoranu

Publisher's Note
This book has been prepared from camera-ready copy provided by the author

Contents

Preface

Adela-Maria Isvoranu[1], Sacha Epskamp[1,2], Lourens J. Waldorp[1], &
Denny Borsboom[1]

1. University of Amsterdam, Department of Psychology

2. University of Amsterdam, Centre for Urban Mental Health

Network psychometrics

This book is the result of a decade of research into the possibilities of using network approaches in the analysis of multivariate data, with specific applications in the realm of psychometric analysis. This approach originally arose from taking a network point of view, in which psychological constructs like depression, intelligence, and personality are conceptualized as systems in which elementary building blocks form a system of causally interacting components. This viewpoint naturally leads to the question of how data can be used to chart the systems in question. For instance, if a construct such as depression really is formed by interacting symptoms, how can we found out the structure of these interactions? How should we describe the construct as a network? How can we describe differences between the network components in an optimal fashion?

Network psychometrics, as discussed in this book, represents an approach designed to answer these questions systematically. It arises from the application of central themes of network thinking to systems of variables as typically encountered in psychometric applications. In this approach, network components are variables, while connections between these components are operationalized in terms of statistical relations between variables. Many technical and conceptual questions can be raised in the process, and these questions largely define the subject matter of network psychometrics: what statistical techniques should one use to determine relations between variables? How should one analyze the stability and replicability of networks? How do networks that represent relations between variables differ from networks that represent relations between concrete entities and does that matter for the interpretation of results?

This textbook aims to extensively cover these topics and provide a first comprehensive collection of materials explaining both the conceptual and methodological aspects network psychometrics, satisfying the increased demand from researchers and students for these materials. After working through this book, readers will be able to understand the theoretical foundations behind network modeling, infer network topology and estimate network parameters from different sources of data, and analyze the network structure and its stability.

Book description

This book is organized in four parts, each consisting of several chapters. The chapters contain conceptual explanations of research methods, with technical details explained in technical boxes and practical details explained in tutorial boxes. Each chapter is accompanied by a set of exercises. This section will explain each part of this setup in more detail.

Organization of the textbook

This textbook is organized into four broad parts:

I. **Network Science in R**. The first part provides the basic knowledge needed to understand and work through the remainder of this book. This includes theoretical foundations of network analysis, the programming background and skills necessary to independently carry out the practical exercises and analyses in R, chapters to introduce descriptive analyses of network structures and the fundamentals of constructing and drawing networks using R, as well as basic statistical knowledge about independence and conditional independence as central concepts in the estimation of psychometric network models.

II. **Estimating Undirected Network Models**. The second part focuses on estimating undirected networks, usually from cross-sectional data. The chapters introduce the reader to the class of statistical models most commonly used to infer network structures (i.e., pairwise Markov random fields), to the multitude of existing estimation methods, network comparison, as well as post-hoc stability and accuracy checks.

III. **Network Models for Longitudinal Data**. The third part moves the focus from cross-sectional data sets to data sets of one or more people measured repeatedly over time. In addition to discussing ways to estimate (time-varying) network models from longitudinal data, the chapters extensively discuss the difference between within- and between-subject effects and the generalizability of results based on cross-sectional data.

IV. **Theory and Causality**. The last part concludes the book with network approaches that explicitly go beyond statistically descriptive analysis tools. Two such approaches are discussed. First causal models, which represent causal relations between variables in directed acyclic graphs, and second Ising models, which are based on symmetric interactions between variables.

Technical details and tutorials

In order to cater to both a novice audience, as well as an audience with a more extensive statistical background, technical details such as formulas and advanced statistical details are included in light red text boxes across all chapters. The box below gives an example of what a technical box looks like throughout the text. The information provided in the technical boxes is not needed to understand the basic material and to be able to carry out the analyses in this textbook. Therefore, the reader can skip the technical boxes and only focus on the written material in the textbook.

> Technical boxes, such as this box, provide extra technical information that is complementary to the text in a chapter. Usually, this means that the technical box will give the mathematical description of what is explained in the main text conceptually. The contents of the technical boxes are not required to be read while working through the book.

Example of a technical box.

The conceptual explanation of the methods discussed throughout this book goes hand in hand with practical applications of the methods. To this end, tutorial boxes, displayed in the same style as technical boxes, but in cyan, contain code examples and tutorials explaining how the methods can be used. These boxes are useful for all readers and provide tips and details on how to carry out analyses, what functions to use, and so forth. We recommend all readers to make use of these text boxes. Of note, the tutorial boxes will focus on the implementation of the methods in R. The methods discussed in the chapter, however, are not limited per se to R and could also be implemented in other programming languages. The content of the tutorial boxes is therefore more specific (application in certain R packages) than the content of the chapters themselves (general description of the methods).

> Tutorial boxes, such as this one, contain code examples and tutorials on how the methods discussed throughout this book can be applied. Usually, these boxes will contain R code examples, explaining the main uses of certain R packages and functions.

Example of a tutorial box.

Exercises

Each chapter is accompanied by theoretical and practical exercises. At the end of each chapter, the reader is provided with open-end questions that encourage thinking more in-depth about the concepts learned, as well as with true/false statements to assess familiarity with the chapter's main content. For several chapters, practical exercises are available in the appropriate folder of each chapter, available on the online *Companion Website*.

About the authors

This book is the result of a collaboration of several authors that stood at the forefront of the development of network psychometrics in the past decade. The book was edited by four main editors:

- **Adela-Maria Isvoranu** is postdoctoral researcher of psychology at the University of Amsterdam. She has been at the forefront of applying complex systems thinking to the study of mental health, in an aim to understand and combat psychological disorders. She organized and taught workshops on network psychometrics across the globe.

- **Sacha Epskamp** is assistant professor of psychology at the University of Amsterdam. He has pioneered the field of Network Psychometrics through both novel methodological research, as well as by developing several software packages implementing the methods discussed in this book.

- **Lourens J. Waldorp** is associate professor of psychology at the University of Amsterdam. He has worked on a variety of theoretical and applied topics in the analysis of multivariate data, and was at the forefront of the development of network modeling techniques for psychology.

- **Denny Borsboom** is professor of psychology at the University of Amsterdam. His work has included conceptual analyses of psychometric models, development of psychological theory, and construction of network models in psychology. He is the founder of the Psychosystems Project, which pioneered network approaches to the analysis of multivariate data.

For each chapter, a lead author was invited to provide a chapter along with co-authors. In addition to the editors, who also authored several of the chapters, the lead authors consisted of Gabriela Lunansky, Marie K. Deserno, Tessa F. Blanken, Eiko I. Fried, Julian Burger, Jonas M. B. Haslbeck, Fabian Dablander, and Jonas Dalege. In addition to the editors and lead authors described above, who also co-authored several chapters, co-authors on the chapters included Angélique O. J. Cramer, Donald J. Robinaugh, Myrthe Veenman, Claudia D. van Borkulo, Ria H. A. Hoekstra, Alessandra C. Mansueto, Oisín Ryan, Han L. J. van der Maas, Riet van Bork, and Maarten Marsman. Finally, Sara Mehrhof aided in finalizing the book.

ORCID iDs authors

- Adela-Maria Isvoranu: https://orcid.org/0000-0001-7981-9198
- Sacha Epskamp: https://orcid.org/0000-0003-4884-8118
- Lourens J. Waldorp: https://orcid.org/0000-0002-5941-4625
- Denny Borsboom: https://orcid.org/0000-0001-9720-4162
- Gabriela Lunansky: https://orcid.org/0000-0001-6226-2258
- Marie K. Deserno: https://orcid.org/0000-0002-7187-7569
- Tessa F. Blanken: https://orcid.org/0000-0003-1731-0251
- Eiko I. Fried: https://orcid.org/0000-0001-7469-594X
- Julian Burger: https://orcid.org/0000-0001-8177-788X
- Jonas M. B. Haslbeck: https://orcid.org/0000-0001-9096-7837
- Fabian Dablander: https://orcid.org/0000-0003-2650-6491
- Jonas Dalege: https://orcid.org/0000-0002-1844-0528
- Angélique O. J. Cramer: https://orcid.org/0000-0003-2128-0331
- Donald J. Robinaugh: https://orcid.org/0000-0002-5579-7518
- Myrthe Veenman: https://orcid.org/0000-0001-5190-8383
- Claudia D. van Borkulo: https://orcid.org/0000-0003-2214-4438
- Ria H. A. Hoekstra: https://orcid.org/0000-0003-2997-0556
- Alessandra C. Mansueto: https://orcid.org/0000-0003-4156-0031
- Oisín Ryan: https://orcid.org/0000-0003-3698-6396
- Han L. J. van der Maas: https://orcid.org/0000-0001-8278-319X
- Riet van Bork: https://orcid.org/0000-0002-4772-8862
- Maarten Marsman: https://orcid.org/0000-0001-5309-7502

Part I

Network Science in R

Chapter 1

Network Perspectives

Denny Borsboom[1], Angélique O. J. Cramer[2], Eiko I. Fried[3], Adela-Maria Isvoranu[1], Donald J. Robinaugh[4,5], Jonas Dalege[6], & Han L. J. van der Maas[1]

1. University of Amsterdam, Department of Psychology

2. National Institute of Public Health and the Environment

3. Leiden University, Department of Psychology

4. Massachusetts General Hospital, Department of Psychiatry

5. Harvard Medical School

6. Santa Fe Institute

1.1   Introduction

The application of network thinking to psychometric questions has led to an eruption of network approaches in several subfields of psychology, most notably clinical psychology and psychiatry (Robinaugh et al., 2020) where the idea that mental disorders are composed of interactions between components (symptoms or other problems) in a multifactorial system is plausible (Kendler et al., 2011). In many such cases, the statistical application of network models to empirical data is motivated by theoretical concerns: substantive considerations that render the conceptualization of a construct as a network plausible (e.g., because causal connections between relevant variables stand to reason; Cramer et al., 2010; Dalege et al., 2016; Isvoranu et al., 2016; Lange et al., 2020). This entanglement of statistical modeling and substantive concerns is typical of the network literature, and

Cite this chapter as:

> Borsboom, D., Cramer, A. O. J., Fried, E. I., Isvoranu, A. M., Robinaugh, D. J., Dalege, J., & van der Maas, H. L. J. (2022). Chapter 1. Network perspectives. In Isvoranu, A. M., Epskamp, S., Waldorp, L. J., & Borsboom, D. (Eds.). *Network psychometrics with R: guide for behavioral and social scientists*. Routledge, Taylor & Francis Group.

arguably in part responsible for its success: the combination of systems thinking with methodological tools to analyze empirical data are important drives behind the popularity of network approaches. However, the close relation between substance and statistics can also lead to problems, because the distinctions between statistical, conceptual, substantive issues are not always clear. Thus, one may unwittingly mistake conceptual questions for statistical ones, or statistical questions for substantive ones, which may hamper progress. The present chapter aims to make the distinction between substantive network theories and statistical network models explicit, and to discuss ways in which they can be connected.

Consider the network approach to psychopathology. Network theory posits that symptoms of psychopathology are causally related (i.e., activating one symptom increases the likelihood of connected symptoms to arise; Borsboom et al., 2017). However, this is not an assumption that underlies the estimation of the popular pairwise Markov random field (PMRF) as explained in Chapter 6. The assumptions of the estimation procedure are purely statistical and hold only that the joint probability distribution can be described by a set of main effects (node thresholds) and pairwise interactions (edges). Because the network theory and the network model are not equivalent, it is important not to confuse assumptions of one for assumptions of the other. Such confusion arises, for instance, when researchers think that application of the network model requires that the network theory is true. This is incorrect: the PMRF, as network *model* can be successfully estimated in situations where the network *theory* is false; for instance, when all dependencies in the data arise from a latent common cause rather than from causal interactions between components (Fried, 2020; Marsman et al., 2017). In this case, mistaking theoretical assumptions for statistical ones may inadvertently hold back the researcher, who may incorrectly think that it is unjustified to apply a network model in cases where relations between network components are not causal in nature. The converse problem arises when researchers think that the successful application of network models indicates that network theory is true. This is incorrect because the network model only contains statistical relations, and the interpretation of such relations in terms of causality requires a stronger inference than data analysis by itself can provide (i.e., one has to provide causal assumptions as well; Pearl, 2010). Interpretation of network results in terms of network theory may, in such cases, overstep the evidence (Bringmann et al., 2019; Epskamp et al., 2017; Fried, 2020).

For these reasons, it is crucial that the student of network analysis learns to distinguish between different ways in which network thinking can be applied, and to get a clear view of the distinctions between theory and statistical modeling. This chapter aims to clarify these distinctions by discussing three ways in which network thinking may be methodologically useful. First, we discuss network approaches, which simply entails 'viewing' a construct as a network of interacting components as a way of developing one's thinking and creating new ways to understand and investigate the construct. Second, we describe psychometric network models (hereafter, referred to simply as network models): systems of statistical relations between variables defined on empirical data. Third, we describe network theory, where both the components of the system and their connections are substantively interpreted and specified, so that they are able to explain characteristic phenomena involving the construct. We then discuss how these conceptualizations of networks are related, identifying network models and network theory as specializations under the rubric of a network approach that, ideally, serve to inform one another. Finally, we analyze a number of strategies that have been applied to connect network theory and network models.

1.2 Network approaches

The network approach to a given empirical domain simply entails conceptualizing that domain as a network: that is, as a set of components and the relationships among those components. Central to this approach, which others have referred to as 'systems thinking,' is the notion that network behavior is closely tied to network structure (Meadows, 2008). The network approach often entails conceptualizing a given phenomena of interest as an emergent property, with the components of a network 'working together' to generate emergent phenomena that feature surprising levels of organization (Barabási, 2012; Wright & Meadows, 2012). For example, consider the complex and seemingly highly organized behavior exhibited by a flock of birds. A network approach conceptualizes such behavior as an emergent property arising from the interrelationships among the individual birds that constitute the flock. This same lens can be applied to numerous empirical domains. For example, we can apply it in the domain of psychiatry, considering whether the behavioral characteristic of the depression syndrome (i.e., chronically elevated depression symptoms) might arise from interrelationships among the components of the syndrome (i.e., the symptoms themselves). This process can be facilitated using *analogical abduction* (Haig, 2014): establishing a systematic correspondences between a source domain (e.g., a flock of birds) and a target domain (e.g., a set of depression symptoms) so that one can use explanatory models from the source (e.g., flocking models that explain why flight courses of birds are correlated) to better understand phenomena in the target (e.g., symptom network models that explain why depression symptoms are correlated). Indeed, because similar features are consistently observed across networks taken from a wide range of empirical domains, the network approach provides fertile ground for productive analogical abduction (Barabási, 2012; Scheffer, 2020).

When one is initially considering the viability of network approaches, it is useful to consider the applicability of its central concepts. Can one identify at least some of the important components and links between them? Do these components behave as a coherent whole? Do the links between them offer *prima facie* plausible explanatory resources, in the sense that a network structure would 'make sense' of a given behavior or pattern of findings (e.g., correlations in one's data)? Do we see synchronized behavior that may emerge out of a network structure? Are there signs that the system shows behavior commonly exhibited in complex systems, such as non-linear behavior in which there are sudden changes in the state of the system (Scheffer, 2020)? Systematically investigating such questions can help in assessing whether a network approach is plausible and worth pursuing (Fried & Robinaugh, 2020).

If these or other initial considerations suggest the network approach may be a suitable conceptual framework, the researcher can put on a pair of network glasses and start exploring whether network science may offer further possibilities. When embarking on such a discovery process, one typically does not make a particular choice on exactly

which components are in play or how they work together; rather the researcher chooses
to view an empirical domain through the 'lens' of networks. Thus, network approaches
usually do not single out precisely which factors act as components in the system at
the outset, nor do they typically specify precisely how they interact. Instead, these are
thought of as open questions worthy of discussion and research. For example, in the
network approach to psychopathology, symptoms enumerated in diagnostic criteria for
a given disorder were put forward as possible components of the network structure.
However, it has subsequently been argued that this viewpoint may be too narrow and
that other components should be included as well (Fried & Cramer, 2017; Jones et al.,
2017). Similarly, in the mutualism model of intelligence, interactions between cognitive
processes were posited (van der Maas et al., 2006), but the processes themselves were
not directly identified. In both these examples, network approaches were initially 'open';
with the components and links between them subject to discussion and research.

As one is considering which components may be present in the network and how they
may relate to one another, it is important to recognize that the nature of components
and links is not uniform across empirical domains. Indeed, in network science we see a
diverse set of network components: organizations, species, actors, neurons, computers,
geographical areas, and medical diseases, to name only a few. There is similar diversity
in the connections between these components, with links defined by e.g., financial loans
(between organizations), competition (between species), co-occurrence (between actors
in movies), physical connections (axons connecting neurons), information exchange
(between computers), travel (between geographical areas), and comorbidity (between
psychopathological conditions or medical diseases). Thus, it is important to realize that
network approaches do not require a particular physical structure, but rather require the
applicability of a mode of representation, and therefore the question whether a domain
'really is' a network is often moot. The reason that network approaches are so generative
and interesting is precisely that they can apply to different systems in different ways.

1.3   Network models

If a network approach to an empirical domain is taken, the researcher will arrive at a
(possibly rough) idea of which components would plausibly feature in a network. A
natural next step is to assess which of these components are linked. In some cases, one can
observe network relations directly (e.g., in traditional social networks, friendship links
between individuals are typically treated as 'observed'). In other cases, links between
nodes can be assessed on the basis of prior research. For instance, Wittenborn et al.
(2016) constructed a network model for depression based on existing knowledge about
relations between relevant components. However, in many cases connections are not
directly observable and existing research is insufficient to assess whether links are present.
In such cases, one can assess how relevant components covary empirically. It is for this
purpose that *network models* are especially useful.

Network models are statistical structures that characterize a multivariate probability
distribution as a network. In a network model, nodes represent *variables* and links
between nodes represent *statistical relations* between these variables. Note that variables

are typically abstract entities, not concrete things, and statistical relations are estimated, not observed. In this sense, network models as used in the approach covered in this book are different from, for instance, social networks in which network nodes represent concrete individuals and relations between individuals are typically observable (or treated as such).

The simplest way of assessing the network structure in a set of variables is to simply calculate correlation coefficients between variables, and interpret these as (weighted) links between nodes (Epskamp et al., 2012). However, a downside of this approach is that, *if* data are indeed generated from a network of pairwise interactions, the correlation matrix will include many spurious links. For instance, if variables A and C are linked through B, but not directly, a correlation between A and C will nevertheless be observed. A solution to this problem is to calculate the correlation between A and C while conditioning on ('controlling for') B. This approach will correctly return the network structure, because the correlation between A and C will vanish (van Borkulo et al., 2014). Generalizing this idea, one can compute the association between any two variables while conditioning on all other variables in the data. This then returns an estimate of the PMRF (see Chapter 6). In such a PMRF, the absence of a link between nodes represents conditional independence between the corresponding variables and the presence of an edge represents conditional dependence. These PMRF models, also known as graphical models in the field of statistics (Cox & Wermuth, 2014), are the type of network model used most often in this book.

Like any statistical model, network psychometric models are generic: they are not about any given substantive phenomena but rather are tools for representing patterns in data. Because these models are generic, they are not about any empirical application in particular. This is obvious from the fact that PMRFs, for instance, have been used in a wide range of research domains, ranging from physics to neuroimaging all the way to clinical psychology. This generality makes network models useful because it allows researchers to construct software that can estimate network models across many different contexts. However, it also means that the interpretation of statistical network models in terms of an empirical domain requires assumptions. For instance, if one wants to interpret the model in terms of causal relations between network components, this requires one to buy into a nontrivial set of assumptions about the data-generating process. One has to be prepared to assume that measurements of the components have sufficient reliability and validity, that causal relations between components are indeed bidirectional and symmetric, and that one has succeeded in capturing the most important components of the network in one's data. Thus, the interpretation of psychometric networks in terms of conditional associations relies only on statistical model adequacy, but the interpretation that such networks represent the targeted attributes and causal relations between them requires additional assumptions of a theoretical nature.

The application of network models shows which variables are so strongly associated that the association cannot be explained away by other variables in the data, which yields an exploratory approach to detecting network structures. Models that operate in this way have become popular in recent years (Robinaugh et al., 2020); here, we highlight examples of how network models can characterize and visualize patterns of dependency in multivariate data, focusing specifically on the network approach to psychopathology.

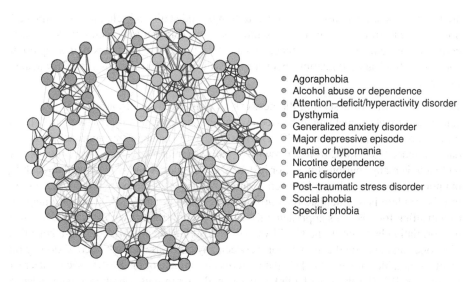

- Agoraphobia
- Alcohol abuse or dependence
- Attention–deficit/hyperactivity disorder
- Dysthymia
- Generalized anxiety disorder
- Major depressive episode
- Mania or hypomania
- Nicotine dependence
- Panic disorder
- Post–traumatic stress disorder
- Social phobia
- Specific phobia

Figure 1.1. DSM-IV symptomatology network structure, adapted from Boschloo et al. (2015).

First, network models have been used to assess the structure of psychopathology networks. An example of this approach is given in Figure 1.1, which displays a network of symptoms defined in the Diagnostic and Statistical Manual of Mental Disorders (DSM-IV, as estimated on a large U.S. community sample; Boschloo et al., 2015). As is evident from the figure, the great majority of symptoms feature positive pairwise interactions (i.e., the presence of symptoms increases the probability of connected symptoms, when controlling for the remaining variables). In addition, the figure shows that symptoms of the same disorder cluster more strongly, while these clusters are not neatly separated (i.e., symptoms between different disorders are conditionally associated). This is consistent with (but does not prove) the idea that comorbidity between disorders may arise through causal connections that cross-cut the borders separating different disorders in systems such as the DSM.

Second, network models have been used to study relations between psychopathology symptoms and external factors (Isvoranu et al., 2016). An example concerns the relation between child abuse and psychotic disorders. Figure 1.2 displays the network of psychotic symptoms (e.g., hallucinations, flat affect), general psychopathology symptoms (e.g., depressed mood, anxiety), and childhood trauma (e.g., sexual abuse, emotional neglect). The network shows all types of trauma are linked to positive and negative symptoms of psychosis through general psychopathology, suggesting general psychopathology symptoms as potential mediators between trauma and psychosis. This aligns well with research showing childhood trauma is connected to a wide array of symptoms present across many mental conditions, and is thus not specific to psychotic symptoms. Further, the trauma nodes themselves are highly interconnected, indicating that the effects of trauma to symptoms can also occur via other types of trauma. Overall, network models including external factors can provide information on how such external factors relate to each other, as well as give insight into potential pathways to a disorder state.

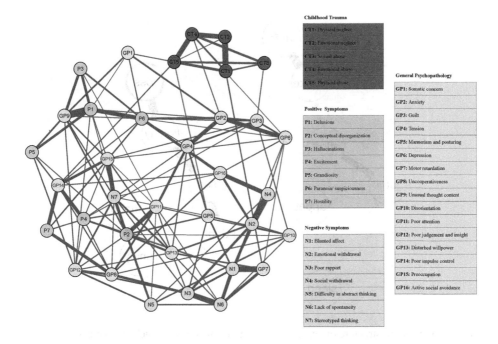

Figure 1.2. Network structure of positive and negative psychotic symptoms, general psychopathology symptoms, and factors involving childhood trauma, adapted from Isvoranu et al. (2016).

Third, network models have been used to examine relations between external shocks and psychopathology. For example, Figure 1.3 shows the relation between the loss of a spouse and a number of symptoms of depression (Fried et al., 2015). The analysis is suggestive of an indirect effect of losing one's spouse on depressive symptoms through feelings of loneliness. Thus, this type of application can lead to hypotheses on the way external shocks may impact the network, which can in turn inform theory formation and further empirical research.

In each of these examples, the application of network models sheds light on the structure of psychopathology networks and the possible ways in which they are influenced by external factors. By constructing such representations, researchers can inform the network approach taken through empirical data analysis. Network models are useful because they can function to inform the researcher with respect to the generic features of the network structure (e.g., is the network dense or sparse?), the position of particular nodes in that structure (e.g., central versus peripheral nodes), and the places in the network that are likely to be perturbed by particular external events (e.g., which variables in the network connect to external shocks?).

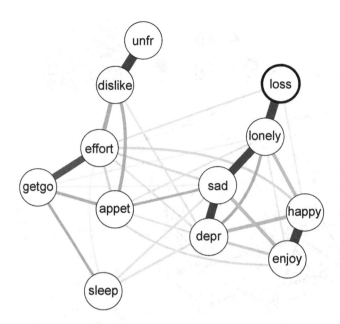

Figure 1.3. Network structure of depression symptoms, feelings of loneliness, and spousal loss, adapted from Fried et al. (2015).

It is important to note that statistical models have limitations. First, it is notoriously hard to establish causal relations from statistical models, especially in quasi-experimental and correlational settings (see also Chapter 12). Thus, although PMRFs may be suggestive of causal structure, they do not establish causal relations directly. Second, although in some circumstances network models *can* correctly estimate networks *if* the data are generated by a particular network model, this does not mean that the application of a network model *will* correctly estimate a generating network in general. For example, it is possible that the links between childhood trauma and psychotic symptoms in Figure 1.2 reflect the operation of an unmodeled common cause (e.g., a genetic disposition that increases both the likelihood of trauma and the likelihood of psychotic symptoms). Third, network models are often explorative statistical tools that try to optimize a search through a very large model space. In general, this means that modeling results should be viewed as hypothesis generating, so that independent research is generally needed to test the hypotheses suggested by the network model. Thus, exploratory uses of network models generate hypotheses, which open up a line of research, rather than firm conclusions that confirm a theory.

In sum, network models are explorative tools that can serve to chart the rough outlines of a network based on empirical data. This renders them highly useful for informing network approaches empirically. By conjoining such empirical results with theoretical considerations, network approaches can gradually become better informed and as such can form the groundwork for building network theories.

1.4 Network theories

Network theories specify a set of components and interactions among components and posit that the resultant network can explain a phenomenon of interest. Network theories are distinguished from simply adopting a network approach by the specification of components and inter-component relationships in the network and by the presence of falsifiable conditions. In other words, whereas the network approach is a lens through which to view a construct of interest, a network theory goes further: it posits what the relevant entities in the network are, it posits how they interact, and, in doing so, it makes predictions that can be corroborated or falsified.

For example, a network approach to depression would entail looking at depression as a system of components and considering whether those components may work together to produce depression akin to the way in which individual birds interact to produce flocking behavior. Such a network approach may offer a tentative set of components and a rough idea of the relations between them, but these are typically sketchy and open-ended. For this reason, network approaches have no clear falsification conditions; they represent a theoretical perspective, rather than a theory. A network theory goes further: it identifies what the relevant entities in the system are and how they interact. These specifications are made by identifying the component set (i.e., deciding which components to include in the network), the type of interaction between components (i.e., specifying what the links in the network represent), and the phenomena to be explained by the theory. The greater the specificity with which the components and inter-component relationships are expressed, the better equipped theorists will be to determine precisely what behavior is predicted by the theory and, thus, the better equipped they will be to determine whether the theory can indeed account for the phenomena of interest. For example, in the context of depression, a very simple kind of network theory could state that depression arises from instantaneous pairwise causal interactions among DSM-5 symptoms. This theory generates an *interpreted* network structure: rather than being an abstract conceptual framework or a statistical model for a data set, the network structure now aims to represent particular entities (DSM-5 symptoms) and their interactions (i.e., causal ones). To strengthen this theory, one can go further, identifying the functional form of those interactions (e.g., linear or nonlinear) and time scale on which they take place (e.g., minutes, days, years). By doing so, theorists can evaluate whether the network theory can indeed account for the core phenomena of interest in depression research: the tendency for depression symptoms to cohere and persist as a syndrome in some individuals.

Naturally, while this step of model interpretation is an important phase towards the construction of a theory, it does not magically render an *adequate* theory. For instance, as previously noted, DSM-5 symptoms may not be optimal components (Fried, 2020; Jones et al., 2017) and several of the observed correlations between them may not be causal but reflect, for instance, semantic overlap or the influence of unmodeled common causes (Fried & Cramer, 2017). Here again, it is important to note that many different choices are possible in the identification of component sets and interactions. For example, the mutualism theory in intelligence research is also a network theory, but it has an entirely different set of components (cognitive processes and abilities) as well as a different type of interactions (mutualistically coupled growth rather than direct causal interaction).

Network theories are often used to explain particular types of empirical phenomena, such as correlation structures, bimodality, and hysteresis. We will examine some of these explanations in detail. First, a network theory of general intelligence has been proposed in van der Maas et al. (2006). The main phenomenon in the study of individual differences in intelligence is the so-called positive manifold, which is the well replicated fact that scores on sub-tests of intelligence tests tend to correlate positively. This phenomenon is traditionally explained by a general factor, which suffices from a statistical point of view in describing the data but lacks a generally accepted substantial interpretation. In the mutualism model, the positive manifold is explained by positive reciprocal interactions between many different cognitive functions during cognitive development. There is ample evidence for such interactions, of which only a few weak ones are needed to lead to the positive manifold data found in intelligence research (van der Maas et al., 2019). The mathematical model is simple. Cognitive functions grow logistically until some limited capacity. The speed of growth and the capacity are strengthened by mutual interactions. van der Maas et al. (2006) also proposed to add a simple linear model for the genetic and environmental effect on the limited capacities, such that the heritability of intelligence could be modeled. Interestingly, this addition to the model naturally leads to an increase of heritability with age, an important finding in genetic studies of intelligence (Haworth et al., 2010).

Second, the network theory of psychopathology (Borsboom et al., 2017) identifies the nodes in the network as clinical symptoms as encoded in diagnostic manuals like the DSM-5. The links between nodes are interpreted as (possibly, but not necessarily) reciprocal causal relations, such that connected symptoms may activate each other. For some disorders, such as panic disorder, such relations have been explicated in some detail (Robinaugh et al., 2019), while for others they remain sketchy. Similar to the mutualism case, this theoretical interpretation naturally explains the fact that psychopathology symptoms form a positive manifold (Caspi et al., 2014; van Bork et al., 2017). In addition, the theory is consistent with the presence of extensive comorbidity between disorders, as symptoms that belong to multiple disorders may act as bridge symptoms that transfer activation from one problem area to another (Cramer et al., 2010). Finally, the theory offers a potential explanation of the onset and maintenance of mental disorders. For instance, Cramer et al. (2016) found that strongly connected networks, in which symptoms easily activate each other, potentially generate sudden transitions into a disorder state, in which they can get stuck due to a hysteresis effect. This naturally leads to the conjecture that mental disorders *are* stable states of symptom activation in strongly connected symptom networks (Borsboom et al., 2017).

Third, a network theory of attitude dynamics has been proposed in Dalege et al. (2016, 2018). This network theory of attitudes relies on the central principle that pairwise interactions between affective, cognitive, and behavioral attitude elements increase when individuals pay direct attention to the attitude object and when the attitude is important to the individual. As is discussed in detail in Chapter 13, this principle explains several well-established findings in the attitude literature. For example, heightened interactions between attitude elements lead to a more extreme attitude, because all attitude elements are pressured to assume the same state. This process provides a mechanistic explanation for the finding that attitudes become more extreme when individuals think about their attitudes (Tesser, 1978).

As these examples illustrate, network theories are explanatory structures aimed at improving our understanding of empirical domains. If successful, this increased understanding may contribute to improved prediction and control. For example, in the case of psychopathology, this would imply the development of better treatments; in the case of attitudes, better instruments of persuasion. Therefore, the construction of network theories is an activity with a deeply practical goal; namely, that of increasing both our understanding of complex multivariate processes and our ability to execute controlled interventions on these processes.

1.5 Relations between network approaches, models, and theories

The fact that network approaches, network models, and network theories are rarely separated neatly has the potential to generate confusion, because it is not always clear how they relate to each other. This problem has been exacerbated by the fact that the term 'network model' has been used to describe all three domains we list here: (a) a broad conceptual network model, (b) a psychometric network model, and (c) a theoretical network model. This section outlines how we can think about the relations among these three domains.

The relation between network approaches on the one hand, and network theories and network models on the other, is relatively straightforward: network approaches define an overarching category, and then further *specialize* into network theories and into network models. A very large set of phenomena can be viewed through the lens of networks, systems science, or complexity science. Nested within these approaches are numerous theories, and the methodological network toolbox in turn comprises many statistical models that lend themselves well to investigate phenomena as networks.

On its surface, the relation between network models and network theories is similarly straightforward. Network models are representations of one's data. In contrast, network theories are representations of the real-world components that one believes give rise to a phenomenon of interest. However, when we interrogate this relationship further and consider how network models can best inform, or even serve as the basis for network theories, things become less clear. There are two broad viewpoints we can consider on this matter.

The first viewpoint posits that one can view the relation between models and theories as direct. Here the transition from network model to network theory is simply an act of interpretation, interpreting the network model as a representation of the real-world system of interest. For example, if we fit a PMRF to the data of the DSM-5 depression symptoms assessed once in a sample of depressed patients, we will obtain statistical relations among these symptoms. We may find, for instance, that 'loss of energy' shows the strongest relations to all other symptoms (or, in network science terminology, has the highest centrality). If we assume the statistical and theoretical models coincide, we can interpret the statistical model *as* a theoretical model, treating the structure of the model as the causal structure of our real-world network of interest. This interpretation, in turn, implies that loss of energy is the most obvious treatment target: the symptom has the largest number of connections; connections are causal relations, according to network theory; hence a successful intervention on loss of energy (i.e., one that persists in deactivating the symptom) should not only alleviate this problem, but also improve connected symptoms.

The direct interpretation of statistical models as theoretical models can be useful in situations where one wants to study the properties that a model could have but has no idea on how to parameterize it. For instance, Borsboom et al. (2011) filled in network relations gleaned from DSM-IV symptom overlap with parameters taken from statistical regression modeling to investigate whether such a model could explain comorbidity patterns (it could). Similarly, Cramer et al. (2016) used an Ising model (see Chapter 6 and Chapter 13) to investigate whether such a model could exhibit hysteresis effects (it did). As a proof-of-principle, they are highly useful because they show that certain phenomena are within the reach of the explanatory model and specify targets for further investigation.

However, a significant number of obstacles must be overcome to justify accepting such a model as a valid description of reality, rather than as a proof-of-principle, which we refer to as an inference gap between statistical and the theoretical domains (Fried, 2020). Broadly speaking, inferences follow from assumptions, and the assumptions for the above type of model are both numerous and implausible. We list but a few here. First, one must assume that a network process generated the data in the first place, yet there are numerous alternative causal mechanisms that can give rise to data that, if analyzed with network models, produce a network—a problem known as statistical equivalence (Fried, 2020; van Bork et al., 2021). More fundamentally, just because one can fit a regression line through the joint distribution of two variables does not mean the resulting coefficient represents a meaningful causal effect, whether in network models or any other statistical model. Second, one must assume that the undirected edges of the PMRFs indicate bidirectional and symmetric causal relationships. However, an undirected edge in a PMRF could arise from a variety of sources. For example, loss of energy could be the causal endpoint of all other symptoms it is connected to, rather than a causal origin. If this were the case, interventions on such a causal endpoint should not be expected to propagate through the system at all. Third, one must assume that the network model estimated from data of multiple people measured once coincides with the within-person structure of causal relationships among depression symptoms. However, this assumption holds under circumstances unlikely to be observed in psychological research (Molenaar, 2004; further discussed in Chapter 9). Further, there is reason to believe that network processes differ (at least to some degree) across people with depression, which would mean that the estimated network structure at the between-subjects level may not be informative about interventions at the individual level (Fisher et al., 2018; Fisher et al., 2017; Fried & Robinaugh, 2020; Henry et al., 2021). Fourth, the PMRF used in the above example estimates linear, pairwise relations. If more complicated processes are part of the data generating structure, such as non-linear dynamics or higher-order interactions, the estimated structure will be biased or incorrect (Haslbeck et al., 2021). Many further assumptions, are described in detail elsewhere (Fried, 2020; Haslbeck et al., 2021; Robinaugh et al., 2020). Drawing inferences from network models thus requires spelling out the auxiliary assumptions a researcher brings to the table that are necessary to make these inferences work. Doing so transparently enables readers to vet whether the assumptions are sufficiently plausible to warrant the conclusions.

The second viewpoint on the network model-network theory relationship posits that the relationship is indirect. From this perspective, the network model is seen as an 'intermediary' between the theory and the empirical data: a data model that organizes multivariate dependencies in an optimal way for network theories to latch onto. Network models provide rich information that serves to inform and constrain the development of network theories, but the theories have a structure that is independent to that of the network model and may include features (e.g., asymmetric and non-linear relationships) not present in the network model. If the theory is able to explain the observed network model derived from empirical data, our confidence in the theory is strengthened. If it fails, we can reason about the best explanation for this explanatory failure, and use this abductive inference to guide improvements to the theory that bring it in line with the network model and other findings from empirical research.

The advantage of the second viewpoint is that it does not require adherence to assumptions that may be implausible in a given domain, such as those reviewed above. The challenge in this perspective is that the systems that give rise to psychometric constructs like intelligence, personality traits, or mental disorders are almost certainly highly complex and heterogeneous biopsychosocial systems whose structure is extremely resistant to discovery. Indeed, a precise and detailed explication of these systems may not be feasible, at least in coming years. This, in our view, does not diminish the role that theories must play in our efforts to unravel the complex systems that give rise to psychopathology. To the contrary, we believe this difficulty elevates the importance of theories. Efforts to simply uncover the structure of such highly complex systems from data models alone will be especially (indeed, perhaps prohibitively) difficult. The key, in our view, is in leveraging the advantages of theories and data models that, by themselves are limited, but can serve to inform and advance one another over time. To illustrate, consider the role of smoking and lung cancer. The statistical relation between smoking and lung cancer, first observed in cross-sectional data and estimated via simple statistical models such as linear regression, did not provide insights into mechanisms, and did not perfectly capture individual relations between the constructs. It failed to take complex interactions with many moderating factors into account. Nonetheless, it was crucial for our research into the causal mechanisms that govern the relationship and the development of theories that could explain this association. Newton's theory of universal gravitation is another example. Newton's theory describes and predicts the motion of the planets in our solar system well, but has important explanatory failures in special cases, e.g., when strong gravitational fields and small distances come together. Because these explanatory shortcomings were clear, a path for improvement was clear and Newton's theory was eventually superseded by Einstein's theory of general relativity, which more accurately explains planetary motion in these special cases. In this way, Newton's theory was not the final word, but a critical stepping stone toward a theory that could provide a more comprehensive account of the known phenomena. Analogously, initial network theories developed to account for robustly observed network models and other empirical phenomena are all but guaranteed to have important explanatory shortcomings, but can hopefully lay the groundwork for better empirical research and stronger network theories that address these shortcomings. For example, an initial network theory of panic attacks introduced in Robinaugh et al. (2019) will not be the final theory of this phenomenon, but provides a starting point to evaluate what the theory can explain and what it cannot, thereby enabling further theory development and identifying empirical research that must be conducted if we are to further inform the theory.

The direct and indirect paths to connect network theories to network models have somewhat distinct implications for how to proceed in applying the network approach to a given empirical domain. If one is sufficiently confident that one has access to the important nodes in the system, and prepared to assume that the relations between them indeed reflect symmetric causal interactions, then the direct interpretation of the statistical model can be feasible and may be preferable. In such cases, a well-developed theory requires only a well-executed empirical research effort in which a set of components are rigorously measured and the structure of relationships among them is robustly estimated. Even in cases where the assumptions required for direct inference are violated, however, it may be that these methods provide a sufficiently faithful representation of the real-world network that it can be useful for advancing our understanding of that network and informing our ability to predict its behavior and intervene upon it; for instance, by providing 'toy models' that can reveal interesting possibilities for further modeling and research. This direct route then emphasizes the importance of rigorous data collection, precise estimation of network models, and research evaluating how well the inferences made from these models can give us purchase in understanding, predicting, and controlling the phenomena that arise from that network. With improvements in network data collection procedures and in the network model methodological toolbox, this direct route may become increasingly plausible.

The indirect path to connect network theories to network models calls for a somewhat different approach, arguing that practical, ethical, and technical limitations may render the prospect of data and models that can directly estimate the causal system unrealistic. In this case, the route forward may not lie primarily in data and model improvements, but in establishing phenomena that are sufficiently robust against model misspecifications and data problems that they can serve as explanatory targets with which to inform and validate theories. For example, we may never gather data good enough to distinguish between different functional forms for the relation between, say, insomnia and depressed mood (e.g., linear, logistic, power functions, etc.) but the fact remains that, whatever form we choose, they remain positively associated. Thus, at a higher level of abstraction, robust phenomena can be identified even if their precise details remain obscure. These phenomena can be represented in many different data models, including networks (Haslbeck et al., 2021) and the challenge of moving from network models to network theory lies in the construction of plausible theoretical models that are able to account for these (Borsboom et al., 2021). Thus, this route towards improvement relies on robustness analyses and theoretical progress. The challenge for this indirect path will be to determine whether these more precise efforts at theory specification can improve upon the insights we can gain from the rough but more accessible direct path of treating network models themselves as theories. In other words, for both the indirect and direct paths, the ultimate arbiter of success will be whether these theories are able to support the pragmatic aims of explaining, predicting, and controlling the phenomena of interest. Because it is likely to be a longer and more resource intensive process, it will be incumbent on those taking this indirect path to demonstrate the added value it provides in moving toward these practical aims.

Naturally, the two routes sketched here are not mutually exclusive, and progress is most likely to ensue by pursuing them in parallel. Ideally, this also leads to productive interaction between theoretical and empirical advances, where, in a true mutualistic fashion, each can inform and stimulate the other's growth (Chang, 2005).

1.6 Conclusion

In this chapter, we have presented and analyzed the different ways in which networks can be used in scientific research. First, networks can offer a novel perspective on empirical domains, just because they generate a different way of looking at the domain. Especially in areas where the classic method of isolating parts of the system for empirical study are hard, because everything seems to be connected to everything else, adoption of a network approach can be fruitful. Second, one can further inform such network approaches through the application of network models, which are statistical techniques to assess conditional dependence relations between putative components of the network. Such techniques are useful because they can broadly identify connectivity patterns from empirical data, and thus can inform network approaches to a higher level of empirical adequacy. Third, through a suitable combination of theoretical principles and empirical information, network approaches can be further specified into network theories: systems in which both the components of the system as well as their interrelations are specified to a level of detail that allows one to explain empirical phenomena. Ideally, the development of such theories will increase our understanding of the system studied, inform our empirical efforts to investigate it further, and strengthen our ability to plan controlled interventions on the system.

1.7 Exercises

Conceptual

1.1. Consider the following statements:

a "Suppose that Alice displays two depression symptoms—depressed mood and loss of interest—while Bob displays two other depression symptoms—psycho-motor retardation and weight problems. On an intuitive level, it is plausible that Alice's symptoms are more likely than Bob's to eventually result in a full-fledged depression." (Cramer et al., 2010) b "Most links we identified in our data are links between the polygenic risk score and positive psychotic symptoms, especially symptoms related to notions of conspiracy and paranoia." (Isvoranu et al., 2020)

c "We found that particular symptoms such as loneliness, sadness, and loss of appetite were especially elevated in the context of bereavement, and that the effects from loss on these symptoms were not conveyed via a latent variable, but through a network. Loneliness played a key role: bereavement mainly affected loneliness, which in turn activated other depressive symptoms." (Fried et al., 2015)

Discuss for each of these cases whether they are best interpreted in terms of a network model or in terms of a network theory.

1.2. Choose a construct that you think may be plausibly represented as a system. Suggest a putative set of system components and relations between them, and evaluate whether a network approach would be feasible. Next, describe how one could gather data to estimate a network model empirically. Do you think the estimated model would be directly interpretable as a network theory? Why (not)?

1.3. Search the literature for a paper that applies network approaches to an empirical topic. Identify the main conclusions of the paper. Are these conclusions best interpreted as being about network theories or about network models? Why?

1.4. Network theories and network models do not have a one-to-one relationship. One can for instance test implications of network theories without using network models at all. Can you think of examples?

1.5. Network models can be used in cases where network theories are known to be false. For instance, suppose one hypothesizes that a set of variables is determined by a latent variable (a common cause) and there are no direct relations at all between the variables. From this hypothesis, it is possible to deduce the implied network model for the observed variables, which can be used to test the latent variable hypothesis. What is your intuition about the network model that would be implied in this case? Would it be expected to contain many edges, a few, or none?

True or false

1.6. Network models can be thought of as tools for representing patterns in data.

1.7. To apply network models, one needs to assume that a network theory is true.

1.8. The difference between a network approach and a network theory is that a network theory aims to specify precisely which components feature as nodes in the network and what the links between them mean.

1.9. In network models, a link between two nodes represents a causal interaction.

1.10. If one interprets an estimated network as giving a truthful picture of how variables influence each other, one follows a *direct* interpretation of the relation between network models and network theory.

References

Barabási, A.-L. (2012). The network takeover. *Nature Physics*, *8*(1), 14–16.

Borsboom, D., Epskamp, S., Kievit, R. A., Cramer, A. O. J., & Schmittmann, V. D. (2011). Transdiagnostic networks: Commentary on Nolen-Hoeksema and Watkins. *Perspectives on Psychological Science*, *6*(6), 610–614.

Borsboom, D., Fried, E. I., Epskamp, S., Waldorp, L., van Borkulo, C. D., van der Maas, H., & Cramer, A. (2017). False alarm? a comprehensive reanalysis of "evidence that psychopathology symptom networks have limited replicability" by Forbes, Wright, Markon, and Krueger. *Journal of Abnormal Psychology*, *126*(7), 989–999.

Borsboom, D., van der Maas, H. L. J., Dalege, J., Kievit, R. A., & Haig, B. D. (2021). Theory construction methodology: A practical framework for building theories in psychology. *Perspectives on Psychological Science*, *16*(4), 756–766.

Boschloo, L., van Borkulo, C. D., Rhemtulla, M., Keyes, K. M., Borsboom, D., & Schoevers, R. A. (2015). The network structure of symptoms of the diagnostic and statistical manual of mental disorders. *PLoS One*, *10*(9), e0137621.

Bringmann, L. F., Elmer, T., Epskamp, S., Krause, R. W., Schoch, D., Wichers, M., Wigman, J. T., & Snippe, E. (2019). What do centrality measures measure in psychological networks? *Journal of Abnormal Psychology*, *128*(8), 892–903.

Caspi, A., Houts, R. M., Belsky, D. W., Goldman-Mellor, S. J., Harrington, H., Israel, S., Meier, M. H., Ramrakha, S., Shalev, I., Poulton, R., & Moffitt, T. E. (2014). The p factor: One general psychopathology factor in the structure of psychiatric disorders? *Clinical psychological science*, *2*(2), 119–137.

Chang, H. (2005). *Inventing temperature: Measurement and scientific progress*. Oxford University Press.

Cox, D. R., & Wermuth, N. (2014). *Multivariate dependencies: Models, analysis and interpretation*. Chapman; Hall/CRC.

Cramer, A. O. J., van Borkulo, C. D., Giltay, E. J., van der Maas, H. L. J., Kendler, K. S., Scheffer, M., & Borsboom, D. (2016). Major depression as a complex dynamic system. *PLoS One*, *11*(12), e0167490.

Cramer, A. O. J., Waldorp, L. J., van der Maas, H. L. J., & Borsboom, D. (2010). Comorbidity: A network perspective. *Behavioral and Brain Sciences*, *33*(2-3), 137–150.

Dalege, J., Borsboom, D., van Harreveld, F., van den Berg, H., Conner, M., & van der Maas, H. L. J. (2016). Toward a formalized account of attitudes: The causal attitude network (CAN) model. *Psychological Review*, *123*(1), 2–22.

Dalege, J., Borsboom, D., van Harreveld, F., & van der Maas, H. L. J. (2018). The attitudinal entropy (AE) framework as a general theory of individual attitudes. *Psychological Inquiry*, *29*(4), 175–193.

Epskamp, S., Cramer, A. O. J., Waldorp, L. J., Schmittmann, V. D., Borsboom, D., Waldrop, L. J., Schmittmann, V. D., & Borsboom, D. (2012). qgraph : Network visualizations of relationships in psychometric data. *Journal of Statistical Software*, *48*(4), 1–18.

Epskamp, S., Kruis, J., & Marsman, M. (2017). Estimating psychopathological networks: Be careful what you wish for. *PLoS One*, *12*(6), e0179891.

Fisher, A. J., Medaglia, J. D., & Jeronimus, B. F. (2018). Lack of group-to-individual generalizability is a threat to human subjects research. *Proceedings of the National Academy of Sciences*, *115*(27), E6106–E6115.

Fisher, A. J., Reeves, J. W., Lawyer, G., Medaglia, J. D., & Rubel, J. A. (2017). Exploring the idiographic dynamics of mood and anxiety via network analysis. *Journal of Abnormal Psychology*, *126*(8), 1044–1056.

Fried, E. I. (2020). Lack of theory building and testing impedes progress in the factor and network literature. *Psychological Inquiry*, *31*(4), 271–288.

Fried, E. I., & Cramer, A. O. J. (2017). Moving forward: Challenges and directions for psychopathological network theory and methodology. *Perspectives on Psychological Science*, *12*(6), 999–1020.

Fried, E. I., & Robinaugh, D. J. (2020). Systems all the way down: Embracing complexity in mental health research. *BMC Medicine*, *18*, 205.

Fried, E. I. I., Bockting, C., Arjadi, R., Borsboom, D., Amshoff, M., Cramer, A. O. J., Epskamp, S., Tuerlinckx, F., Carr, D., & Stroebe, M. (2015). From loss to loneliness: The relationship between bereavement and depressive symptoms. *Journal of Abnormal Psychology*, *124*(2), 256–265.

Haig, B. D. (2014). *Investigating the psychological world: Scientific method in the behavioral sciences*. MIT Press.

Haslbeck, J. M. B., Ryan, O., Robinaugh, D. J., Waldorp, L., & Borsboom, D. (2021). Modeling psychopathology: From data models to formal theories. *Psychological Methods*. https://doi.org/10.1037/met0000303

Haworth, C. M., Wright, M. J., Luciano, M., Martin, N. G., De Geus, E. J., van Beijster-veldt, C. E., Bartels, M., Posthuma, D., Boomsma, D. I., Davis, O. S., Kovas, Y., Corley, R. P., Defries, J. C., Hewitt, J. K., Olson, R. K., Rhea, S. A., Wadsworth, S. J., Iacono, W. G., McGue, M., ... Plomin, R. (2010). The heritability of general cognitive ability increases linearly from childhood to young adulthood. *Molecular Psychiatry*, *15*, 1112–1120.

Henry, T., Robinaugh, D. J., & Fried, E. I. (2021). On the control of psychological networks. *Psychometrika*. https://doi.org/10.1007/s11336-021-09796-9

Isvoranu, A. M., Guloksuz, S., Epskamp, S., van Os, J., Borsboom, D., & GROUP Investigators. (2020). Toward incorporating genetic risk scores into symptom networks of psychosis. *Psychological Medicine*, *50*(4), 636–643.

Isvoranu, A. M., van Borkulo, C. D., Boyette, L., Wigman, J. T. W., Vinkers, C. H., Borsboom, D., & GROUP Investigators. (2016). A network approach to psychosis: Pathways between childhood trauma and psychotic symptoms. *Schizophrenia Bulletin*, *43*(1), 187–196.

Jones, P. J., Heeren, A., & McNally, R. J. (2017). Commentary: A network theory of mental disorders. *Frontiers in Psychology*, *8*, 1305.

Kendler, K. S., Zachar, P., & Craver, C. (2011). What kinds of things are psychiatric disorders? *Psychological Medicine*, *41*(6), 1143–1150.

Lange, J., Dalege, J., Borsboom, D., van Kleef, G. A., & Fischer, A. H. (2020). Toward an integrative psychometric model of emotions. *Perspectives on Psychological Science*, *15*(2), 444–468.

Marsman, M., Waldorp, L., & Maris, G. (2017). A note on large-scale logistic prediction: Using an approximate graphical model to deal with collinearity and missing data. *Behaviormetrika*, *44*(2), 513–534.

Meadows, D. H. (2008). *Thinking in systems: A primer*. Chelsea Green Publishing.

Molenaar, P. C. M. (2004). A manifesto on psychology as idiographic science: Bringing the person back into scientific psychology, this time forever. *Measurement: Interdisciplinary Research & Perspective*, *2*(4), 201–218.

Pearl, J. (2010). Causal inference (I. Guyon, D. Janzing, & B. Schölkopf, Eds.). In I. Guyon, D. Janzing, & B. Schölkopf (Eds.), *Proceedings of workshop on causality: Objectives and assessment at nips 2008*, PMLR.

Robinaugh, D. J., Haslbeck, J. M. B., Waldorp, L., Kossakowski, J. J., Fried, E. I., Millner, A., McNally, R., van Nes, E., Scheffer, M., Kendler, K., & Borsboom, D. (2019). Advancing the network theory of mental disorders: A computational model of panic disorder. *PsyArXiv*. https://doi.org/10.31234/osf.io/km37w

Robinaugh, D. J., Hoekstra, H. A., Toner, E. R., & Borsboom, D. (2020). The network approach to psychopathology: A review of the literature 2008–2018 and an agenda for future research. *Psychological Medicine*, *50*(3), 353–366.

Scheffer, M. (2020). *Critical transitions in nature and society*. Princeton University Press.

Tesser, A. (1978). Self-generated attitude change. *Advances in Experimental Social Psychology*, *11*, 289–338.

van Bork, R., Epskamp, S., Rhemtulla, M., Borsboom, D., & van der Maas, H. L. J. (2017). What is the p-factor of psychopathology? some risks of general factor modeling. *Theory & Psychology*, *27*(6), 759–773.

van Bork, R., Rhemtulla, M., Waldorp, L. J., Kruis, J., Rezvanifar, S., & Borsboom, D. (2021). Latent variable models and networks: Statistical equivalence and testability. *Multivariate Behavioral Research*, *56*(2), 175–198.

van Borkulo, C. D., Borsboom, D., Epskamp, S., Blanken, T. F., Boschloo, L., Schoevers, R. A., & Waldorp, L. J. (2014). A new method for constructing networks from binary data. *Nature: Scientific Reports*, *4*(5918).

van der Maas, H. L. J., Dolan, C. V., Grasman, R. P., Wicherts, J. M., Huizenga, H. M., & Raijmakers, M. E. (2006). A dynamical model of general intelligence: The positive manifold of intelligence by mutualism. *Psychological Review*, *113*(4), 842–861.

van der Maas, H. L. J., Savi, A. O., Hofman, A., Kan, K.-J., & Marsman, M. (2019). The network approach to general intelligence. In D. J. McFarland (Ed.), *General and specific mental abilities*. Cambridge Scholars Publishing.

Wittenborn, A. K., Rahmandad, H., Rick, J., & Hosseinichimeh, N. (2016). Depression as a systemic syndrome: Mapping the feedback loops of major depressive disorder. *Psychological Medicine*, *46*(3), 551–562.

Wright, D., & Meadows, D. H. (2012). *Thinking in systems*. Earthscan.

Chapter 2

Short Introduction to R

Gabriela Lunansky[1], Sacha Epskamp[1,2], & Adela-Maria Isvoranu[1]

1. University of Amsterdam, Department of Psychology

2. University of Amsterdam, Centre for Urban Mental Health

2.1   Introduction

This chapter aims to provide the reader with the programming background and skills necessary to independently carry out the practical exercises and analyses in this textbook. To date, the network approach is almost uniquely implemented in R, making it an essential tool for carrying out psychological network analyses. Readers who are already familiar with R can skip this chapter and continue with Chapter 3 of this textbook.

2.2   The R environment

Why use R?

Using R for psychometric analyses is no longer reserved for specialists or extremely enthusiastic methodologists. During the past decade, psychometric analyses in R have expansively increased, making it, currently, the norm for doing general psychometric analyses (Mair, 2018). There are good reasons for this: R is a powerful programming language for statistical analyses, data visualization, data mining, and general programming. Furthermore, R is freely available, open source, and is accompanied by a large and lively community. Many statistical analyses, such as the ones discussed in this book, are implemented in R packages, making the use of novel statistical methods easy.

Cite this chapter as:

Lunansky, G., Epskamp, S., & Isvoranu, A. M. (2022). Chapter 2. Short introduction to R. In Isvoranu, A. M., Epskamp, S., Waldorp, L. J., & Borsboom, D. (Eds.). *Network psychometrics with R: A guide for behavioral and social scientists*. Routledge, Taylor & Francis Group.

Installing and setting up R and RStudio

We suggest installing two different programs for using R: the base program R itself, as well as an integrated development environment (IDE): RStudio. R is the base programming language, which can be operated through the terminal or command prompt. The popular IDE RStudio presents a clear and easy-to-use environment to work in, which includes in addition to the R console itself also a plain text editor for editing R code, several useful panes for displaying plots, help files, loaded objects, and more. While it is possible to carry out all analyses presented in this book without using RStudio (e.g., by directly working in the computer terminal), we suggest using RStudio and assume it is used throughout this book.

Please note that R and RStudio need to be installed separately from different websites, and that these programs have to be updated separately as well. The latest version of R can be installed from https://www.r-project.org/, and the latest version from RStudio can be installed from https://rstudio.com/products/rstudio/download/. It is advisable to always work with the latest version of both programs.

After installing both R and RStudio, you can open RStudio to get started.[1] It can then immediately be seen that the RStudio program consists of four main panes:

Console The console pane processes commands, meaning that you can enter and execute commands here. However, we suggest using the Source pane for executing (and saving) your commands. The console is similar to the terminal of the R base program and it will not allow saving your script.

Source The source pane is a plain text editor, meaning it shows plain text in the form of numbers, symbols, and letters. Here, you can write and edit your code, as well as save it in the form of a script. It is highly recommended to work from your script and send your commands to the console, instead of directly working from the console.

Plots/Help This pane has two functions. The first is to show graphical output, for example, figures such as scatterplots or barplots created from your code. Graphical output can be saved in several formats, such as `.pdf`, `.tiff`, or `.jpeg`. The second function of this pane is to show you documentation of functions (functions will be further discussed in Section 2.5). Any function in R is accompanied by documentation. Documentation gives information on what functions do, which arguments can be specified, and what the output will be. Many manuals also include example code on how to use the function. Documentation for every function can be found under the `help` tab or by using the question mark followed by the name of the function `?name`. For example, running the following command `?mean` gives the documentation for the function which calculates the mean of an object.

Workspace The workspace shows which objects are currently loaded in your environment. Objects can consist of, for example, loaded data sets or created objects

---

[1]Note: on some operating systems, an icon labeled "R" will also be created. It is important to note that this usually is not R, but rather an older IDE that comes with the default R installation. We recommend to use RStudio instead of this IDE.

such as matrices and vectors. Please note that it is not recommended to save your workspace when closing RStudio, as in every future session the same objects will be reloaded and this may create issues in new scripts or overwrite functions. In addition, always loading your objects from your script is better practice for reproducibility.

It is recommended to have the console and source panes on top, since they are the most important, and plots and workspace panes below (see Figure 2.1). Pane layouts can be set with *Tools → Global Options → Pane Layout*. In *Tools → Global Options → Appearance* the theme of RStudio, including background colors and text colors, can be changed.

2.3 Basics of R programming

This section will discuss some of the basics of R programming, starting with how R can be used as a calculator, and ending with how to write the first forms of an R script that can be saved and loaded later.

Using R as a calculator

To start programming in R, experiment with the console pane. For example, write the following command, followed by pressing enter:

```
1 + 1
```

Figure 2.1. Example of RStudio with the four panes ordered in the recommended setup, clockwise from top left: the R Console pane, the Script pane, the Workspace pane, and the Plots/Help pane. Note that the color of RStudio is set here according to a theme, which can be set using *Tools → Global Options → Appearance*.

R will now return the number 2, telling you that the sum of 1 and 1 equals 2. The full output in the console is:

    [1] 2

The 2 refers to the answer of our question ('what is 1 + 1?'). The [1] indicates that the first element of the answer is the number 2. This is specific to R: R will often return *vectors*, series of numbers, even if the vector is only one element long (i.e., a single number). So in full, this output tells us that a vector is returned, and that its first element equals 2. For now, you can ignore the [1] completely.

Next, try to enter:

    1 +

followed by pressing *enter*. Now, something else happened: the console prompt > changed into +. This is because R is still expecting input. If you type another number and press enter the command will finish and output will be returned. Alternatively, if you press escape the command will be canceled, allowing you to enter new commands into R.

Of course, R can do more than just add numbers. Several other operators work as might be expected. For example, * can be used to multiply numbers, / can be used to divide numbers, ^ can be used to raise numbers to some power, and brackets (and) can be used to group commands and give precedence over evaluating some commands first. In addition, there are several *functions*, which will be explained in more detail later, that can be used for mathematical operations: sqrt(...) computes a square root ($\sqrt{...}$), exp(...) computes the exponential function ($e^{...}$), log(...) computes a logarithm (ln(...)), and so forth.

Writing R code in a script

While the console is the pane that actually accepts R commands, as well as the pane in which most output is returned, it is highly recommended to never write code in the console pane directly. Instead, R code should be written in an R script such that the commands can be saved and used later again. In addition, scripts allow for more complicated sequences of R commands to be written. Often, you need to evaluate many commands sequentially, e.g., commands to read, transform, plot, or analyze data. Furthermore, saving code in scripts makes your code reproducible for other researchers.

To create an R script, select *File → New File → R script*. Immediately also save the script using *File → Save As*. Always use the .R extension to save R scripts. Now, R commands can be written in the script pane instead of the console pane. Sending commands from the source pane to the console is done by selecting the relevant code and pressing "Run", or alternatively, pressing control+enter/ cmd+enter. This sends the selected commands to the console, where they will be processed.

Comments

Including comments in your script helps other researchers, or your future self, understand your code. Comments are added by using the hashtag # before writing code; any line of R code will no longer be evaluated from the moment # is encountered. These comments can then be used to explain what the purpose of the code is or why it is added. Alternatively, comments can be used to omit part of the code temporarily (this is termed 'commenting out' some code). Tutorial Box 2.1 gives some examples of how a comment can be used.

Any code past a # symbol will not be evaluated by R. For example the code:

```
1 + 1 # + 1
```

will return 2, not 3, as the code 1 + 1 is evaluated, and the last bit is not. As such, the # can be used to clarify code. For example, a clarification can be added after a line of code:

```
1 + 1 # This sums the numbers 1 and 1
```

or before a line of code:

```
# Sum the numbers 1 and 1:
1 + 1
```

We recommend to use comments very liberally in the code. For example, it is not uncommon for almost every line of R code in an analysis script to be accompanied by a comment.

Tutorial Box 2.1. Placing comments in the code to clarify code.

Programming style and coding conventions

Carrying out statistical analyses in R implies writing code. This means not only having to learn the correct programming commands for conducting specific analyses, but also learning rules on what code should look like. The set of rules that determine the coding format are called coding conventions, which are related to general programming style. Just like there are guidelines for how to write research papers (e.g., American Psychological Association, 2020), many guidelines also exist for how to write clear code. While it is never mandatory to adhere to a specific coding convention, writing code according to coding conventions does greatly increase its readability and clarity, making it easier to share with other people and to maintain code over time.

Although there is no clear best style guide for programming in R, the "tidyverse style guide" by Hadley Wickham is often viewed as one of the most important ones.[2] It should be noted, however, that style guides are inherently opinionated, and therefore arguments can be made in favor and against every element included in any style guide. This book will not rely on strong rules on particular programming style. However, we would like to make readers aware that style guides exist, and encourage thinking about the format of code when doing analyses in R.

---

[2]https://style.tidyverse.org/

2.4   Basic R data structures

While it certainly can be nice and useful to write mathematical expressions in R, the output of such expressions has to be stored such that it can be used in later commands. In addition, when data are analyzed, they need to be stored inside R as well, such that they can be called later. Saving the output from commands or storing data in R can be done by using *objects*. This section discusses objects in more detail.

Assigning objects

Objects can contain anything in R. For example, a single number can be stored in an object, but also more complicated data structures and books worth of text. The <- operator is used to store values into objects. For example, the following statement saves the number 1 in the object a:

```
a <- 1
```

Now, instead of writing 1, the object a can be used. For example:

```
1 + a
```

will again return the number 2. Alternatively, the = operator also functions to store values into objects. We do not recommend using =, however, because <- is unambiguous, explicating the left part becomes what is on the right part, while the = operator is ambiguous. Furthermore, = cannot be used within function calls to assign objects.[3]

R expressions that are not stored into an object are printed in the console. When entering a command where an expression is saved into an object, the result of the object is not printed in the console. To see the value of the object, you need to run the name of the object into the console. For example, the following statement evaluates $1 + 1 = 2$ and stores the result into the object b, but does not print the result:

```
b <- 1 + 1
```

To get the result, we can ask R to print the result with `print(b)` or just by typing b. All currently loaded objects are listed in the workspace pane. When quitting R, you will be asked if you would like to save the objects in your workspace. As emphasized above, it is recommended to never do this.

Naming objects

You can use any combination of letters, numbers, and some symbols (_ and ˙) to form object names, as long as the object does not start with a number. It is important to give your objects informed names, which describe the content of your object. In this way, it will be easier for other people to read and understand your code. Various conventions and standards exist regarding object naming. Object names in R are case sensitive: `object`, `Object`, and `OBJECT` are different objects. The tidyverse style guide recommends to only use lowercase letters, numbers, and underscores. Underscores should be used to separate

---

[3]In function calls, = assigns function arguments instead of objects.

words, for example, `data_wave_1` instead of `datawaveone`. Another frequently used style, without using underscores or other operators, is *lowerCamelCase*. Here, the first letter of the first word is lowercase, and the following first letters of words are uppercase. For example: `sampleSize`, `rawData`, and `nMales`.

Object modes

Objects in R can be of different types, called object modes. There are three main object modes for the standard output in R (a vector): numeric, character, and logical. Tutorial Box 2.2 gives examples of each of these object modes. Numeric objects store numbers, on which you can apply mathematical operations. Character objects, also called strings, store any form of text between tick marks (which can be double tick marks, ", or single tick marks, '). You cannot apply mathematical functions on character objects, since character strings are not numbers (even if they look like numbers). Logical objects indicate if something is true or false, and consist of the Boolean objects TRUE or FALSE. Commonly used shortcuts you may see in code are T and F. However, we strongly advise not to use these shortcuts. This is because T can be overwritten and stored as another object, for example F <- 1. In this case, F no longer refers to FALSE but to the number 1. This is problematic, as R sometimes interprets the number 1 as TRUE without warning. When a logical statement is preceded by an exclamation mark (!) the logical result is reversed (TRUE becomes FALSE and FALSE becomes TRUE). Logical modes are used in two ways: in functions, to assign logical modes to arguments, and in performing logical tests.

The following code creates a *numeric* object:

```
numericObject <- 1
```

This object can subsequently be used as a number:

```
numericObject + 1 # This will return the value 2
```

The following object is a string and not a number:

```
characterObject <- "1"
```

This object cannot be used as a number:

```
characterObject + 1 # This will result in an error.
```

Finally, we can also store a logical object:

```
logicalObject <- TRUE
```

Interestingly, this object *can* be used as a number, as TRUE also refers to *1* and FALSE to *0*. In addition, the logical values are also returned when asking R a logical test. For example:

```
1 == 0 # This will return the message FALSE
```

Tutorial Box 2.2. Examples of three object modes that can be used in R: numeric, character, and logical.

Missing data

Missing data are encoded in R with NA, which means 'not available.' Missing data are handled differently for different functions. To find the right argument for handling missing data in the function you are using, review the documentation for that specific function using ?.

Vectors

A vector is an object that stores multiple values. These values can include numbers, but also characters such as letters, or missing data (encoded with NA). To assign a series of values to a vector, you can use the *combine* function c(...) by simply adding the series you want to combine into a vector. Every element of the series is separated by a comma. A second way to create a vector, is to use the colon : to create a series of successive numbers. Vectors can also be *indexed* using square brackets ([and]), which means selecting a certain cell or collection of cells from the vector. This can be used to check the values of these cells, to use them for analyses, or to change them. Tutorial Box 2.3 gives some examples of how vectors can be used.

2.5   Functions and packages

The introduction of vectors also introduced the concept of *functions*. A function is a small program: it takes input, does something, and gives output. For example, the *combine* function c(...) takes some values, combines them, and gives a vector consisting of those values as output. Some other examples of common functions are mean(x), sd(x), and sum(x) to compute the mean, standard deviation, and sum over elements of a vector called x. Functions always have the same form, namely, their name, and then the corresponding arguments within brackets: name(argument, argument, argument, ...). Some arguments have default settings, meaning that the parameters of that argument are set. This makes the functions more generic to use, however, you can always change the parameters of every argument when using functions.

To know which arguments can be provided, and which default arguments apply, every function in R is accompanied by documentation. Reference cards also give a good overview of R functions for frequently used analyses, which can be found online. Furthermore, you can use online search engines and the R community to find the exact function names and arguments for the analyses you want to execute. You can also write your own functions using function(). However, this is part of advanced programming skills and will not be discussed throughout this book. Several freely available online resources on this topic exist.

Packages are extensions contributed to R containing extra functions. Developmental versions of R packages can often be found on Github, and stable versions of R packages are commonly stored on the Comprehensive R Archive Network (CRAN). Several packages are necessary for carrying out the analyses described in this book. All packages

The combine function (c) can be used to create a vector. For example, the following code will create the vector $\begin{bmatrix} 1 & 2 & 3 & 4 & 5 \end{bmatrix}$:

```
numericVector <- c(1, 2, 3, 4, 5)
```

Because this is an integer sequence, the same vector could also be formed using:

```
numericVector <- 1:5
```

A vector can also contain missing elements, which are encoded as NA:

```
vectorMissing <- c(1, 2, 3, NA, 5, 6, NA, 8, 9, 10)
```

Many functions in R tend to return errors when elements of a vector are missing. For example, the mean function can be used to compute the mean of a vector, but using it on a vector with missing elements will lead to an error:

```
mean(vectorMissing) # Results in an error
```

Instead, missing data must be handled in a way that is acceptable for the function used. For the example above, we could remove all missing elements using na.omit:

```
mean(na.omit(vectorMissing))
```

or an argument of the mean function can be used to do the same:

```
mean(vectorMissing, na.rm = TRUE)
```

Always refer to the help file of a function for information on how to handle missing data. Finally, vectors can be indexed using square brackets that follow the name of the vector. The square brackets can contain integers indicating the elements of the vector (starting with 1), or a logical vector of the same length as the original vector with TRUE indicating an element should be returned. For example, vectorMissing[1:3] selects only the first three elements of the vector and vectorMissing[!is.na(vectorMissing)] selects all elements that are not NA.

Tutorial Box 2.3. Examples of how to use vectors in R.

need to be installed once by using install.packages().[4] For example, the following command installs the package *bootnet*, which we will use in the remainder of this book:

```
install.packages("bootnet")
```

This may take a long time, and only has to be run occasionally, to ensure the package is up to date. It is not recommended to leave a call to install.packages(...) in an R script (or if it is included, include a comment sign # before the call so it is not always evaluated). After installing a package, the package also needs to be loaded using the

---

[4]Sometimes R may struggle to install an R package and return an error. If R asks if you want to install a package from source, it is best to answer 'no' unless you have your system set up to install packages from source. Answering 'no' does not stop installation but rather continues with installing pre-compiled packages from CRAN, which is easier. Most R packages depend on other R packages, which should be installed automatically. Sometimes, however, this does not work. Whenever R returns an error that some package is not installed or cannot be loaded, try installing that package first. Sometimes then a new error may be returned pointing out a different package that needs to be installed.

function library(...).[5] For example, the *bootnet* package can be loaded with:

```
library("bootnet")
```

This makes all exported functions from the *bootnet* package available to the user. Contrary to install.packages(...), the library(...) command does have to be used at the beginning of every script that uses functions from a package.

2.6   Advanced object structures

We already discussed different modes of objects in R and vectors that combined several objects in Section 2.4. Typically, data in R are presented in more advanced structures than vectors. For example, networks can be encoded using two-dimensional matrices, and data are typically stored in a form of a matrix, in which columns can have different modes (data frames). This section will introduce these more advanced object structures.

Matrices

An important function when doing network analyses is the matrix() function. Technically, a matrix is a vector with two dimensional attributes. Rows indicate horizontal lines of cells, while columns indicate vertical lines of cells. The first argument of a matrix is a vector (i.e., the data) to fill the matrix with, the second argument the number of rows, and the third argument the number of columns. Indexing in matrices can be done using square brackets, where the first value indicates the row number and the second value the column number, separated by a comma. Some examples of how to use matrices are shown in Tutorial Box 2.4, and documentation for the matrix function can be found with ?matrix.

The matrix function can be used to create a matrix:

```
myMatrix <- matrix(1:9, nrow = 3, ncol = 3)
```

Note that the matrix is filled columnwise. To fill the matrix rowwise, we can instead use:

```
myMatrix <- matrix(1:9, nrow = 3, ncol = 3, byrow = TRUE)
```

Next, we can index the matrix using square brackets. For example, myMatrix[1,2] selects the cell at row 1 and column 2, myMatrix[1:2,1:2] select the block with the first two rows and columns, and myMatrix[1:2,] selects the first two rows and all columns.

Tutorial Box 2.4. Example code for creating and indexing matrices.

---

[5]The function require() can also be used to load an R package.

We can create a list with two objects, one vector consisting of character elements, and one matrix consisting of numeric elements, with the following code:

```
myList <- list(
    characterVector = c("a", "b", "c", "d"),
    numericMatrix = matrix(data = c(1, 2, 3, 4),
    nrow = 2, ncol = 2))
```

To confirm that the list consists of two objects, one character vector and one numeric matrix, we can use the structure function with `str(myList)`. To index the list, we can use double square brackets. For example, the following selects only the first element of the list:

```
myList[[1]]
```

We can do the same by using the name of the element:

```
myList$characterVector
```

Finally, we can also index elements of lists. For example, the following selects the first element of the first object of the list:

```
myList[[1]][1]
```

Tutorial Box 2.5. Examples of constructing and indexing lists.

Lists

Lists can consist of any (combination of) data modes. Lists are like coat racks that can store any type and combination of object modes, even other lists! For example, numeric matrices and vectors consisting of characters can be combined into a list. The first element will be the matrix, while the second element will be the vector. Every element of a list can be named. To index from a list, the $ operator or double square brackets ([[and]]) can be used. An example can be seen in Tutorial Box 2.5.

Data frames

Data frames are the most used objects for storing data sets; most data sets, such as data sets imported from the statistical program SPSS, will be represented as data frames in R. Technically, a data frame is a list in which each element is a vector of the same size. This allows the data frame to also be represented (and indexed) as a matrix. Data frames can store different variables, such as numeric variables, indicating scores on a questionnaire, but also characters, such as "male" and "female". Since they are technically a list, you can index data frames using the $ operator. However, you can also index data frames in the same way matrices are indexed. Tutorial Box 2.6 shows how a data frame can be created.

We can create a data frame with two variables indicating a participant's score and gender, consisting of a numeric vector and a character vector:

```
myDataFrame <- data.frame(
    score = c(3, 6, 2, 4),
    gender = c("male", "female", "other", "female"))
```

To index the data frame, the $ operator, single square brackets and double square brackets can be used. For example, all these commands will index the second column (gender):

```
myDataFrame$gender
myDataFrame[,"gender"]
myDataFrame[["gender"]]
myDataFrame[,2]
myDataFrame[[2]]
```

A popular R package for manipulating data frames is the *dplyr* package (Wickham et al., 2021). The *dplyr* package contains several powerful functions for manipulating data. For example, the `select` function can also be used to select a variable:

```
select(myDataFrame, gender)
```

and the `group_by` and `summarize` commands can be used to compute something for every level of one or more grouping variables:

```
summarize(group_by(myDataFrame, gender), mean = mean(score))
```

This code computes the mean for every level of `gender`. The *dplyr* package exports a handy *pipe* operator, `%>%`, which can be used to express, for example, `f(g(x))` as `x %>% g %>% f`, in which `x` is some R object and `f` and `g` are some R functions. This can be used to write chains of commands easier (reading from left to right instead of from inside to outside):

```
myDataFrame %>% group_by(gender) %>% summarize(mean = mean(score))
```

The pipe operator syntax is used in some of the examples of this book. Of note, recent versions of R also include the pipe operator as `|>`. The *dplyr* package is part of a collection or R packages that all work well together, termed the *tidyverse* (Wickham et al., 2019). Other popular tidyverse packages are *ggplot2* for data visualization, and *tidyr* for data reshaping.

Tutorial Box 2.6. Working with data frames.

2.7   Working with data in R

Now that you are familiar with the way R works, it is time to start looking at real data. To do this, data need to be loaded into R as an object, after which it can be used for analysis.

Working directory

The working directory is the folder on your computer in which R is currently operating. This means that your data will be loaded from this folder, and any output created (e.g., new data and plots) will be saved to this folder. You can request your current working directory

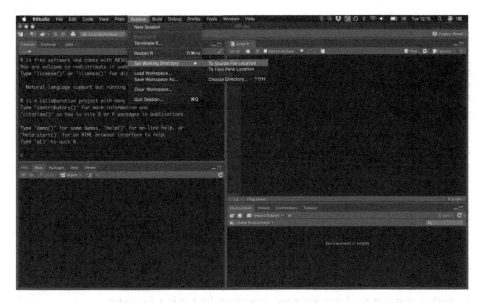

Figure 2.2. Setting up the working directory.

with the function `getwd()`. A common error that can occur is that a file is requested which is not located in the working directory. To solve this issue, you need to change your working directory or add the needed (data)file to your current working directory. To set your current working directory, you can use the function `setwd()`. Another way to set your working directory is by clicking *Session → Set Working Directory → Choose Directory*. This will allow you to set your working directory to a location of choice. Finally, as also shown in Figure 2.2, you can also set your working directory by clicking *Session → Set Working Directory → To Source File Location*. This sets your working directory to the same folder as where your current script is saved, which is convenient, since this allows you to easily load and save objects, (data)files, and scripts within the same folder.

Importing data into R

After the working directory is correctly specified, there are several ways to load data sets into R. First, data sets can be loaded into R from different sources (e.g., CSV, SAS, SPSS, Microsoft Excel) by clicking *File → Import Dataset*. This option will in addition provide you the code to import data, which you can also use directly. Second, data sets can be loaded into R directly, by using a command to read your data. The most common format to read data into R is the Comma-Delimited (CSV) format. Please note that reading SPSS or Microsoft Excel data files into R requires installing and loading dedicated R packages. Tutorial Box 2.7 shows examples of code that can be used to read data into R.

If data `mydata` is stored in a plain text file with the extension `.csv` (comma separated values), and located in the same directory as the script, then, after setting the working directory to the same location as the script with *Session → Set Working Directory → To Source File Location*, the data can usually be loaded into R and stored in an object called data with:

```
# Read a CSV data file into R
data <- read.csv("mydata.csv")
```

Possibly, some arguments need to be used to specify how exactly the data are stored. See for more information `?read.csv`.

If the data `mydata` are instead stored in an SPSS file with the extension `.sav`, the following commands can be used to read the data and store them in an object called `data`:

```
# Read an SPSS data file into R
install.packages("foreign")
library("foreign")
data <- read.spss("mydata.sav", to.data.frame=TRUE)
```

Both the function `read.csv` and `read.sav` return the data in a data frame

Tutorial Box 2.7. Importing data from plain text files and SPSS files.

Correlation & covariance

After the data are loaded into R, they can be used for statistical analysis. For example, the data could be used to estimate a correlation matrix, which will play an important role in some of the analyses discussed in this book. The function `cor()` computes a correlation from a data frame (or any other type of numerical data) and the function `cov()` computes the covariance. The argument `method` selects the method for computing the correlation or covariance. The default is using Pearson correlations, (`method = "pearson"`), but other options include Spearman (`method = "spearman"`) and Kendall (`method = "kendall"`) correlations.

2.8   Conclusion

This chapter introduced the reader to basic concepts of the statistical programming language R. The discussed topics should be sufficient for most of the R analyses discussed in this book. However, it can be noted that R is a very extensive programming language, and the full extent of programming in R cannot readily be captured in a single chapter. For example, we did not discuss actual programming in R (such as using `if` statements and `for` loops), how to write functions, how to write efficient R code, or how to do more complicated statistical analyses. As R is a very popular open-source programming language, there is a wealth of freely available guides available online that teach these more advanced topics of programming in R for the interested reader.

2.9   Exercises

Conceptual

2.1. List three advantages of using R over using an interface based software such as SPSS. Can you also think of a disadvantage?

2.2. What are the three main object modes for a vector in R? Provide a short R-code example for every object mode.

2.3. The following code gives an error:

```
x <- "1"
1 + x
```

Explain why this error occurs. Can you transform the object x such that 1 + x does not give an error?

2.4. The following code gives an error:

```
x <- c(1,10,NA,5,2,9)
sd(x)
```

Look at the help file of sd and find an argument that solves this error.

2.5. Given the following three vectors:

```
A <- rnorm(100)
B <- A + rnorm(100)
C <- B + rnorm(100)
```

Find out if the correlation between A and C is significant? What about the partial correlation between A and C, controlling for B?

True or false

2.6. R is a freely available, open source program.

2.7. The source pane in R automatically processes commands, but does not allow saving your script.

2.8. The <- and = operators can be used interchangeably.

2.9. Using the shortcuts of logical objects (i.e., T or F) is recommended, as they are shorter and cannot be overwritten.

2.10. Packages need to be both installed and loaded every time you open R.

Practical

For practical exercises in R, please navigate to the appropriate folder of this chapter, available on the online *Companion Website*.

References

American Psychological Association. (2020). *Publication manual of the American Psychological Association (7th ed.)*. APA.

Mair, P. (2018). *Modern psychometrics with R*. Springer.

Wickham, H., Averick, M., Bryan, J., Chang, W., McGowan, L. D., François, R., Grolemund, G., Hayes, A., Henry, L., Hester, J., Kuhn, M., Pedersen, T. L., Miller, E., Bache, S. M., Müller, K., Ooms, J., Robinson, D., Seidel, D. P., Spinu, V., . . . Yutani, H. (2019). Welcome to the tidyverse. *Journal of Open Source Software*, *4*(43), 1686.

Wickham, H., François, R., Henry, L., & Müller, K. (2021). *dplyr: A grammar of data manipulation* [R package version 1.0.7]. R package version 1.0.7. https://CRAN.R-project.org/package=dplyr

Chapter 3

Descriptive Analysis of Network Structures

Marie K. Deserno[1], Adela-Maria Isvoranu[2], Sacha Epskamp[1,3], & Tessa F. Blanken[2]

1. Max Planck Institute for Human Development, Berlin

2. University of Amsterdam, Department of Psychology

3. University of Amsterdam, Centre for Urban Mental Health

3.1 Introduction

This chapter introduces networks, how they can be constructed, and how they can subsequently be analyzed. Networks consist of nodes (also called *vertices*) and edges (also called *links*). Often in the literature, networks can also be called *graphs*, though the former generally refers to the visual representation, while the latter generally refers to the mathematical notation. Virtually anything can be represented as a set of nodes and edges. For example, Figure 3.1 displays interactions between characters of a book series. In real life we encounter networks constantly: transportation networks consisting of train stations (nodes) and railways between them (edges); lights (nodes) that are connected through wires (edges); or internet cables (edges) that connect homes (nodes) to the internet. Networks can also consist of edges that are not directly visible: friends (nodes) that are connected through telephone calls (edges); or a social network consisting of scientists (nodes) that are connected through co-authorships (links). Finally, and central to this book, networks can consist of estimated statistical relationships (edges) among variables (nodes).

Cite this chapter as:

Deserno, M. K., Isvoranu, A. M., Epskamp, S., & Blanken, T. F. (2022). Chapter 3. Descriptive analyses of network structures. In Isvoranu, A. M., Epskamp, S., Waldorp, L. J., & Borsboom, D. (Eds.). *Network psychometrics with R: A guide for behavioral and social scientists*. Routledge, Taylor & Francis Group.

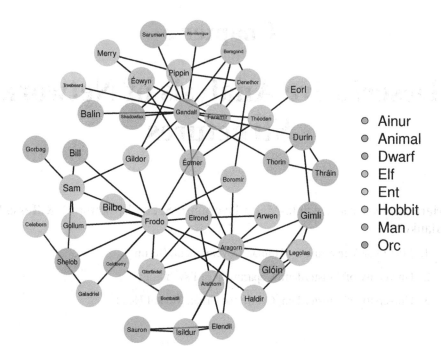

Figure 3.1. A network depicting character interactions in the *Lord of the Rings* book series: nodes represent characters, and edges represent that these characters were often mentioned together in the same paragraph. Based on the work of Calvo Tello (2016). The data can be downloaded from Github at https://github.com/morethanbooks/projects/tree/master/LotR.

The chapter starts with a description of the origin and context in which network analysis is most applied. Next, we describe the differences between the setting in which we introduce network analysis tools in this chapter, *Network Science*, compared to the setting which is the focus of the remainder of this book, *Network Psychometrics*. Subsequently, we discuss different types of networks, how they can be encoded, and several of the most prominent methods in which networks are analyzed. We conclude this chapter with an introduction to network analysis of psychological variables, which will form the core of the remainder of this book.

3.2   Complex systems and network science

Increasingly, scientific questions are targeted at the structure and evolution of complex systems. Theoretical advances lie in the conceptual integration of complex and multivariate mechanisms. As such, many of the big scientific questions of this century are rooted in a general interest in patterns within such complex system. Now, more than ever, the availability of multi-scale and multi-modal data and powerful computing capacity enable scientists to empirically test theories about how components of a complex system, such as cells, human beings, or species, interact. These advances have led to a rapidly emerging field spanning a wide range of applied disciplines: *Network Science* (Barabási, 2012).

The fundamental study of networks is by no means new. Graph theory—dating back to the solution of the Königsberg bridge problem by Euler (1736)—has been a substantial part of mathematics and adopted by the social sciences for most of the twentieth century. Recent years, however, have witnessed an unprecedented fast-paced expansion and application of the mathematical framework: ecological networks of food webs or ecosystems in ecology (Ings et al., 2009), semantic association networks in linguistics (Steyvers & Tenenbaum, 2005), social networks in sociology (Scott, 1988), and symptom networks in psychology (Borsboom, 2017). All of these networks display characteristics, organized patterns emerging from the system's diverse interconnectedness. Fuelled by the substantial questions and data from different fields, not only the network toolbox, but also network theory is rapidly expanding. There are multiple applied examples of the complexity-credo: "The whole is more than the sum of its parts." Primarily, because modern network approaches provide fundamental insights into the dynamics and emergent properties that result from the interaction of simple elements. As such, the flocking of birds, for example, produces a swarm with collective intelligence and the collective actions of nerves create consciousness—all through multi-scale network interactions. Such complex phenomena can best be understood by studying the integrative dynamics and functions of the system that produces it.

The translation of this mathematical framework into network analysis techniques has allowed scholars from different scientific fields to formalize and apply their hypotheses grounded in system-focused thinking. For example, Watts and Strogatz (1998) generalized the basic idea of network structures to a variety of data sets and demonstrated that many real-world networks display similar properties (see Section 3.5). Despite the differences in what networks represent across disciplines, the network analytical framework allows to describe and predict the inner workings of the system's interconnectedness. During the past decades, scholars across different scientific fields have invented a new language to communicate and formalize their theories grounded in systems-focused thinking and analysis. With a focus on the predictability of patterns, analytic schools based on differential equations and network analysis have advanced the translation of systems-thinking into toy models and analytic toolboxes. Its empirical application has grown even more, after Watts and Strogatz (1998) generalized the basic idea of network structures to a variety of data sets. What distinguishes network analysis from previous attempts at accommodating complex systems theory is its data-inspired methodology. From early on, network analysis has been rooted in empirical evidence for the system properties its theory predicts: the changing distribution of connections when more variables are added to the network, for example, has been reported across a diverse range of disciplines and their data. The decades-old questions fuelled by complex systems theory have been reassembled by the toolbox of network science. With its strong empirical basis, network science has allowed researchers to develop theoretical bits and pieces about not only effects and workings of complex systems and their interconnectedness but also about

individual nodes and links. In other words, the rapidly advancing network methodology
has become indispensable in the study of complex systems, relating local dynamics and
properties to global effects and structures, and vice versa.

3.3   From network science to network psychometrics

In many networks, nodes are well-defined entities. In a transportation network, for
example, it is clearly defined what makes up a node (e.g., a train station). Two nodes
can be easily separated from each other, and what constitutes the network can be clearly
defined. If we were to map out the subway system in London, for example, it is clear that
we (a) consider subway stations; and (b) consider the subway stations that are situated in
London, not those in Glasgow. These clear distinctions and definitions, however, are not
a given. In the psychological networks discussed in this book, it is not always clear (a)
what a node entails, and (b) what the scope of a network should be. Rather than nodes
representing *entities* (e.g., people, cities, species), in such psychological networks nodes
typically represent *variables* that can take more than one state (e.g., absence or presence
of a psychological symptom). Moving away from representing entities as nodes, it may be
unclear what the nodes then should represent. Constructing a network of depression, for
example, one may choose to include 'symptoms' as defined in nosologies and assessed by
a clinician, or to include items of a self-reported depression questionnaire. Similarly, one
may choose to restrict to depression symptoms only, or to consider anxiety symptoms
important to the network of depression as well.

The same holds for the edges in a network. These can be clearly defined, for example
when they are directly observed (e.g., rails in a transportation network) or follow a clear
rule (e.g., co-authorships), but may be less straightforward when they represent statistical
relationships between variables that need be estimated from data. Edges representing
statistical relationships bring several complications to the interpretation of the network.
For example, the interpretation of the interaction between connected nodes depends on
the type of statistical relationship that is estimated. These edges now no longer denote
ways in which two entities can interact with one another (e.g., two friends meeting
and potentially infecting one another with a virus), but instead represent probabilistic
association (e.g., the presence of symptom A increases the probability of the presence of
symptom B). Estimating edges from data through the use of statistics also adds a layer of
complexity in the form of sampling variation and uncertainty in the estimated values—a
topic discussed in more detail in Chapter 8.

Because there can be such striking differences between what networks encode, it is
important to make the setting in which network analysis is applied explicit. This chapter
introduces some of the core methods of analyzing networks in the field of *Network
Science*. Network Science is a very broad field of research on network structures, but
mostly relates to networks in which nodes and edges are quite well defined (often clear
entities linked through observable or well-defined links). Statistical modeling in this field
often takes the edges to be the variables, which can take, for example, the values 'present'
and 'absent.' The remainder of this book will focus on the estimation of network models
from data, in which not the edges but rather the nodes are the variables (e.g., symptoms).

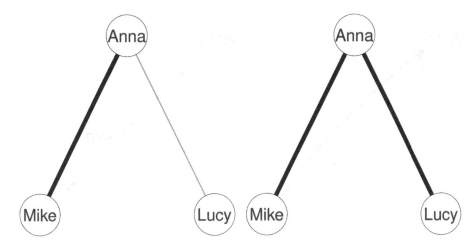

Figure 3.2. The difference between weighted (left) and unweighted (right) networks. In weighted networks, the strength of connections can differ across edges in the network. For example, Anna could interact more with Mike than with Lucy, and as such if Anna is infected with a virus she is more likely to infect Mike than Lucy.

The field of study that is concerned with the estimation of such networks from data is termed *Network Psychometrics*. While this difference between networks typically analyzed in network science and networks typically obtained in network psychometrics may seem subtle, it substantively changes the interpretation of what a network is. Methods from network science can be, and routinely are, applied to networks estimated from data, but doing so takes a certain leap of interpretation. To this end, it is vital to learn about these metrics in the setting in which they were developed, and keep a critical eye to when they are being applied outside of this scope.

3.4   Constructing networks

Constructing a network starts with the selection of a set of nodes which represent certain entities that are connected in some way through edges. The edges in a network structure can be either *weighted* or *unweighted*. Let's take the basic example in Figure 3.2, assuming the edges in the network represent *friendship*. In the network structure on the left side, where we have a weighted network, we would take the interpretation that Anna and Mike are better friends than Anna and Lucy, as the edge between Anna and Mike is stronger. In the network structure on the right side, where we have an unweighted network, we would take the general interpretation of friendships between people, without a focus on whether some people are better friends than others: Anna and Mike are friends, Anna and Lucy are also friends, and there is no friendship relationship between Mike and Lucy.

Further, edges can have both a *sign* and a *direction*. Throughout this book, as well as in many of the software packages that we will use in this course, positive links will be by

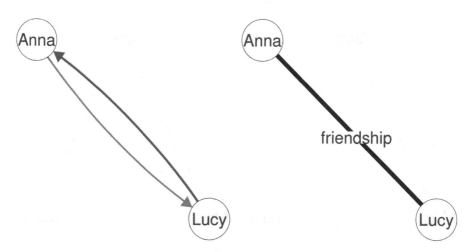

Figure 3.3. The difference between weighted directed (left) and unweighted undirected (right) networks. In addition to differing in the strength of connections, edges can also differ in the direction of the edge. For example, a relationship from *A* to *B* may be of a different strength or absent entirely in comparison with a relationship from *B* to *A*. In this example: Lucy likes Anna, but Anna does not like Lucy.

default represented by *blue edges* and negative links will be by default represented by *red edges*.[1] Let's take the basic example in Figure 3.3, assuming the edges in the network still represent *friendship*. In the network structure on the left side, we would take the interpretation that Anna and Lucy experience their relationship differently: While Lucy really likes Anna and thinks of her as a friend, Anna doesn't really like Lucy and does not reciprocate the relationship. In the network structure on the right side, where we have no direction or sign, the edge would simply represent a friendship relation between Anna and Lucy.

With the basic building blocks of a network at hand, the network can now be represented mathematically, as is further discussed in Technical Box 3.1. Such mathematical representations can be used to encode a large variety of network structures, such as large and small networks, weighted and unweighted networks, and directed and undirected networks. Throughout this book, we will mainly focus on undirected weighted networks estimated from cross-sectional data (Part II), and both directed and undirected weighted networks estimated from longitudinal data (Part III). In the following sections, we will discuss how networks can further be analyzed.

3.5   Analyzing networks

Network construction or estimation is typically followed by network inferences to quantify or summarize the network's interconnectedness. To this end, different metrics can be

---

[1]Some other color codings are used in the literature. Older papers often use green for positive effects instead of blue, and some papers use red for positive edges and blue for negative edges.

Mathematically, a *graph* (or network) can be defined as a set G that consists of a set of *vertices* (nodes) V and a set of *edges* (links) E:

$$G = \{V, E\}.$$

For example, the network on the right of Figure 3.2 could be represented with the following sets:

$$V = \{\text{Mike}, \text{Anna}, \text{Lucy}\}$$
$$E = \{(\text{Mike} - \text{Anna}), (\text{Anna} - \text{Lucy})\}.$$

A typical way of encoding the network mathematically is through the use of an *adjacency matrix*, A, which contains a row/column for each node, and in which a 1 indicates two nodes are connected and a 0 indicates two nodes are not connected:

$$A = \begin{array}{c} \\ \text{Mike} \\ \text{Anna} \\ \text{Lucy} \end{array} \begin{array}{ccc} \text{Mike} & \text{Anna} & \text{Lucy} \\ \left[\begin{array}{ccc} 0 & 1 & 0 \\ 1 & 0 & 1 \\ 0 & 1 & 0 \end{array} \right] \end{array}.$$

If the network is *directed*, the adjacency matrix could be asymmetrical, in which case the rows indicate the node of origin and the columns the node of destination. For *weighted* networks, additional weights can be added to every edge in the graph. These can be encoded through a *weights matrix* W, in which 0 indicates no strength of connection. For example, suppose the left network in Figure 3.2 represents the number of interactions in a week. Then the corresponding weights matrix could be:

$$W = \begin{array}{c} \\ \text{Mike} \\ \text{Anna} \\ \text{Lucy} \end{array} \begin{array}{ccc} \text{Mike} & \text{Anna} & \text{Lucy} \\ \left[\begin{array}{ccc} 0 & 4 & 0 \\ 4 & 0 & 1 \\ 0 & 1 & 0 \end{array} \right] \end{array}.$$

Typically, if a weights matrix is supplied an adjacency matrix is no longer needed, as a weight of 0 already indicates the absence of an edge. To this end, the weights matrix alone is typically enough to encode a network. Occasionally, the weights matrix is also called the (weighted) adjacency matrix.

Technical Box 3.1. Mathematical encoding of networks.

computed to make inferences about the structure of the network, or regarding the role that specific nodes have within the network. Roughly, these metrics can be divided into 'local' and 'global' metrics. Local metrics concern specific parts of the network, whereas global metrics relate to the network as a whole.

In network inference, it is again important to keep in mind what the networks represent, as well as the research question that is being asked. For example, when interested in the overall network structure, the appropriate metric to quantify this structure may be different for transportation than for psychological networks. Consequently, within different contexts (e.g., social networks, brain networks, psychology networks), different metrics have been proposed. Metrics originally proposed in relation to e.g., social networks can be informative for psychological networks too. Yet, it is important to critically consider how the metric is computed, and what the interpretation for your network could be. The metrics currently used to describe psychological networks are by no means set in stone but rather part of an ongoing discussion. As there are many metrics available, here we only list a selection. This list is thus by no means exhaustive, and the purpose is not to direct to all relevant metrics out there. Rather, the goal is to familiarize with the different available questions that can be asked about network properties, and match them with examples of metrics that pick up on those properties.

Local network properties

Research questions can relate to the role that specific nodes have in the estimated network. Initially, many of the local inferences made in psychological networks were based on centrality metrics developed in social network science, of which strength, closeness, and betweenness are most common (Opsahl et al., 2010). The computation and interpretation of these metrics are explained in the sections below. However, to quantify the role of specific nodes, there are many other metrics to turn to, of which some are specifically developed in the context of psychological networks, for example: expected influence (Robinaugh et al., 2016), predictability of nodes (Haslbeck et al., 2021), stabilizing and communicating nodes (Blanken et al., 2018). Alternatively, existing metrics can be adopted and adapted to suit specific study hypotheses (e.g., Letina et al., 2019). Different metrics will shed different light on the role a node might have, and as such can be used to answer different research questions.

Centrality

Centrality measures can be used to estimate the position and role of a node in a network. As detailed further in Chapter 4, a two-dimensional representation of the network cannot judge how 'central' a node is in the network: nodes placed in the center of the visualization are not necessarily important to the network architecture or well connected. Centrality metrics aim to quantify how 'central' a node is in the network. While many centrality metrics exist, we only focus here on a select few commonly used centrality metrics that have been generalized to weighted networks and directed networks (Opsahl et al., 2010; Robinaugh et al., 2016). These metrics can roughly be divided into two categories: metrics for directed connectivity, and metrics for indirect connectivity. For example, in the network $A - B - C$, a centrality metric of direct connectivity of the node A would only take its immediate connection to node B into account, whereas a centrality metric of indirect connectivity would also take its indirect connection to C (via B) into account.

Centrality metrics for direct connectivity.   Metrics for direct connectivity only investigate the immediate connections of a node. The most common metrics of direct connectivity are *node degree*, tallying the number of connected nodes regardless of their weight, *node strength*, summing the absolute edge weights connected to a node, and *one-step expected*

Opsahl et al. (2010) describe several generalizations of common centrality metrics for weighted graphs. These all use a tuning parameter α that can be used to place more emphasis on the presence/absence of connection in A ($\alpha = 0$) and the strength of connection in W ($\alpha = 1$). Unweighted variants can be obtained by setting $W = A$ or $\alpha = 0$. For all metrics below, let n be the number of nodes and i a node of interest.

One of the main metrics used in network science is the *node degree*, which counts the number of connected edges to a node (in this case, node i):

$$\text{Degree}(i) = \sum_{j=1}^{n} a_{ij},$$

in which a_{ij} is the element at row i and column j of the adjacency matrix A. The typical weighted variant is termed *node strength*, which sums over the absolute weights matrix instead of the adjacency matrix:

$$\text{Strength}(i) = \sum_{j=1}^{n} |w_{ij}|,$$

in which w_{ij} is the element at row i and column j of the weights matrix W. Opsahl's variant of node degree/strength is as follows:

$$\text{WeightedDegree}(i) = \sum_{j=1}^{n} a_{ij}^{1-\alpha} |w_{ij}|^{\alpha},$$

which reduces to the degree with $\alpha = 0$ and strength with $\alpha = 1$.
An alternative measure to node strength is one-step *expected influence*, which is virtually the same as node strength except that no absolute value is used (Robinaugh et al., 2016):

$$\text{ExpectedInfluence}_1(i) = \sum_{j=1}^{n} a_{ij} w_{ij}$$

Technical Box 3.2. Explanation of how to calculate centrality metrics that encode strength of direct connectivity.

influence, summing the edge weights connected to a node without taking the absolute value. If a node ranks high on metrics of direct centrality, this implies that it has (many) strong relations to other nodes in the network. In psychological networks, researchers have used these metrics aiming to extract information on the importance of a node for the state of all other nodes. Technical Box 3.2 explains these metrics of direct centrality in more detail.

Centrality metrics for indirect connectivity. In addition to centrality metrics that are based on direct connectivity, there are also several centrality metrics that are based on indirect connectivity. That is, these centrality metrics do not only take into account the nodes a node of interest is immediately connected to (sometimes termed the 'neighbors' of a node), but also the nodes that a node of interest is connected to via other nodes (e.g., neighbors of neighbors). The metric *two-step expected influence*, for example, takes into account every node that is connected in two steps to the node of interest. Other metrics of indirect centrality rely on the concept of *distance* between two nodes: the minimum number of steps it takes to go from one node to another node. In weighted graphs, the distance is determined by the length of each edge, which is typically quantified as the inverse of the absolute edge-weight. The metric of *closeness* quantifies how far removed a node is from every other node in the network, by taking the inverse of the sum of all distances from a node of interest to all other nodes. As such, from a node with a high closeness you can reach all other nodes relatively fast. The *betweenness*

The most important indirect centrality metrics rely on the concept of *shortest path length* or *geodesic distance* between two nodes: what is the shortest distance to go from one node to another node. To compute this, we first need to translate the weight of an edge to a hypothetical length of the edge. Opsahl et al. (2010) describe the following function to define the length of an edge between nodes i and j (including the absolute value operator to make edges positive):

$$\text{Length}(i, j) = \frac{1}{|w_{ij}|^\alpha}.$$

For unweighted networks $A = W$ can be used. As such, for unweighted networks (or when $\alpha = 0$) the length of an edge is 1 when the edge is present and ∞ when the edge is absent. For weighted networks, the edge is longer for edges with weaker weights. The shortest path length is then the minimal distance between two nodes:

$$\text{Distance}(i, j) = \min\left(w_{ik} + \ldots + w_{lj}\right).$$

The common centrality metric *closeness* makes use of this metric. Closeness is computed by taking the inverse of the sum of all distances from one node to all other nodes (also termed *farness*):

$$\text{Closeness}(i) = \frac{1}{\sum_{j=1}^{n} \text{Distance}(i, j)}.$$

Another common centrality metric is *betweenness*, which is computed by investigating how many shortest paths go through a node of interest:

$$\text{Betweenness}(i) = \sum_{<j,k>} \frac{\text{\# of shortest paths between nodes } j \text{ and } k \text{ that go through } i}{\text{\# of shortest paths between nodes } j \text{ and } k}.$$

Finally, an alternative metric for indirect connectivity is two-step *expected influence*, which looks at the strength of connection two steps away from a node (Robinaugh et al., 2016):

$$\text{ExpectedInfluence}_2(i) = \sum_{j=1}^{n} a_{ij} w_{ij} + \sum_{j=1}^{n} a_{ij} w_{ij} \sum_{k=1}^{n} a_{jk} w_{jk}$$

Technical Box 3.3. Explanation of how to calculate centrality metrics that encode strength of indirect connectivity.

centrality quantifies how often a node lies on the shortest path connecting any two other nodes, which directly reflects on the extent to which that node funnels the activity or influence between any two sets of nodes (Opsahl et al., 2010). As such, a node with high betweenness is a node that tends to connect clusters of nodes together. Technical Box 3.3 explains these metrics of indirect centrality in more detail.

Bridge centrality.   The above described centrality indices each quantify the connectivity of one node to potentially all other nodes in the network. Sometimes, however, it may not be interesting to look at how well a node connects to all other nodes in the network. For example, in symptom networks of multiple psychological disorders, we may expect that symptoms connect well with other symptoms from the same disorder (Epskamp et al., 2017). The topic of interest may be to only investigate how well symptoms connect to symptoms from *other* disorders, indicating that such symptoms may form bridges between clusters of disorders (Borsboom et al., 2011; Cramer et al., 2010). Jones et al. (2021) proposed a set of adaptions for the above described centrality indices that specifically look at connectivity across predefined clusters of nodes—*bridge centrality*. *Bridge strength* and *bridge expected influence* investigate how many and how strong the edges are between a node and nodes from different clusters, *bridge closeness* investigates how easy it is to reach all nodes belonging to other clusters from a particular node, and *bridge betweenness* investigates how often a node lies on the shortest paths between two different clusters.

Positive and negative edges.   One topic of interest is how some of the discussed centrality metrics differ is the way in which negative edge-weights are handled when computing the centrality indices. It may not be clear how negative edge-weights should be handled when computing centrality. This is because in most network applications studied in network science, edges can typically have only positive weights. For example, two people cannot interact less than 0 times per week with one another, and the distance between two cities, usually quantified with the inverse of the edge-weight, can at most be ∞, leading to a weight of 0. As we will learn later in this book, psychological networks can feature negative edges. For example, the association between two variables can be negative, implying that higher levels of one variable (e.g., amount of coffee someone drinks in a day) is negatively related to another variable (e.g., quality of sleep). It can be noted that we could arbitrarily re-code variables in such psychological networks to make this association positive. For example, instead of 'quality of sleep' a node could represent 'sleep problems,' making the association positive. To this end, a typical manner in which negative edges are handled is by taking the absolute value (making negative values positive). This way, a negative effect of, say, -0.2 is interpreted as just as strong as a positive effect of 0.2. This interpretation is used in default computations of node strength, but also closeness and betweenness, as these metrics rely on the definition of the length of an edge, which is typically defined as the inverse of the absolute edge weight. By not taking the absolute value, expected influence interprets negative edges and positive edges to potentially cancel one another out. This interpretation is sensible if the nodes in the network cannot arbitrarily be re-coded. For example, in a network in which nodes represent symptoms, the interpretation of the scales of the nodes is the same for every node (higher values indicate worse symptomatology). This makes negative edges substantively interpretable and not just an artifact due to encoding of the variables represented by the nodes.

Clustering

In addition to centrality metrics, another local property of nodes that is often investigated —although not very often in psychological networks—is the *clustering* of nodes. That is, to what extent do nodes in the network tend to cluster together? The *local clustering coefficient* takes one node of interest as a starting point and quantifies the proportion of nodes that is connected to that specific node and also to each other. In other words, it

---

The *local clustering coefficient* quantifies how well the nodes connected to a node of interest are also connected to one another. To explain this, we need to make a distinction between *triplets* and *triangles* in a network. A triplet is any sequence of three nodes that are connected in a chain, such as $A — B — C$. It does not matter for the triplet if A and C are connected as well. A triangle is a set of three nodes that are all connected to one another (e.g., $A — B — C — A$). As such, every triangle leads to three triplets, each containing one of the three nodes as middle node once: $A — B — C$, $B — C — A$, and $C — A — B$. Let $\tau_\Delta(i)$ indicate the number of times node i is in a triangle, and let $\tau_3(i)$ indicate the number of times node i is the middle node of a triplet. The local clustering coefficient can then be computed as follows:

$$\text{Clustering}(i) = \frac{\tau_\Delta(i)}{\tau_3(i)}.$$

The *global clustering coefficient* computes how well nodes cluster together on average in a network. One way to compute this is is by simply averaging the local clustering coefficients:

$$\text{Clustering}(G) = \frac{1}{n} \sum_{i=1}^{n} \text{Clustering}(i).$$

A problem with this metric is that it is an average of averages, and does not take into account that some nodes are more often the middle node of a triplet (i.e., are more central with more directed connections). To this end, the *transitivity* metric computes the global clustering directly using the number of triangles, $\tau_\Delta(G)$, and the number of triplets, $\tau_3(G)$, that are present in the graph, taking into account that there are three times more potential triplets in the graph than there are triangles:

$$\text{Transitivity}(G) = \frac{3 \times \tau_\Delta(G)}{\tau_3(G)}.$$

Of note, the clustering coefficients here are well defined for unweighted networks, but less well defined for weighted networks. While weighted variants exist, they are not without limitations and make interpretation of clustering harder. To this end, we do not discuss these weighted variants in this book.

Technical Box 3.4. Explanation of how to calculate the local and global clustering coefficient.

quantifies the proportion of neighbors of a node that are also neighbors to each other. In contrast to centrality metrics, local clustering can be interpreted as a metric of redundancy of a node. For example, in a social network of friendships, a person (node) with a high local clustering coefficient would have friends that are also friends with each other. The so-called redundancy of this person's role in the network can be illustrated by considering the spread of a virus through their network: a virus can more easily spread in a cluster of people that are all friends with one another, as there are many ways in which two people can infect each other in such a well-connected cluster; if an individual is removed from the network (e.g., vaccinated), others can still easily infect each other. As such, the role of the individual with high local clustering is less important for the spread of the virus than the role of an individual with low clustering. The local clustering coefficient is explained in more detail in Technical Box 3.4.

Global network properties

In addition to metrics quantifying local properties of networks, there are also several metrics that quantify the network architecture as a whole, termed *global network properties*. This architecture is sometimes referred to as the networks' topological structure: the organization of nodes and edges in the network. Knowing the architecture of a network conveys information on how quickly information or activity can travel through the system. Important features of the network architecture are, for example, the amount of clustering in a network (i.e., whether neighboring nodes are also neighbors), the overall connectivity of the network (i.e., how densely or strongly the nodes are connected to each other) or the existence of hubs (i.e., whether some nodes are more interconnected than others).

The network architecture is thought to be a key property of the network itself. For example, in brain networks the architecture is thought to reflect on the efficiency of information processing (Liu et al., 2017), in social networks the structure might reveal something about how gossip spreads through the network (Doerr et al., 2012), and in symptom networks the strength of the associations might reveal something about the vulnerability of the network (van Borkulo et al., 2014). These structures can be assessed using various global metrics, such as the clustering, degree distribution, or the connectivity of the network. There are some well-known network architectures such as *scale-free* or *small-world* networks, whose characteristic properties have been extensively studied. As such, if a network can be classified to follow a certain known network architecture, the research on the behavior of networks with this architecture can become relevant to the topic studied in an applied network analysis. This section discusses some of the most prominent global network properties.

Degree distributions

As discussed above, the most important and well-studied centrality metric is node degree, which tallies the number of connected nodes to a node of interest. A typical analysis for unweighted networks is to determine how node degree is distributed over the network. This concept is termed the *degree distribution*. The degree distribution dictates the expected number of connections per node, as well as the variance around that expected number. For example, a network in which edges are present or absent at random with

There are several metrics that can be used to quantify global connectivity in a network. For these metrics, we first need to know the total number of possible edges in a network. Let m represent the total number of possible edges. This number is then a direct function of the number of nodes n and the type of network studied. For example, for undirected networks that do not feature loops (edges from and to the same node), this number becomes:

$$m = n(n-1)/2.$$

However, if the network is directed and self-loops are included, this number becomes:

$$m = n^2.$$

The most straightforward metric is the unweighted *density* of a network, which gives a proportion of the number of present edges:

$$\text{Density}(G) = \frac{1}{m} \sum_{<i,j>} a_{ij},$$

in which $\sum_{<i,j>}$ denotes the sum over all unique edges: all $n(n+1)/2$ undirected edges in an undirected network or all n^2 directed edges in a directed network.[a] The *sparsity* of a network is simply the proportion of absent edges:

$$\text{Sparsity}(G) = 1 - \text{Density}(G).$$

For weighted networks, a weighted variant of density can be computed. There are several ways in which this is done, but the most common method is to take the average absolute edge-weight:

$$\text{WeightedDensity}(G) = \frac{1}{m} \sum_{<i,j>} |w_{ij}|.$$

Another metric of global connectivity that is often studied is the *average shortest path length* (APL), which is quantified by taking the average of all shortest path lengths (geodesic distance) between each pair of nodes:

$$\text{APL}(G) = \frac{1}{m} \sum_{<i,j>} \text{Distance}(i, j).$$

---

[a]Of note: the inclusion of self-loops in network density is questionable, and some software packages will only compute density for edges between different nodes by default.

Technical Box 3.5. Description of measures of global connectivity.

some probability, also termed an Erdös-Rényi model, will feature a degree distribution that is binomial, which looks similar to a normal distribution (bell shaped). In such a network, we expect every node to have similar degrees: some nodes will have more connections than others, but we don't expect some nodes to have many more connections than others. Decades of literature investigating the degree distributions of natural network structures have shown that 'real' networks rarely adhere to such a distribution. More common is a *power-law* or exponential distribution, in which some nodes (hubs) have many connections and thus a high degree and many nodes (spokes) have only few connections and thus a low degree. Such networks are termed *scale-free* networks.

Connectivity

In addition to studying average properties of the nodes in a network, it may also be interesting to study average properties of the edges in a network, for example by looking at if a network features many or few connections. Important metrics that are often discussed are the *density* and *sparsity* of a network. The density of a network quantifies the proportion of present connections, whereas the sparsity quantifies the proportion of absent connections. For weighted networks, a weighted density can also be computed by averaging the absolute edge weights. Density plays an important role in simulations of network dynamics, as further discussed in Chapter 13. Sparsity, on the other hand, plays an important role in the performance of network estimation procedures, as further discussed in Chapter 7. A final metric of connectivity is the *average shortest path length* (APL), which takes the average of the shortest distances between every pair of nodes. Technical Box 3.5 introduces these metrics in more detail.

Clustering and small-worldness

In addition to investigating how well nodes cluster around an individual node using local clustering coefficients, it may also be interesting to investigate how well nodes cluster together in a network on average. Technical Box 3.4 discusses the *global clustering coefficient* and *transitivity* of a network, two metrics for determining if nodes tend to cluster together. Watts and Strogatz (1998) describe an interesting relationship between the global clustering in a network and the APL of a network. They noted that in a network generated at random (Erdös-Rényi model), both the APL and the global clustering tends to be low. That is: on average it is easy to reach one node from another node, but nodes also do not tend to cluster together. On the other hand, a network can also be constructed that is highly organized, for example a network in which people only interact with their literal neighbors and neighbors of neighbors. Such a network will have a high clustering, but also a very high APL (it will take a very long time to go from one node to another node on average). Watts and Strogatz (1998) noted that many networks have properties somewhere in between these random and organized networks: networks are overall organized, but may include some random connections. This leads to a network structure in which both APL is low and global clustering is high, which is termed a *small-world* network. The small-world architecture is named after the six-degrees of separation phenomenon; the phenomenon that all people are, on average, only six social contacts away from each other. Such a phenomenon is only possible in a social network with high clustering and short characteristic path-lengths. A technical description of how small-worldness can be quantified can be seen in Technical Box 3.6.

Community detection

A final topic of interest in network analysis is the detection of clusters in a network. When a network is highly clustered, one can aim to identify these clusters using community detection. In community detection, the goal is to identify highly connected clusters (or communities) that exhibit greater connectivity within than between clusters. Statistically, many community detection algorithms have been developed that allow identifying such a structure, see for example Fortunato (2010) for an extensive overview. In psychological network analysis, community detection has become popular through the introduction of *exploratory graph analysis* (EGA; Golino & Demetriou, 2017; Golino & Epskamp, 2017), which utilizes cluster detection on estimated psychological networks to provide an alternative to exploratory factor analysis: to detect a potential latent variable structure underlying the data.

To quantify small-worldness of a network G, the APL and transitivity of that network can be compared to the APL and transitivity of a comparable random network (Erdös-Rényi model) with the same number of nodes and edges, G_R. A network can be said to feature a small world if the network has a comparable APL as a corresponding random network:

$$\text{APL}(G) \approx \text{APL}(G_R), \tag{3.1}$$

but also a much higher clustering than the comparable random network:

$$\text{Transitivity}(G) \gg \text{Transitivity}(G_R). \tag{3.2}$$

One way to summarize these quantities is through the *small-world index*:

$$\text{SmallWorld}(G) = \frac{\text{Transitivity}(G)/\text{Transitivity}(G_R)}{\text{APL}(G)/\text{APL}(G_R)}.$$

The denominator of this expression contains the quantities of Expression (3.1), and should be around 1 if that property holds. The numerator of this expression contains the quantities of Expression (3.2), and is therefore expected to be higher than 1 if this property holds. To this end, higher values of the small-world index indicate larger levels of small-worldness. A small-world index larger than 1 indicates that a network holds some small-world properties, although cutoffs of 3 and 6 are also proposed as more strict criteria.

Technical Box 3.6. Description of quantifying small-worldness.

Assuming the weights matrix of an unweighted and undirected network (in this case the *Lord of the Rings* network) is called W, the resulting network plot is called graph, and differing clusters are encoded in an object called clusters, we can use the code below to compute network metrics of interest. Please note that both the *qgraph* and *networktools* R packages need to be installed and loaded for the code to run:

Load packages:

```
library("qgraph"); library("networktools")
```

Number of nodes:

```
ncol(W)
```

Number of edges:

```
sum(W[lower.tri(W)])
```

Density:

```
mean(W[lower.tri(W)])
```

Centrality:

```
centrality(W)
```

Bridge centrality:

```
bridge(graph, communities = clusters,
  useCommunities = c("Elf","Dwarf"))
```

APL, transitivity and small-worldness:

```
smallworldIndex(qgraph(W))
```

N.B.: The .R file including all code and the data file to run this example are available on the *Companion Website*.

Tutorial Box 3.1. Computing network metrics for the *Lord of the Rings* network.

3.6 *Lord of the Rings* example

Figure 3.1 displays an example of a network that shows interactions between characters of the *Lord of the Rings* book series. This example is based on the work of Calvo Tello (2016), who provided the data online.[2] The original network structure was weighted with the edge weight indicating the number of times two characters were mentioned in the same paragraph. First, we transformed this network into an unweighted network by normalizing every edge: i.e., we dived the weight by the smallest number of times one of the two characters was mentioned (the maximum possible number of times two characters could be mentioned in a paragraph together). Subsequently, we connected two nodes together if the normalized number of interactions between these characters exceeded 0.15. The resulting network has 43 nodes and 75 edges, leading to a density of 0.08. By using

[2]https://github.com/morethanbooks/projects/tree/master/LotR

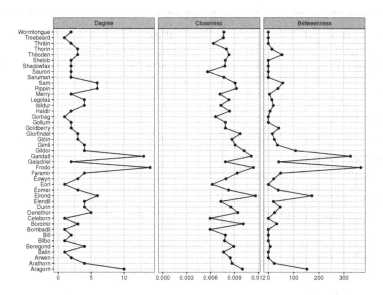

Figure 3.4. Centrality estimates of the *Lord of the Rings* network shown in Figure 3.1. This plot was created using the `centralityPlot` function in the *qgraph* package, which is further discussed in Chapter 4.

R, as further detailed in Tutorial Box 3.1, we can then compute several network metrics. The APL of the network is 2.95 and the transitivity of the network is 0.21. A comparable random network would have an APL of 3.05 and a transitivity of 0.08. The small world index becomes 2.67 (using unrounded APL and transitivity values), indicating that the network contains some small world properties. Figure 3.4 shows estimated centrality metrics (we will learn how to make this plot in the next chapter), indicating that the most central nodes are Frodo, Gandalf, and Aragorn, also the three main characters of the book series. We can in addition note the central role of Elrond, especially in terms of closeness and betweenness. Investigating the bridge centrality between the pre-defined clusters 'Dwarf' and 'Elf,' we find that the characters Legolas and Gimli feature high levels of bridge betweenness, which is in line with the theme of the friendship between these two characters forming a bridge between the rather disjoint societies of elves and dwarfs.

3.7   Conclusion

This chapter introduced networks and some of the most prominent ways of analyzing network structures in network science, including quantifying local network properties such as centrality and clustering of nodes, and global network properties such as the degree distribution and small-worldness of a network. The topics introduced here form the basics of network analysis, but do not nearly cover the full breadth of possibility network science has to offer. To this end, several books have been written that cover descriptive analysis of network structures in far more detail (e.g., Newman, 2010).

In psychological science, many scholars have voiced the need to conceptualize the cognitive and behavioral characteristics of individuals as complex and ever-evolving systems (Ferguson, 1954). The first instantiation of the data-driven methodology from network science followed from the introduction of the mutualism model by van der Maas et al. (2006). This model formalizes the idea that the cognitive system consists of many basic processes that, through their direct relations, form a network of cognitive components that cannot be understood without its interconnectedness. First taken up by the field of psychopathology, this idea has been applied to data on behavioral symptoms from individuals with diagnosed depression (Cramer et al., 2010). This work has caused a surge of empirical research on psychological systems as complex networks. As such, network science is fundamentally reshaping our approach to the ontology, etiology, and development of psychological phenomena (Borsboom, 2017). The remainder of this book will expand on both the methodological and theoretical developments in the field.

3.8 Exercises

Conceptual

3.1. What is the main difference between network structures analyzed in, e.g., social network or railroad network analysis, and the psychological networks analyzed in fields such as psychopathology?

3.2. What additional challenges does this difference present?

3.3. Describe why the absolute value is needed to translate a negative edge weight to an edge length.

3.4. In weighted networks in which the edge weights are real numbers (any continuous quantity), the betweenness metric typically is an integer (whole number). Describe why this is the case.

3.5. Describe the difference between the global clustering coefficient and transitivity.

True or false

3.6. Nodes can also be called *vertices*.

3.7. Node strength is usually calculated by summing up all the edge weights of edges connected to a given node.

3.8. In psychological networks nodes are always well-defined entities.

3.9. The local clustering coefficient can be seen as a measure of redundancy.

3.10. For a network to be a *small-world network* it is sufficient to display very high clustering.

Practical

For exercises in R, please navigate to the appropriate folder of this chapter, available on the online *Companion Website*.

References

Barabási, A.-L. (2012). The network takeover. *Nature Physics, 8*(1), 14–16.

Blanken, T. F., Deserno, M. K., Dalege, J., Borsboom, D., Blanken, P., Kerkhof, G. A., & Cramer, A. O. J. (2018). The role of stabilizing and communicating symptoms given overlapping communities in psychopathology networks. *Scientific Reports, 8*(1), 5854.

Borsboom, D. (2017). A network theory of mental disorders. *World Psychiatry, 16*(1), 5–13.

Borsboom, D., Cramer, A. O. J., Schmittmann, V. D., Epskamp, S., & Waldorp, L. J. (2011). The small world of psychopathology. *PLoS One, 6*(11), e27407.

Calvo Tello, J. (2016). Graph – network of the Lord of the Rings. http://www.morethanb ooks.eu/graph-network-of-the-lord-of-the-rings/

Cramer, A. O. J., Waldorp, L. J., van der Maas, H. L. J., & Borsboom, D. (2010). Comorbidity: A network perspective. *Behavioral and Brain Sciences, 33*(2-3), 137–150.

Doerr, B., Fouz, M., & Friedrich, T. (2012). Why rumors spread so quickly in social networks. *Communications of the ACM, 55*(6), 70–75.

Epskamp, S., Kruis, J., & Marsman, M. (2017). Estimating psychopathological networks: Be careful what you wish for. *PLoS One, 12*(6), e0179891.

Euler, L. (1736). Solutio problematis ad geometriam situs pertinentis. *Commentarii Academiae Scientiarum Petropolitanae, 8*, 128–140.

Ferguson, G. A. (1954). On learning and human ability. *Canadian Journal of Psychology/Revue canadienne de psychologie, 8*(2), 95–112.

Fortunato, S. (2010). Community detection in graphs. *Physics Reports, 486*(3-5), 75–174.

Golino, H. F., & Demetriou, A. (2017). Estimating the dimensionality of intelligence like data using exploratory graph analysis. *Intelligence, 62*, 54–70.

Golino, H. F., & Epskamp, S. (2017). Exploratory graph analysis: A new approach for estimating the number of dimensions in psychological research. *PLoS One, 12*(6), e0174035.

Haslbeck, J. M. B., Bringmann, L. F., & Waldorp, L. J. (2021). A tutorial on estimating time-varying vector autoregressive models. *Multivariate Behavioral Research, 56*(1), 120–149.

Ings, T. C., Montoya, J. M., Bascompte, J., Blüthgen, N., Brown, L., Dormann, C. F., Edwards, F., Figueroa, D., Jacob, U., Jones, J. I., et al. (2009). Ecological networks–beyond food webs. *Journal of Animal Ecology, 78*(1), 253–269.

Jones, P. J., Ma, R., & McNally, R. J. (2021). Bridge centrality: A network approach to understanding comorbidity. *Multivariate Behavioral Research, 56*(2), 353–367.

Letina, S., Blanken, T. F., Deserno, M. K., & Borsboom, D. (2019). Expanding network analysis tools in psychological networks: Minimal spanning trees, participation coefficients, and motif analysis applied to a network of 26 psychological attributes. *Complexity, 2019,* 9424605.

Liu, J., Li, M., Pan, Y., Lan, W., Zheng, R., Wu, F.-X., & Wang, J. (2017). Complex brain network analysis and its applications to brain disorders: A survey. *Complexity, 2017,* 8362741.

Newman, M. (2010). *Networks: An introduction.* Oxford University Press.

Opsahl, T., Agneessens, F., & Skvoretz, J. (2010). Node centrality in weighted networks: Generalizing degree and shortest paths. *Social Networks, 32*(3), 245–251.

Robinaugh, D. J., Millner, A. J., & McNally, R. J. (2016). Identifying highly influential nodes in the complicated grief network. *Journal of Abnormal Psychology, 125*(6), 747–757.

Scott, J. (1988). Social network analysis. *Sociology, 22*(1), 109–127.

Steyvers, M., & Tenenbaum, J. B. (2005). The large-scale structure of semantic networks: Statistical analyses and a model of semantic growth. *Cognitive Science, 29*(1), 41–78.

van Borkulo, C. D., Borsboom, D., Epskamp, S., Blanken, T. F., Boschloo, L., Schoevers, R. A., & Waldorp, L. J. (2014). A new method for constructing networks from binary data. *Nature: Scientific Reports, 4*(5918).

van der Maas, H. L. J., Dolan, C. V., Grasman, R. P., Wicherts, J. M., Huizenga, H. M., & Raijmakers, M. E. (2006). A dynamical model of general intelligence: The positive manifold of intelligence by mutualism. *Psychological Review, 113*(4), 842–861.

Watts, D. J., & Strogatz, S. H. (1998). Collective dynamics of 'small-world' networks. *Nature, 393*(6684), 440–442.

Chapter 4

Constructing and Drawing Networks in *qgraph*

Adela-Maria Isvoranu[1] & Sacha Epskamp[1,2]

1. University of Amsterdam, Department of Psychology

2. University of Amsterdam, Centre for Urban Mental Health

4.1 Introduction

While many more visualization tools and packages exist for network analysis, this textbook will focus on *qgraph* as the main visualization software. *qgraph* is a package for R, developed in the context of network approaches to psychology and designed as an interface to visualize data through network modeling techniques (Epskamp et al., 2012). The *qgraph* package was developed with the goal to enable researchers new to R to easily visualize non-sparse weighted graphs—the main network structures discussed throughout this textbook. Further, while offering easy usability for beginner R users, *qgraph* also offers more advanced customization options for experienced R users. This chapter covers some of the basic functionality of *qgraph* that can be used to visualize and analyze network structures.

4.2 *qgraph* functionality

Tutorial Box 4.1 explains how the *qgraph* package can be loaded in R. The main function in *qgraph* is called qgraph(). Most of the other functions that can be used are either wrapping functions around qgraph() or functions used in qgraph(). While a lot of

Cite this chapter as:

Isvoranu, A. M., & Epskamp, S. (2022). Chapter 4. Constructing and drawing networks in *qgraph*. In Isvoranu, A. M., Epskamp, S., Waldorp, L. J., & Borsboom, D. (Eds.). *Network psychometrics with R: A guide for behavioral and social scientists.* Routledge, Taylor & Francis Group.

other arguments can be specified within qgraph(), the only mandatory argument is the *input* argument. The *input* argument can be an edge-list or a weights matrix.

---

qgraph is available from the Comprehensive R Archive Network (CRAN) at http://CRAN. R-project.org/package=qgraph. You can install the latest version of *qgraph* from CRAN using the code below in RStudio:

```
install.packages("qgraph", dep=TRUE)
```

Please note that having up-to-date versions of R, RStudio, and *qgraph* is extremely important, as most of the errors encountered when trying to install new packages result from outdated versions of software or packages. In addition, if R asks whether any packages should be installed from source you can decline this, as installing packages from source can create problems on some computers and it is usually not a necessary step in installation.

After installing *qgraph*, you can load the package with the following command:

```
library("qgraph")
```

As highlighted in Chapter 2, it is sufficient to install the package once, but loading the package is required every time you open a new RStudio session. You can check the package version of *qgraph* with the following code:

```
packageVersion("qgraph")
```

Tutorial Box 4.1. Installing and loading the *qgraph* package.

Input. An edge-list is a matrix with two or three columns, in which each row represents an edge, the first column the node of origin, the second column the node of destination, and the optional third column the edge weight. The weights matrix, further detailed in Tutorial Box 4.2, is a square matrix that encodes the strength of connection between nodes, as previously explained in Chapter 3. Such weights matrices occur naturally in statistics. For example, correlations, covariances, (lag-1) regression parameters and so forth are all common statistics that can be used as a weight matrix input in *qgraph*. As such, *qgraph* can be used to visualize such parameters using network representations (Epskamp et al., 2012). Of note, while such matrices can be used as input to *qgraph*, they do not yet represent the main network structures we will focus on in the remainder of this book (for continuous data: partial correlations rather than marginal correlations).

Edge colors. The edges within a network plotted using qgraph() are colored according to the sign of the edge weight, without the need of any additional arguments: green is used to indicate a positive relation and red is used to indicate a negative relation. The thickness of the edges is used as an indication of the absolute magnitude of the relation (e.g., for the case of a correlation, thicker edges would represent higher correlations). Of note, because green and red are problematic colors for colorblindness, newer standard practices in the field of network psychometrics recommend using colorblind friendly edge colors. An additional argument in qgraph() can be used for this, specifically the theme="colorblind" argument, also shown in Tutorial Box 4.3. This will plot positive edges as blue and negative edges as red. This is also the format in which all network structures will be presented throughout this textbook, and we recommend using it when constructing your own network structures.

A weights matrix can be used to code the connectivity structures between nodes in a network structure. A weights matrix is a square $n \times n$ matrix (where n represents the number of nodes), in which each element indicates a relationship between two nodes. The rows indicate the node of origin, while the columns indicate the node of destination. Any value can be used as long as 0 is used to indicate the absence of a connection and absolute negative values are similar in strength to positive values.

Of note, the structure of the matrix will drive the resulting plot. If a non-symmetric matrix is provided as input, a *directed* network will be plotted. If a symmetric matrix is provided as input, an *undirected* network will be plotted. If all diagonal elements are 0 or 1 self-loops are not included in the network unless diag=TRUE. Finally, if all elements of the matrix are 0 and 1, an *unweighted* network will be plotted.

As a running example, consider the following weights matrix:

$$
W = \begin{array}{c c} & \begin{array}{cccccc} \text{A1} & \text{A2} & \text{A3} & \text{B1} & \text{B2} & \text{B3} \end{array} \\ \begin{array}{c} \text{A1} \\ \text{A2} \\ \text{A3} \\ \text{B1} \\ \text{B2} \\ \text{B3} \end{array} & \left[\begin{array}{cccccc} 0 & 0.5 & 0.4 & 0 & 0 & -0.1 \\ 0.5 & 0 & 0.3 & -0.3 & 0 & 0 \\ 0.4 & 0.3 & 0 & 0 & 0 & 0 \\ 0 & -0.3 & 0 & 0 & 0.4 & 0.3 \\ 0 & 0 & 0 & 0.4 & 0 & 0.2 \\ -0.1 & 0 & 0 & 0.3 & 0.2 & 0 \end{array} \right] \end{array}.
$$

This matrix, which encodes the network shown in Figure 4.1, can be loaded into R with the following command:

```
W <- matrix(
  c(0,    0.5, 0.4,  0,    0,   -0.1,
    0.5, 0,    0.3, -0.3, 0,    0,
    0.4, 0.3, 0,    0,    0,    0,
    0,   -0.3, 0,    0,    0.4, 0.3,
    0,    0,   0,    0.4, 0,    0.2,
   -0.1, 0,   0,    0.3, 0.2, 0),
  nrow = 6, ncol = 6, byrow = TRUE
)
```

Subsequently, the matrix can be visualized in *qgraph* with:

```
qgraph(W)
```

Tutorial Box 4.2. Weights matrices as input to qgraph.

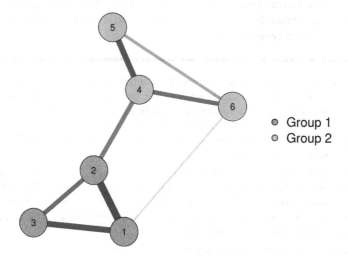

Figure 4.1. Visualization of the running example, created with the code from Tutorial Box 4.4.

To aid data interpretation and visualization, further arguments can be of help. The `groups` argument allows specifying which nodes belong together (e.g., in the same cluster). Nodes defined as belonging together will be plotted using the same color, and a legend is included with the names of the cluster and/or the names of every element (see Tutorial Box 4.3).

Node placement.   The location on which each individual node is placed in the network visualization is termed the *layout* of the network. For weighted undirected networks, the predefined layout in `qgraph()` is the *circular* layout. This means that without the need of any additional arguments, all nodes will be placed in a circle when plotting a network structure. If the `groups` argument, further explained in Tutorial Box 4.3, is specified alongside the input argument, then nodes belonging together will be placed together in smaller circles. For other types of networks (unweighted and directed networks), the default layout is a spring layout as discussed in more detail below.

The layout can be changed according to preference, by using the `layout` argument in `qgraph()`. This can be an $n \times 2$ matrix (where n represents the number of nodes) indicating the x and y position of each node on a coordinate plane. These coordinates can be on any scale and will be by default rescaled to fit the network. Manually specifying the layout of every node can be a lot of work, especially in the case of larger network structures and as such is not common practice. Alternatively, the layout can be a character indicating one of the two default layouts: `default="circular"` or `default="spring"`. The latter argument is a popular algorithm when visualizing psychological networks, and is a modified version of the force-embedded algorithm proposed by Fruchterman and Reingold (1991). This algorithm—also termed the Fruchterman-Reingold algorithm—uses an iterative process to compute a layout such that nodes with higher centrality (i.e., more connected nodes) will be pulled towards the centre of the network and the more disconnected nodes will be placed closer to the periphery of the network. Plotting a network using this force-embedded algorithm is shown in Tutorial Box 4.3.

Important to note is that this algorithm exhibits chaotic behavior. This means that with the exact input the exact same placement of nodes is obtained, but also that with tiny differences in the input a very different node placement can be returned (e.g., the butterfly effect). For example, even a change of 001 in an edge weight may result in a different placement of the nodes. This can have implications for comparing two (or more network structures), as differing layouts may give the impression of more differences between the structures than actual differences. Therefore when comparing network structures, we always recommend using the same layout. *qgraph* allows forcing another network to have the same layout as the first network, or to average the layout across multiple network structures (see Tutorial Box 4.3).

Other useful arguments, alongside their descriptions, are presented in Table 4.1. The qgraph() documentation help file (which can be accessed using the code ?qgraph) includes a list of all arguments that can be used within the function.

We can form a *groups* list to encode which nodes belong together. This information is used for the coloring of the nodes, the legend next to the network, and the placement of the nodes if a circular layout is used. There are two options to encode the groups argument. The first is through a list in which each element contains an integer vector encoding which nodes belong to a group:

```
groups <- list("Group 1" = 1:3, "Group 2" = 4:6)
```

The second option is by using a vector with the group membership per node:

```
groups <- c("Group 1", "Group 1", "Group 1",
            "Group 2", "Group 2", "Group 2")
```

Both specifications will lead to the same output. Next we can use this object in qgraph():

```
qgraph(W, groups = groups, theme = "colorblind", layout = "spring")
```

Here, the argument theme = "colorblind" encodes that a colorblind friendly theme is used, and the argument layout = "spring" encodes that the placement of the nodes is controlled through the Fruchterman-Reingold algorithm. Within the layout argument an object containing an exact placement of the nodes can also be specified. For example, such an object can be obtained through the averageLayout function, which runs the Fruchterman-Reingold algorithm on an averaged network. Suppose we have three more networks, W2, W3 and W4, then we can compute the averaged layout as follows:

```
L <- averageLayout(W, W2, W3, W4)
```

which could subsequently be used in qgraph() with the argument layout = L.

Tutorial Box 4.3. Example of specifying groups and a force-embedded layout for placing the nodes.

4.3   *qgraph* **interpretation**

In order to interpret the edges drawn in weighted *qgraph* networks, three arguments are essential: the *minimum*, *maximum*, and *cut* arguments. This section will detail the use of these arguments. Figure 4.2 displays two examples of the scaling of the edge width and color. Figure 4.2a displays the edge scaling for a network structure with no minimum and maximum values specified and cut disabled, while Figure 4.2b displays the edge scaling for a network structure with a minimum value of 0.1, a cut value of 0.4, and a maximum value of 1. Note that while Figure 4.2b creates the illusion that edges scale in both width and saturation, in reality the edges with an absolute strength above 0.4 only scale in width (same color) while the other edges only scale in color (same width).

Table 4.1 Common arguments used in the `qgraph()` function

Argument	Description
asize	Sets the size of arrows
bidirectional	Defines if edges are bidirectional
color	Sets the color of nodes
curve	Sets the curvature of multiple edges between two nodes
cut	Splits scaling in color and width of edges
details	Set to TRUE to display minimum, cut, and maximum
directed	Defines if edges are directed or undirected
edge.color	Sets the color of edges
edge.labels	Adds edge labels to the edges
edge.label.cex	Sets the size of the edge labels
esize	Sets the size of edges
fade	Logical that can be used to disable fading of edges (not recommended)
filename	Name of the file to save the plot to
filetype	Type of file to save the plot to
GLratio	The relative width of the network compared to the legend
groups	Colors nodes and adds a legend
layout	Specifies how nodes should be placed in the network
legend	TRUE or FALSE to control if a legend is plotted
legend.cex	Size of the legend
mar	Defines the size of the margins around the network
maximum	Treated as invisible edge that can fix scaling of edge color/width
minimum	Defines the smallest absolute edge weight that is visualized in the network
negCol	Sets the color of negative edges
nodeNames	Adds a legend with specific names per node
palette	Sets the color palette used to color nodes of different groups
parallelEdge	Makes multiple edges between nodes parallel instead of curved
pie	Displays values in a pie chart around each node
posCol	Sets the color of positive edges
repulsion	Controls the repulsion of nodes in legend = "spring"
shape	Sets the shape of the nodes
theme	Overwrites posCol, negCol, unCol, palette and some other arguments
threshold	Removes edges with an absolute weight lower than this value
vsize	Sets the size of nodes
unCol	Sets the color of unweigthed edges
XKCD	Makes edges and nodes appear handdrawn

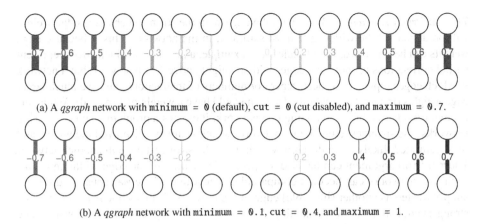

(a) A *qgraph* network with `minimum = 0` (default), `cut = 0` (cut disabled), and `maximum = 0.7`.

(b) A *qgraph* network with `minimum = 0.1`, `cut = 0.4`, and `maximum = 1`.

Figure 4.2. Contrasting the visualization of network structures under different *qgraph* arguments.

The `minimum` *argument.* By default, edges are displayed with wider and/or more colorful lines if the corresponding edge weight is stronger. An edge with the weight of exactly 0 is not displayed, and an edge with a weight very close to 0 is displayed as very thin and almost white—usually barely visible. The `minimum` argument can be used to change this lower point of the scaling. For example, if `minimum = 0.2`, any edge with an absolute edge weight below 0.2 will not be drawn, and edges with absolute weights near 0.2 will be very thin and/or hardly visible. The `minimum` argument can therefore be used to effectively omit edges with absolute weights equal to and under this value. Note that using this argument will hide edges, but they will not be removed (i.e., thresholded) from the network—it is simply a visualization aid. Using the minimum value is only recommended in very dense networks (e.g., a visualization of a marginal correlation matrix), and not recommended for the network structures discussed in this textbook (e.g., a sparse pairwise Markov random field), as other statistical tools (discussed in later chapters) will be employed to account for potential spurious associations.

The `cut` *argument.* The `cut` argument is used to split the scaling of width and saturation. When used, edges with an absolute weight equal to and under this value will have the smallest width, but will continue to scale in color (i.e., will become more saturated as they reach the cut value). Edges with an absolute weight above this value will have full color saturation, but will continue to scale in width (i.e., will become wider with stronger edge weights). This allows highlighting important edges, making it a useful argument especially in very large network structures. Setting `cut = 0` will disable the cutoff, making all edges scale in both width and saturation instead.[1] The `cut` argument defaults to 0 (disabled) for network structures with less than 20 nodes, but it is automatically set to a convenient value for larger network structures. We recommend, however, to set `cut = 0` to disable this behavior, and only use this behavior when needed.

---

[1] Of note, any value for `cut` other than 0 will enable cutting scaling in width and color. Therefore, `cut = 0` and `cut = .0001` will lead to very different results.

The `maximum` *argument.*   By default, the edge with the strongest absolute edge weight will be displayed the widest and most saturated in the network. This is because edge weights can be on very different scales. For example, a network in which edges represent partial correlations cannot have edges with a weight above 1 or below −1, but a network in which edges represent co-occurrences or numbers of interactions can have much larger edge weights (in fact, the smallest edge then would have a weight of 1 instead). While this behavior works well for visualizing one network, it creates a problem when comparing networks: the strongest edge in one network, which is always displayed the widest and most saturated, likely has a different weight than the strongest edge in another network. The `maximum` argument can be used to specify the scaling of the edge width and color such that networks can become comparable. The value of the `maximum` argument is simply treated as another (invisible) edge in the network: if this value is lower than the strongest edge in the network, nothing changes, but if it is higher than the strongest edge in the network, edges will instead scale to this maximum.

The best way to store a network is by explicitly saving the plot to a graphical device. For example, the R function `pdf` can be used to open a pdf device, in which you can subsequently store plots. The R function `dev.off()` finally closes the device and finishes the file:

```
# Create an empty pdf file in your working directory:
pdf("qgraph_output.pdf", width = 1.4 * 4, height = 4)

# Plot your network structure in the pdf file opened above:
qgraph(W, groups = groups, theme = "colorblind", layout = "spring")

# Close your pdf file:
dev.off()
```

Here we made the width of the PDF file 1.4 times the height of the PDF file to ensure the aspect ratio of the network is correct. Please note that R can sometimes return faulty output, indicating that the PDF file was not closed. If this happens, make sure to run `dev.off()` enough times until R returns the message *NULL DEVICE*. An alternative to the code above is to use the `qgraph` arguments `filename` and `filetype`:

```
qgraph(W, groups = groups, theme = "colorblind", layout = "spring",
filename = "qgraph_output", filetype = "pdf", width = 4, height = 4)
```

Now, *qgraph* recognized that a legend was included and automatically increased the width of the canvas to match this. The figure created with this code can be seen in Figure 4.1. The `filetype` argument allows for some other devices to be used, such as *png*, *jpeg*, and *tiff* devices. However, the first version described in this Tutorial Box is more general, as any device can then be used to store the plots, including more advanced graphical devices such as `CairoPNG()` from the *cairo* package.

Tutorial Box 4.4. Storing a *qgraph* network in a PDF file.

The details *argument.* If set to TRUE, the details argument will print the minimum, maximum, and cut values under the network structure.

To summarize, by default, the color saturation and the width of the edge weights will scale from the value specified by the minimum argument to the highest absolute weight in your particular network structure (e.g., in the case of a correlation this could be 0.4, 0.9, or 1) or the value of the maximum argument. If the cut argument is used (or if the network contains more than 20 nodes), the scaling in width and saturation is cut based on the value of the cut argument. Setting all three arguments is therefore essential when aiming to make two network structures comparable.

4.4 Saving *qgraph* networks

Finally, after the network is constructed in R the last step is to save the network visualization to a file. This is not entirely trivial to do using *qgraph*. An important reason for this is that when creating the visualization, the qgraph() function takes the dimensions of the plotting canvas into account. Because of this, graphs made using *qgraph* cannot be manually rescaled, and therefore also the RStudio *Export* functionality cannot be used to directly save your network graph. Doing so will lead to very ugly networks, in which nodes are no longer circles and edges may not connect well to the borders of nodes. As such, networks should be stored using R syntax, as explained in more detail in Tutorial Box 4.4. The aspect ratio of the visualization should be square if no legend is used. If a legend is used with default arguments, the width should be 1.4 times the height of the file.[2] For best results and high-resolution, publication-ready images we recommend always saving your network structure in a *PDF* device, as such the file will contain all elements of the networks (circles and lines) rather than rasterized versions of the network figure. To this end, a network stored in PDF format can always be displayed with perfect resolution even when zoomed in. Alternatively, the *Cairo* package for R (Urbanek & Horner, 2020) provides some powerful capabilities of storing an R plot in a rasterized file (e.g., PNG, JPEG, TIFF) that tend to work better than the options provided by base R.

4.5 Descriptive analysis of networks using *qgraph*

While the *qgraph* package is mostly designed for visualization and for some network estimation procedures, the package also contains limited methods for analyzing network structures. Mainly, as further detailed in Tutorial Box 4.5, the weighted variants of centrality indices discussed in Chapter 3 are included in the centrality() function. The centralityPlot() function can subsequently be used to visualize the centrality estimates. Of note, this function by default displays the centrality estimates as *z*-scores, which is not recommended. To this end, we always recommend using the argument scale = "raw" or scale = "raw0" to plot centrality indices on their proper scale. A similar function, clusteringPlot exists in the *qgraph* package for clustering coefficients. For

---

[2]The relative width of the network compared to the legend is controlled with the GLratio argument. The default value of 2.5 indicates that the network canvas is 2.5 times wider than the legend canvas. This indicates that the width of the total canvas is $(2.5 + 1)/2.5 = 1.4$ times the height of the total canvas.

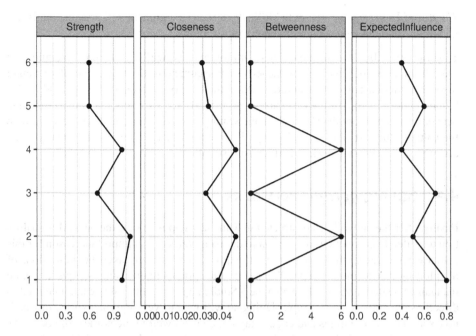

Figure 4.3. Centrality plot of centrality metrics in the running example.

more advanced methods of analyzing network structures, we recommend the popular R package *igraph* (Csardi & Nepusz, 2006). The function `as.igraph` in the *qgraph* package can be used to create an *igraph* R object from the output of *qgraph*.

4.6 Conclusion

This chapter introduced the *qgraph* package for R, which can be used to visualize networks. The package relies on one main function, `qgraph()`, which takes a weights matrix as input and plots the network. Several arguments can be used to control the visualization, as well as to make networks comparable. While certainly not the only network visualization tool available, *qgraph* is convenient to use in network psychometrics as the package has been developed alongside many of the methods discussed in the remainder of this book. The latest, developmental version of the package can be found on the Github website,[3] which can also be used for questions and/or bug reports.

_____

[3]https://github.com/SachaEpskamp/qgraph

The *qgraph* package can be used to investigate the centrality of nodes. The weights matrix W or the output of qgraph(W, ...) can be used as input to the centrality function to compute a set of centrality metrics:[a]

```
centrality(W, alpha = 1)
```

The argument alpha = 1 sets the α parameter discussed in Chapter 3. Alternatively, the centrality_auto function (which only uses the commonly used $\alpha = 1$) can be used, which is a wrapper around centrality that automizes some things:

```
centrality_auto(W)
```

For example, centrality_auto automatically picks the correct names for centrality indices (e.g., node strength instead of degree), for unconnected graphs centrality_auto computes closeness only for the largest component of connected nodes, and for undirected graphs betweenness is computed counting paths between two nodes once instead of twice. The centralityPlot function uses centrality_auto to visualize centrality indices in a *ggplot2* object (Wickham, 2016):

```
centralityPlot(W, scale = "raw0", include = c("Strength",
                "Closeness", "Betweenness", "ExpectedInfluence"))
```

The scale = "raw0" argument specifies that centrality indices are drawn using their original scale and that zero is included on the x-axis (the default is to plot z-values of the centrality indices, which is not recommended), and the include argument specifies which centrality indices should be included. The resulting figure can be seen in Figure 4.3. For clustering coefficients, *qgraph* includes the functions clustcoef_auto and clusteringPlot which work comparable to centrality_auto and centralityPlot.

---

[a]Sometimes qgraph() is used with a correlation matrix as input coupled with the graph argument to create, for example, a partial correlation matrix. This is outdated functionality that is no longer recommended. When this is used, it is important to note that the input correlation matrix is *not* the weights matrix of the network. To this end, the output of qgraph() should then be used as input to centrality().

Tutorial Box 4.5. Using *qgraph* to obtain and visualize centrality estimates.

4.7 Exercises

Conceptual

4.1. What are the two main types of input that we can use in qgraph()? Which type of input will we mainly use in this course and why?

4.2. Explain the difference between the minimum argument and the threshold argument in qgraph().

4.3. Suppose the argument GLratio = 3 is used. Would then (a) the width of the legend canvas be smaller or larger compared to default setup, and (b) how large should the width of the plot be with respect to the height to retain proper aspect ratio?

4.4. Describe how Figure 4.2a would change if the argument `maximum = 0.3` was used.

4.5. Change the edge-weight between nodes 1 and 2 in W to 0.5001, and plot the network using the Fruchterman-Reingold algorithm. Is the placement of the nodes very different as the original placement? And is the network structure itself very different than the original network structure? Explain why.

True or false

4.6. The `qgraph()` function in R requires several arguments to be specified in order to return a network structure.

4.7. If a non-symmetric matrix in provided as input in `qgraph()`, a directed network will be plotted.

4.8. If diagonal elements of a matrix used as input in `qgraph()` are different than 0 or 1, self-loops will be included in the network structure automatically.

4.9. For weighted undirected networks, the predefined layout in `qgraph()` is the *spring* layout.

4.10. It is recommended to use the RStudio *Export* functionality to directly save your *qgraph* network.

Practical

For practical exercises in R, please navigate to the appropriate folder of this chapter, available on the online *Companion Website*.

References

Csardi, G., & Nepusz, T. (2006). The igraph software package for complex network research. *InterJournal, Complex Systems*, 1695.

Epskamp, S., Cramer, A. O. J., Waldorp, L. J., Schmittmann, V. D., Borsboom, D., Waldrop, L. J., Schmittmann, V. D., & Borsboom, D. (2012). qgraph : Network visualizations of relationships in psychometric data. *Journal of Statistical Software*, *48*(4), 1–18.

Fruchterman, T., & Reingold, E. (1991). Graph drawing by force-directed placement. *Software: Practice and Experience*, *21*(11), 1129–64.

Urbanek, S., & Horner, J. (2020). *Cairo: R graphics device using Cairo graphics library for creating high-quality bitmap (PNG, JPEG, TIFF), vector (PDF, SVG, PostScript) and display (X11 and Win32) output* [R package version 1.5-12.2]. R package version 1.5-12.2. https://CRAN.R-project.org/package=Cairo

Wickham, H. (2016). *ggplot2: Elegant graphics for data analysis*. Springer-Verlag New York.

Chapter 5

Association and Conditional Independence

Lourens J. Waldorp[1], Denny Borsboom[1], & Sacha Epskamp[1,2]

1. University of Amsterdam, Department of Psychology

2. University of Amsterdam, Centre for Urban Mental Health

5.1 Introduction

As described in the previous chapters, a network consists of nodes and edges. Nodes represent entities, and edges represent relations between those entities. In the remainder of this book, we will take nodes to represent variables (e.g., symptoms, attitudes), and edges to represent the strength of association between two variables, after controlling for all other variables (or all other variables at the previous time-point in the case of time series analysis). Two variables are *associated* (or dependent) if learning something about one of the variables allows one to make a better prediction of the value of the other variable. *Conditional association* is the same, but now we control for a third (and fourth, fifth, etc.) variable.

Figure 5.1 shows examples of these concepts (inspired by an example of Koller and Friedman, 2009). The visualizations show hypothetical data of students measured on their motivation to work hard for a particular class, the difficulty of that class, the grade obtained for that class, and if students eventually obtained a diploma for the program. Tutorial Box 5.1 at the end of this chapter shows how these data can be generated. The left panel shows that the motivation of students is *marginally* (without controlling for other variables) not associated with (independent of) the difficulty of the class. Interestingly,

---

Cite this chapter as:

    Waldorp, L. J., Borsboom, D., & Epskamp, S. (2022). Chapter 5. Association and conditional independence. In Isvoranu, A. M., Epskamp, S., Waldorp, L. J., & Borsboom, D. (Eds.). *Network psychometrics with R: A guide for behavioral and social scientists*. Routledge, Taylor & Francis Group.

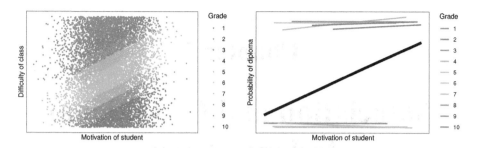

Figure 5.1. Two visualizations of the data generated in Tutorial Box 5.1. Left: motivation of students is independent of difficulty of class, but no longer after conditioning on grade. Right: there is an association between motivation of student and probability of getting a diploma (black line), but no longer when controlling for grade (colored lines).

however, these two variables become associated when controlling for grade: if we know the grade a student obtained, we can suddenly see a strong association between the two variables. As such, in the network model we would draw an edge between difficulty of class and motivation of students, as they are conditionally associated.

The absence of an edge will indicate some form of conditional independence: after controlling for other variables there is no dependency (correlation when variables are continuous) between the two variables represented by the nodes in the network. This concept can be seen on the right panel of Figure 5.1: after controlling for the grade of a student, the motivation of that student does not matter for the probability of obtaining a diploma. As such, in a network representation we would then not draw an edge between motivation of students and probability of obtaining a diploma.

As independence and conditional independence are central to the interpretation of psychometric network models, we will provide a short introduction to these concepts in this chapter.

5.2   Independence and dependence

There are many ways in which variables can statistically depend on each other, and one could easily spend a lifetime studying those; many readers will have come across things like odds-ratios, tetrachoric and polychoric correlations, Kendall's tau coefficients, Pearson and Spearman correlations, mutual information measures, and a host of other statistical metrics for capturing the many ways in which dependence can arise. Indeed, many of these metrics play a role in this book. While there are many ways to represent dependence, there is only one way to define *in*dependence. And since that definition is crucial to every application of network modeling, we will start by defining what independence means.

Two variables are statistically independent if learning the value of one of them gives you no information about the other. The classic example is throwing two coins: Coin *A* and Coin *B*. Suppose that both these coins can be flipped and can land either on 'heads' or 'tails.' To model this behavior, we need to model the probability of reaching such outcomes. Let P represent a probability function. For example, for Coin A we can state that the probability of heads is 0.5: $P(\text{Coin } A = \text{heads}) = 0.5$. To simplify notation, let A represent specifically the event that Coin A lands on heads. Then we can simplify this expression as $P(A) = 0.5$. We can also define the probability of landing on tails as $P(\neg A) = 0.5$, where $\neg A$ stands for 'not A.' Whether Coin A falls heads or tails tells us nothing about what Coin B will do or vice versa. In statistical terms, this means that the probability that Coin A will fall heads, given that Coin B has fallen heads (B)—denoted $P(A \mid B)$—is the same as the probability that Coin A will fall heads, given that Coin B has fallen tails—denoted $P(A \mid \neg B)$. That is: $P(A) = P(A \mid B) = P(A \mid \neg B) = 0.5$. This is an intuitive definition and you would do well to pause and ponder it, because understanding this definition and keeping it in mind throughout this book will help you understand the models conceptually, even if you do not see through all the details. The probability $P(A \mid B)$ is called a *conditional probability*, because to compute it we only consider the frequency with which we find that A occurs, in the subset of cases where B occurs.

Table 5.1 and Table 5.2 represent situations in which we encounter independence and dependence. Table 5.1 describes a hypothetical probability distribution of two variables, and denotes the probability that an individual has insomnia (I) and whether they have depressed mood (D). For example, the table shows that if we would sample 100 people, we would expect 60 to endorse depressed mood, 20 to endorse insomnia, and 12 to endorse both depressed mood and insomnia.[1] Now the question of independence is whether the probability of endorsing one variable *changes* when we learn about the other variable in the table. In other words, does this probability of having depressed mood change if we are given the additional information that the person has insomnia?

Table 5.1 Probabilities of co-occurrences of insomnia (I) and depressed mood (D) represented in a probability table. In this table, the co-occurrences are statistically independent because the joint probabilities exactly equal the product of marginal probabilities (e.g., 0.6 × 0.2 = 0.12)

	I	$\neg I$	total
D	0.12	0.48	0.6
$\neg D$	0.8	0.32	0.4
total	0.2	0.8	1

Table 5.2 Alternative probabilities of co-occurrences of insomnia (I) and depressed mood (D) represented in a probability table. In this table, the co-occurrences are statistically dependent, because the joint probabilities do not exactly equal the product of marginal probabilities (e.g., 0.4 × 0.3 ≠ 0.2)

	I	$\neg I$	total
D	0.2	0.1	0.3
$\neg D$	0.2	0.5	0.7
total	0.4	0.6	1

---

[1] The exact numbers in a sample will likely be different due to sampling variation.

To evaluate this question, we compare the probability of having depressed mood, given that a person has insomnia, with the probability of having depressed mood, given that a person does not have insomnia. We first compute the conditional probability of D given I, $P(D \mid I)$. This probability can be obtained by considering how often depressed mood occurs among those with insomnia. We can compute this probability by dividing the probability a person endorses both depressed mood and insomnia (.12) with the total probability a person endorses insomnia (regardless of depressed mood; .2). We then get

$$P(D \mid I) = \frac{0.12}{0.2} = 0.6.$$

It turns out that this probability is the same as the probability of depressed mood that we can see in the right margin of Table 5.1. So, we can expect a 60% probability that a person has depressed mood regardless of whether we know that that person has insomnia. Thus, learning that a person has insomnia, in this case, adds no useful information for the prediction of depressed mood. Hence, depressed mood and insomnia are *statistically independent* in this sample. Of course, this is just an example, and not something we would expect to see in a real data set, as symptoms of the same disorder are typically correlated.

Informally, we call D and I independent if it is of no consequence for $P(D)$ whether we condition on I or $\neg I$. We denote independence between two variables as:

$$P(D \mid I) = P(D \mid \neg I) = P(D) \quad \text{is equivalent to} \quad D \perp\!\!\!\perp I.$$

This notation was first introduced by Dawid (1979). The symbol $\perp\!\!\!\perp$ is derived from linear algebra, in which two independent variable are also said to be *orthogonal*.

Now, statistical *dependence* is generally defined as a violation of independence. Statistical dependence thus means that two variables carry information about each other: learning the value of one variable alters the probability distribution for the other variable. For example, suppose that instead of the probability distribution in Table 5.1, the alternative probability distribution in Table 5.2 best characterizes the co-occurrence between depressed mood and insomnia. In Table 5.2, the probability of depressed mood is 0.3. However, the probability of depressed mood within the subgroup of people with insomnia is $P(D \mid I) = 0.2/0.4 = 0.5$, while the probability of depressed mood within the subgroup without insomnia is $P(D \mid \neg I) = 0.1/0.6 \approx 0.17$. Thus, in this case, learning that a person has insomnia raises the probability that the person has depressed mood, while learning that a person does not have insomnia lowers it. In this case, D and I are statistically dependent. This is a more realistic situation, that one typically encounters for symptoms in actual research.

If two variables are dependent, then we represent this as follows:

$$P(D \mid I) \neq P(D \mid \neg I) \quad \text{and} \quad P(D \mid I) \neq P(D) \quad \text{are equivalent to} \quad D \not\!\perp\!\!\!\perp I$$

The symbol $\not\!\perp\!\!\!\perp$ can be read as 'is not independent from.' This notation is convenient and will be used in other parts of the book.

Table 5.3 Probabilities of co-occurrences of depressed mood (D) and insomnia (I) among those with fatigue (F; left), among those without fatigue (¬F; middle), and in the combined group (F and ¬F taken together; right)

	D	¬D	total		D	¬D	total		D	¬D	total
I	0.07	0.28	0.35	I	0.01	0.09	0.1	I	0.08	0.37	0.45
¬I	0.03	0.12	0.15	¬I	0.04	0.36	0.4	¬I	0.07	0.48	0.55
total	0.1	0.4	0.5	total	0.05	0.45	0.5	total	0.15	0.85	1
		F				¬F			F and ¬F taken together		

5.3   Conditional independence

In the previous section, we introduced independence and dependence as it applied to a pair of variables. Here, we generalize the notion of conditional probability to more than two variables and explain the concept of *conditional independence*. The basic idea is similar to the case of two variables, where in the case of independence we could write $P(D \mid I) = P(D)$. Conditional independence means that this relation of independence holds between two variables, if we condition on a third. Conditioning on a variable means that we only consider subgroups with a specific value of that variable separately.

For example, suppose that in addition to depressed mood and insomnia, we are also interested in whether a person is fatigued or not (F or ¬F). We can then expand the probability table to encompass all three dimensions, in which we represent how the individuals are distributed over the variables D and I: one for the group with fatigue, and one for the group without. These separate tables and the combined table for the whole group are represented in Table 5.3.

First, consider the relation between D and I when we look at the combined population F and ¬F in Table 5.3 (right panel). As we did in the previous section, we can determine whether the variables D and I are statistically independent by considering whether the probability of depressed mood is the same among people with and without insomnia. We find that:

$$P(D \mid I) = \frac{0.08}{0.45} \approx 0.178 \quad \text{and} \quad P(D \mid \neg I) = \frac{0.07}{0.55} \approx 0.127$$

Since the probabilities are not the same, we conclude that depressed mood and insomnia are dependent in the table: depressed mood arises more often in cases of insomnia and vice versa.

Although depressed mood and insomnia are dependent, it may be the case that fatigue plays a role in creating this dependence. This is what we can investigate using conditional independence. To evaluate this question, we consider the separate tables in Table 5.3 for individuals who do and do not suffer from fatigue. In both of these tables, we evaluate whether D and I are statistically independent.

The probability table in the left panel, which only describes probabilities of depressed mood and insomnia in people with fatigue, shows that the probability of depressed mood is the same among those with and without insomnia:

$$P(D \mid I, F) = \frac{0.07}{0.35} = 0.2 \quad \text{and} \quad P(D \mid \neg I, F) = \frac{0.03}{0.15} = 0.2$$

In other words, in the subgroup of people with fatigue, D and I are statistically independent.

We find the same when we consider the group without fatigue, $\neg F$, which is represented in the middle panel of Table 5.3:

$$P(D \mid I, \neg F) = \frac{0.01}{0.1} = 0.1 \quad \text{and} \quad P(D \mid \neg I, \neg F) = \frac{0.04}{0.4} = 0.1$$

Again, the probability of depressed mood is the same for individuals with and without insomnia. We say in this case that F *screens off* the dependence between D and I. This means that, even though depressed mood and insomnia are dependent in the whole sample, as soon as we create separate contingency tables for those with and without fatigue, that dependence vanishes. Similar to the case for independence with two variables, we write for conditional independence:

$$P(D \mid I, F) = P(D \mid I, \neg F) \quad \text{is equivalent to} \quad D \perp\!\!\!\perp I \mid F.$$

In this case, we say that D and I are conditionally independent given F, or, alternatively, that conditioning on F renders D and I independent. Thus, in the case of binary variables, *conditioning on a variable* means that one makes separate probability tables for each of the levels of that variable. If, in all of these, we find that the other variables are independent, then that implies conditional independence. Conversely, if in at least one of these separate probability tables statistical independence is violated, then we say that the variables are conditionally dependent. Thus, conditional dependence means that, even if we take the conditioning variable into account, the remaining variables still carry information about each other.

5.4   Testing for statistical dependencies

The previous section described a situation in which we know the true probability distribution, such that we can see that, for example, the product of the marginal probabilities should exactly equal the joint probability when two variables are independent (e.g., $P(D) \times P(I) = P(D, I)$). In reality, the true probability distribution is not known, and needs to be estimated from the data. These estimates are never perfect. For example, if we take a sample of 100 people from the probability distribution in Table 5.1, we may find 13 people that endorse both depressed mood and insomnia, 58 people in total that endorse depressed mood, and 22 people in total that endorse insomnia, leading to estimates $P(D, I) \approx 0.13, P(D) \approx 0.58$, and $P(I) = 0.22$. Using these quantities to approximate Table 5.1, we would no longer find exact independence, as $0.58 \times 0.22 = 0.1276 \neq 0.13$. The approximate of the joint probability $P(D, I)$ is close to the approximate of the product of marginal probabilities $P(D) \times P(I)$ however. The continuing question in statistical inference then always is: is it close enough?

When dealing with samples, statistical inference will be required to make claims on (violations of) independence between two or more variables. Typically, this will involve parameterizing a statistical model in such a way that the association of interest is captured in some parameter, say ω, which equals 0 when (conditional) independence holds. In the case of binary data, such as discussed above, we can form a log-linear model with such a parameter such that when $\omega = 0$ the expected probability distribution would lead to exact matches between products of marginal probabilities and joint probabilities. In the case of continuous data, we can no longer make a table such as the tables shown above, as we now have to consider possibly infinite many outcomes. To this end, the probability distribution P is then replaced with a density function f. Mostly, the rules of the density function are the same as the rules of a probability function[2]. As such, independence would hold if $f(D) \times f(I) = f(D, I)$ for all possible outcomes. A correlation coefficient can then be used as parameter ω in addition to an assumed multivariate normal distribution, because then when $\omega = 0$ this property of independence will hold. With multiple variables, ω could instead represent a partial correlation coefficient that characterizes the correlation between two variables after controlling for all other variables in the data set. Such parameters (log-linear relationships and partial correlations) will form the main form of parameters we will use to draw network structures in the remainder of this book.

Once an (in)dependence relationship is suitably parameterized with some parameter ω, all that is left to do is to perform a statistical test whether $\omega \neq 0$. Indeed, this is exactly the topic of Chapter 7. A plethora of statistical tests exist for testing various such relationships, most of which go beyond the scope of this book. Most of these can be subdivided in *frequentist* and *Bayesian* methods. In frequentist statistics, we use the data to obtain some estimate of the parameter, $\hat{\omega}$, and subsequently compare this estimate to the distribution of expected estimates if the parameter would truly have been zero. That is, maybe we obtain $\hat{\omega} = 0.1$, but maybe we would expect to obtain values for $\hat{\omega}$ between -0.2 and 0.2 if $\omega = 0$ simply due to chance. Then, we cannot reject the hypothesis that $\omega = 0$ (the *null-hypothesis*), as our result is in line with what is expected if $\omega = 0$. If we reject the null-hypothesis, we have evidence that (conditional) independence does not hold. Such a test, however, cannot determine if independence holds, as it could also be that we cannot reject the null-hypothesis due to not having enough data. In Bayesian statistics, instead of relying on a single estimate we assume that the parameter has some distribution that quantifies our (un)certainty of the parameter value. After observing the data, we can use Bayes' rule to update our (un)certainty of the value of the parameter. Similarly, we can also quantify our belief in an hypothesis (e.g., $\omega = 0$) and update our belief in this hypothesis after observing the data. This allows us to, in principle, both reject or accept the hypothesis if our belief is strong enough. As such, Bayesian statistics could in principle also be used to obtain evidence for independence.

---

[2]A notable exception is that sum signs are replaced with integrals.

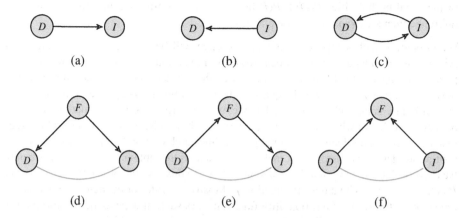

Figure 5.2. Several ways in which dependence or correlation can arise. In (a) D causes I and the reverse holds for (b). In (c) D and I have a cyclic relation. In (d) F is a common cause of D and I. In (e) F mediates the relation between D and I. In (f) F is a common effect where conditioning on F results in a dependence between D and I. The red curved lines indicate the possible spurious correlation inferred with the configuration of only considering D and I.

5.5   Where do conditional dependencies come from?

The importance of conditional dependence and independence for the interpretation of the edges in a network becomes apparent when we consider the possible underlying structures that might induce dependence. For example, suppose we find an association between depressed mood and insomnia. There can be different ways in which this association might arise. Consider, for instance, the three graphs (a), (b), and (c) in the top row of Figure 5.2. Each shows a type of relation between two variables that reflects a true dependence between the variables.

As shown in the figure, depression may cause insomnia (a), or insomnia may cause depression (b), or both variables may be involved in a cyclic relation where they influence each other (c). But there are different possibilities that induce a dependence that does not arise from a direct connection between the two variables. These are shown in the bottom row of Figure 5.2. For instance, it can also be the case that the dependence between the variables is produced by a third variable that acts as a *common cause*. In this case, we would expect that conditioning on this third variable—say, fatigue—would screen off the relation between depressed mood and insomnia (c); if this is true, we expect that depressed mood and insomnia are conditionally independent given fatigue. However, finding such conditional independence does not *prove* that fatigue actually *is* a common cause of depressed mood and insomnia; it could also be the case that fatigue *mediates* the effect of depressed mood on insomnia (e). Finally, it is possible that a dependence between depressed mood and insomnia arises *because of* conditioning (f). This latter case is sometimes referred to as Berkson's bias—a topic that will be further discussed in Chapter 6 and Chapter 12. Revisiting Figure 5.1 coupled with seeing the data generating code shown in Tutorial Box 5.1, we can see that the conditional dependency between

The data used in Figure 5.1, inspired by an example of Koller and Friedman (2009), can be generated using the following R code:

```
set.seed(1)
N <- 10000
motivation <- rnorm(N,0,1)
difficulty <- runif(N,0,10)
grade <- round(10 - difficulty + motivation)
grade <- pmin(10, pmax(1, grade))
diploma <- runif(N) < ifelse(grade >= 5.5, 0.75, 0.25)
```

Tutorial Box 5.1. R code to generate the data underlying Figure 5.1.

difficulty of class and motivation of students after conditioning on grades emerged due to conditioning on a *common effect* (Berkson's bias). On the other hand, the conditional independency between the motivation of students and whether or not they obtain a diploma after conditioning on grade is due to a mediation effect.

The possibilities in Figure 5.2 highlight two important facts. First, combining multiple variables and considering the pattern of conditional independence relations that they are involved in can yield clues about the causal organization of the system as a whole. For example, if we considered the variables D and I in isolation, we might suspect that their dependence is direct, as in panels (a) to (c). However, if upon including F in the analysis, the dependence between D and I vanishes, then the patterns in panels (d) and (e) become more likely. In this particular case, bringing in substantive knowledge, the pattern in panel (d) would seem most likely: insomnia is a plausible cause of fatigue, and fatigue is a plausible cause of depressed mood. Thus, combining the information present in patterns of conditional independence with substantive background knowledge can help in coming up with plausible hypotheses on the origin of statistical dependencies.

Second, although patterns of conditional independence can suggest possible hypothetical scenarios in which the associations between variables arise, they cannot by themselves prove that any one of these scenarios is correct. There will usually be multiple explanations that can account for patterns of dependence (as encoded in the fundamental fact that correlation does not imply causation), and in the same way, there will usually be multiple explanations for patterns of conditional independence. This is one reason why seeking patterns of conditional independence, as described by the network models discussed in this book, is best seen as a hypothesis-generating methodology if the goal is to arrive at a causal model. Ideally, in this case, the generated hypotheses are followed up by additional analyses and research projects to establish their validity. This may include experimental data with interventions on nodes, which can be used to inform the direction of effects, and intra-individual time series data, which can be used to get a better grip on patterns of interaction as they develop over time. However, note that causal interpretations of networks are not necessarily required for the interpretation of the pairwise Markov random field (PMRF); this is discussed in greater detail in Chapter 6.

5.6   Conclusion

This chapter has provided an introduction designed to explain the concepts of independence, dependence, and conditional dependence. It is important to remember that independence always has the same meaning: learning about one event does not change the probability distribution of another. In contrast, dependence does *not* always have the same meaning. This is because variables can be related in many different ways. Thus, independence has a clear uniform definition—two variables do not carry information about each other—but dependence does not. You can think of independence as the top of a mountain: there is only one way in which one can be at the top. Dependence is more like 'not being at the top': this state can be realized in indefinitely many ways. Network models, as discussed in this book, attempt to represent conditional dependence and independence relations among larger sets of variables. However, it is useful to keep in mind that, however complicated the estimation algorithms and probability distributions become, conditional independence still always means the same thing: variables do not contain information about each other, given the other variables in the network.

5.7   Exercises

Conceptual

Below is a 2×2 contingency table with frequencies of recovered (R) and not recovered ($\neg R$) participants who had received either treatment A or B.

	R	$\neg R$	total
A	24	17	41
B	12	14	26
total	36	31	67

5.1. Determine the probabilities $P(R)$, $P(R \mid A)$, and $P(R \mid B)$.

5.2. Are recovery and treatment independent in this table?

For the remaining questions, consider the new data below. In the first two tables below, we see the number of pupils that successfully pass (S) or fail (F) a test either in school 1 or school 2, that were taught using method A or B. The third table contains the frequencies of the two other tables combined (1+2).

1	S	F	total
A	21	7	28
B	9	16	25
total	30	23	53

2	S	F	total
A	16	9	25
B	7	20	27
total	23	22	52

1+2	S	F	total
A	37	16	53
B	16	36	52
total	53	52	105

5.3. Determine if there is evidence for method A or B to be better using only the pupils from school 1 (left table). Do the same for school 2 (middle table).

5.4. Determine if there is evidence for method *A* or *B* to be better in the combined sample (right table).

5.5. What can you conclude about conditional independence (dependence) with respect to success, method, and school?

True or false

5.6. The correlation between the number of ice creams sold and the number of shark bites can be explained (i.e., the correlation can be removed) by the hot weather.

5.7. Parents having high income and their kids having a good education (both binary variables) are correlated. This implies that these variables could be independent.

5.8. IQ and shoe size (both normally distributed) are correlated. This implies that there cannot be another variable that explains away this correlation.

5.9. Dopamine level and mood (both normally distributed) are uncorrelated. This implies that the variables are independent.

5.10. A correlation has been obtained between the level of B12 (a vitamin) and sensations at the nerve ends in the finger tips. It is sufficient to conclude that the B12 level causes the sensations at the fingertips to know that these sensations cannot cause the B12 level.

References

Dawid, A. P. (1979). Conditional independence in statistical theory. *Journal of the Royal Statistical Society: Series B (Methodological)*, *41*(1), 1–15.

Koller, D., & Friedman, N. (2009). *Probabilistic graphical models: Principles and techniques*. The MIT press.

Part II

Estimating Undirected Network Models

Part II

Estimating Undirected Network Models

Chapter 6

Pairwise Markov Random Fields

Sacha Epskamp[1,2], Jonas M. B. Haslbeck[1], Adela-Maria Isvoranu[1], &
Claudia D. van Borkulo[1,2]

1. University of Amsterdam, Department of Psychology

2. University of Amsterdam, Centre for Urban Mental Health

6.1   Introduction

In this second part of the textbook, we will focus on the estimation of network models from data. While there are many potential statistical multivariate models that would allow for a network representation—visualizing and analyzing estimated model parameters as a network structure—we focus on one particular type of network model: a pairwise Markov random field (PMRF; Lauritzen, 1996; Murphy, 2012), which is a class of undirected network models in which variables are represented by nodes connected by edges that indicate the (strength of) conditional association between two variables after controlling for all other variables in the network. This chapter will introduce the main types of PMRFs used in network psychometrics, how the resulting network models can be interpreted, and the main methods behind estimating parameters of the PMRF. Chapter 7 will expand on these topics and also discuss how the *structure* (absence and presence of edges) of a network can be determined, and Chapter 8 will conclude the discussion on PMRFs and introduce methods for assessing the stability and accuracy of estimates, as well as discuss how groups can be statistically compared.

Cite this chapter as:

Epskamp, S., Haslbeck, J. M. B., Isvoranu, A. M., & Van Borkulo, C. D. (2022).
Chapter 6. Pairwise Markov random fields. In Isvoranu, A. M., Epskamp, S., Waldorp,
L. J., & Borsboom, D. (Eds.). *Network psychometrics with R: A guide for behavioral
and social scientists*. Routledge, Taylor & Francis Group.

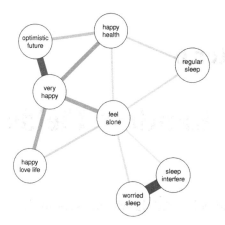

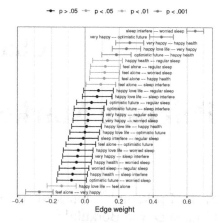

(a) A GGM: nodes represent variables, and edges represent partial correlation coefficients (blue: positive, red: negative) after controlling for all other variables in the network. Only edges with weights significant at $\alpha < 0.05$ are shown.

(b) Parameter estimates, 95% confidence intervals and significance (color of the interval) of each of the estimated edge weights.

Figure 6.1. Example of a Gaussian graphical model (GGM) estimated with the *psychonetrics* package. Based on data collected during the 2020 course on Network Analysis at the University of Amsterdam ($N = 501$), which is available at osf.io/45n6d/.

6.2   Pairwise Markov random fields

A PMRF model is a network model in which nodes represent variables and edges represent the strength of the conditional association between two variables after controlling (conditioning on) all other variables in the network. This means that according to the model, two nodes are connected by an edge only if the corresponding variables are conditionally dependent. As such, the absence of an edge in the PRMF model indicates a conditional independence relationship between two variables after controlling for all other variables in the model.[1] In psychological research, we are often interested in the strength of relationships in addition to the presence and absence of relationships. To this end, the edges in PMRFs are typically weighted, with the weight of the edge quantifying the strength of association between two variables after conditioning on all other variables in the model.

Figure 6.1a gives an example of a PMRF, which is estimated using the techniques described below in Tutorial Box 6.2. This network is estimated from $N = 501$ responses on a set of questions designed by students taking a course on Network Analysis given in 2020 at the University of Amsterdam (Isvoranu, 2021). A description of the nodes can be

[1]Of note, in the next chapter we introduce methods for including edges in a PMRF model, usually by considering if an effect is substantial enough to be included. It could be that edges are not included simply due to a lack of power. To this end, it is important to distinguish between the PMRF as a mathematical model, in which the absence of an edge indicates conditional independence, and an estimated PMRF from data, in which the absence of an edge could also be due to a lack of power.

Table 6.1 Node descriptions for the network structure presented in Figure 6.1

node	description
regular sleep	I try to keep a regular sleep pattern
worried sleep	I am worried about my current sleeping behavior
sleep interfere	My (lack of) sleep interferes with my daily functioning
happy health	I am happy with my physical health
optimistic future	I feel optimistic about the future
very happy	I am very happy
feel alone	I often feel alone
happy love life	I am happy with my love life

seen in Table 6.1. Figure 6.1b shows estimated confidence intervals around the edges, showing also a central theme in network psychometrics: network edges are estimated from data, and the uncertainty around the estimates should be taken into account. This topic will be discussed in more detail in Chapter 8. The network shows several strong links between the items, such as the strong link between 'being very happy' and 'being optimistic about the future,' and the strong link between 'worry about sleeping behavior' and 'sleep interferes with daily functioning.' In addition, we can see that 'being very happy' seems to play a central role in the network (this would also follow from centrality analyses as discussed in Chapter 3).

While many models fall under the general umbrella term of a PMRF with appropriate edge weights, we will focus on only three distinct subclasses: The statistical *Ising model* (Epskamp, Maris, et al., 2018; Ising, 1925; Marsman et al., 2018; Waldorp et al., 2019) for binary data, introduced in more detail in Technical Box 6.1, the *Gaussian graphical model* (GGM; Epskamp, Waldorp, et al., 2018; Lauritzen, 1996) for continuous data, introduced in more detail in Technical Box 6.2, and the *mixed graphical model* (MGM; Haslbeck & Waldorp, 2020) for mixed continuous, categorical and count data, introduced in more detail in Technical Box 6.3. Each of these models includes variables as nodes, linked by edges encoding the strength of conditional association between two variables. In each of the models, an edge-weight of 0 indicates conditional independence, and the more the edge-weight differs from 0 the stronger the strength of conditional dependence. In the Ising model, this strength of association is quantified using a log-linear relationship which can take on values from $-\infty$ to ∞; in the GGM model this strength of association is quantified using partial correlation coefficients bounded between -1 and 1; and in the MGM this strength of association is quantified using regression parameters from generalized linear models of standardized variables (edges between continuous variables will be bounded by -1 and 1, but edges between other types of variables not necessarily so).

6.3   Interpreting pairwise Markov random fields

There are several ways in which PMRF networks can be interpreted. Below, we discuss five interpretations in more detail: (1) as a statistical modeling framework, (2) showcasing

The Ising model (Epskamp, Maris, et al., 2018; Ising, 1925; Marsman et al., 2018) models the joint probability of a set of dichotomous responses (usually encoded −1 and 1, or 0 and 1). The Ising model can be expressed as a joint probability distribution as follows:[a]

$$\Pr(\boldsymbol{Y} = \boldsymbol{y}) = \frac{1}{Z} \exp\left(\sum_i y_i \tau_i + \sum_{<i,j>} y_i y_j \omega_{ij} \right).$$

in which $\boldsymbol{Y}$ represents a vector of dichotomous responses from a random subject, and $\boldsymbol{y}$ represents a vector of dichotomous responses from given subject. The parameter τ_i represents a *threshold* (also termed the *external field* or *intercept*) and encodes the general deposition of variable i to take one of the two outcome values. The parameter ω_{ij}, which we term the *network parameter* (or *slope*), encodes the strength of (dis)similarity between variables i and j. It is this parameter that is used in network visualizations. The value Z, also termed the *partition function* is a normalizing constant with respect to the data (but a function with respect to the parameters), such that the probability function sums to one:

$$Z = \sum_y \exp\left(\sum_i y_i \tau_i + \sum_{<i,j>} y_i y_j \omega_{ij} \right).$$

Here, $\sum_y$ should be read as *the sum over all possible outcomes of* $\boldsymbol{Y}$. This partition function is notoriously hard to compute, and makes multivariate estimation of the Ising model intractable with more than about 20 variables. In univariate estimation, the need to compute Z is avoided, thus simplifying the estimation considerably for larger networks.

---

[a]Chapter 13 discusses how the Ising model can be used to simulate data, in order to study dynamics implied by the model. When doing so, an important additional parameter is added to the model: the inverse temperature β. While this parameter plays a crucial role in simulating Ising model dynamics, it is statistically not identified together with the thresholds and network parameters. To this end, when estimating the Ising model parameters from data, we typically set $\beta = 1$ for identification purposes.

Technical Box 6.1. Explanation of the Ising model.

predictive relationships, (3) generating causal hypotheses, (4) as a data generation model, and (5) as an exploratory tool in factor analysis. These interpretations are not necessarily compatible with one another and are sometimes even opposing one another. To this end, there are many ways in which a PMRF can be interpreted, and a researcher does not, for example, need to take a causal interpretation per se in order to use a PMRF.

Statistical modeling framework

The first way in which a PMRF can be interpreted is as a multivariate modeling framework for pairwise interactions between variables. For example, consider the following simple PMRF:

$$\text{coffee} - \text{energetic} - \text{productive,} \tag{6.1}$$

which encodes relationships with variables such as 'on this day I drank a lot of coffee,' 'on this day I was energetic,' and 'on this day I was productive.' Suppose we expect some sort of interaction between 'coffee' and 'energetic' and some form of interaction between 'energetic' and 'productive.' We would then also expect 'coffee' to be correlated with 'productive.' The PMRF allows for forming such a model in which all marginal correlations are expected to be non-zero in a sparse manner: the above PMRF only has two parameters (one for each edge), while explaining three correlation coefficients. As such, this model has a degree of freedom, which allows for the model to be tested and the fit of the model to be gauged, similar to factor analytic models. This is a form of log-linear modeling which has been used for modeling interactions between categorical variables (Agresti, 1990; Epskamp, Maris, et al., 2018). In contrast to commonly used log-linear models, however, is that the PMRF is usually applied to larger sets of variables (by modeling at most pairwise interactions) and that the PMRF can be applied to continuous data as well. For example, suppose we would take the network shown in Figure 6.1a and form a network model using only the shown edges (not including the thresholded edges that were not significant). We will term this process *pruning* in the next chapter. This model is then a multivariate statistical model containing 12 pairwise interactions, aiming to explain 28 correlation coefficients. (e.g., 'happy love life' and 'optimistic future' will correlate positively given their interaction with 'very happy'). This model has $28 - 12 = 16$ degrees of freedom, and as such the fit of the model can be evaluated, preferably in a new data set (Kan et al., 2020).

Predictive models

While PMRFs are often interpreted in a causal vein, their assumptions do not rely on any causal hypothesis. In essence, the PMRF shows predictive relationships between the variables in the model. This is because univariate distributions implied by PMRFs are equivalent to the most commonly used models for regression analysis: strong edges in the PMRF correspond to strong coefficients in multiple/logistic/generalized regression models. As such, the PMRF offers a powerful tool for visualizing the results of many exploratory regression analyses, not only allowing one to read what variables would likely be significant predictors, but also allowing one insight into how these predictors would in turn predict one another as well—mapping out the multicolinearity of the data.

Consider again the simple three-node PMRF introduced in Equation 6.1. We can read from this PMRF that on days a person drinks coffee, that person tends to be more energetic, and that on days a person is energetic, that person is more productive. Interestingly, however, is that we can also reason in the opposite direction: on days this person is productive, this person is more likely to be energetic, and on days this person is energetic, it is likely that this person drank coffee. For example, if we would perform a (logistic) regression analysis with 'energetic' as dependent variable and 'coffee' and 'productive' as independent variables, we would likely obtain that both predictors are significant. If we instead use 'productive' as dependent variable, we would likely only obtain 'energetic' as significant predictor, but not 'coffee.' The PMRF, however, reveals that even though 'coffee' is not a significant predictor of 'productive,' it is correlated with 'productive'—a correlation that is fully mediated by the variable 'energetic.'

The Gaussian graphical model (GGM; Epskamp, Waldorp, et al., 2018; Lauritzen, 1996) is a model in which relationships between variables are modeled through *partial correlation coefficients*, which could be set to zero and which can be represented graphically through a network visualization. Let Y represent a vector of n responses from a random subject and y a realization. We will assume Y to be normally distributed with mean vector μ and variance–covariance matrix Σ:

$$Y \sim N(\mu, \Sigma).$$

This means that the likelihood function takes the following form:

$$f(Y = y) = \frac{1}{\sqrt{(2\pi)^n |\Sigma|}} \exp\left(-\frac{1}{2}(y - \mu)^\top \Sigma^{-1}(y - \mu)\right).$$

The variance–covariance matrix Σ is of particular importance to this book, as it encodes all marginal and conditional relationships between variables in y. In the GGM, we do not model Σ directly, but rather model standardized elements of its inverse, K (Kappa):

$$K = \Sigma^{-1}$$

This matrix is also termed a *precision matrix*. The precision matrix can be standardized to partial correlations as follows:

$$\omega_{ij} = -\frac{\kappa_{ij}}{\sqrt{\kappa_{ii}\kappa_{jj}}} \quad \text{if } i \neq j.$$

We can also summarize the two expressions above in a single expression (Epskamp, Rhemtulla, et al., 2017):

$$\Sigma = \Delta (I - \Omega)^{-1} \Delta,$$

in which Ω contains partial correlation coefficients on off-diagonal elements and zeroes on the diagonal, and Δ is a diagonal scaling matrix. This expression can directly be used together with the normal likelihood to estimate non-zero elements of Ω through maximum likelihood estimation (Epskamp et al., 2021).

Technical Box 6.2. Explanation of the Gaussian graphical model.

Similarly, the network in Figure 6.1a shows interesting predictive relationships. The strong link between 'worried about sleeping behavior' and 'sleep interferes with daily functioning' indicates that in a multiple regression model with one of these variables as dependent variable, the other variable would be the strongest predictor. This also shows a risk in PMRFs: if two variables are too similar and explain too much variance in one another, they might end up only being connected to one another. We can further see that in a multiple regression model 'feeling optimistic about the future' would likely feature 'being very happy' and 'being happy with physical health' as significant predictors. The multiple regression model, however, would not show that 'feeling alone' would also predict 'being optimistic about the future,' albeit via the node 'being very happy.'

Relationships between causal modeling and PMRFs

While the PMRF is undirected, the model is closely related to causal modeling, which was already briefly introduced in Chapter 5 and will be introduced in more detail in Chapter 12. For example, the PMRF from Equation (6.1) is equivalent to three causal structures:[2]

$$\text{coffee} \rightarrow \text{energetic} \rightarrow \text{productive}$$
$$\text{coffee} \leftarrow \text{energetic} \rightarrow \text{productive}$$
$$\text{coffee} \leftarrow \text{energetic} \leftarrow \text{productive}.$$

When a causal model generated the data, the corresponding PMRF includes an edge whenever there is an edge in the causal model, or if the two variables both cause a third variable (a common effect). As such, a strikingly different interpretation of the PMRF as the two interpretations above is that the model can be indicative of causal relationships. For example, an intuitive hypothesis that could be generated by this PMRF is that drinking coffee leads to being more energetic and that being more energetic leads to increased productivity. Similarly, the network in Figure 6.1a could be used to hypothesize that 'feeling less alone' could make one 'feel very happy,' which in turn could cause 'being optimistic about the future.' It is also very likely that someone sleeping so poorly that this 'interferes with daily functioning' would make that person 'worry about their current sleeping behavior.' Such statements should, of course, be read in the exploratory nature in which PMRF studies are usually performed, and in general it is advisable to limit causal inference from PMRFs as much as possible.

The fact that a common effect leads to an extra edge in the PMRF deserves some further attention. It can be derived that the sign of this edge will equate the negative product of the signs of the two causal effects: two positive and two negative causal effects lead to a negative edge in the PMRF, and a positive and a negative causal effect leads to a positive edge in the PMRF. For example, suppose that the easiness of a class and the motivation of a student both increase that student's grade. Suppose that easiness of class and motivation of the student are also uncorrelated, meaning that we cannot predict how motivated a student is based on how easy the class is. Now suppose that we know the student passed the class with the grade of a 10 (A+), and that we know the student was not at all motivated. Now, we can predict that the class must have been easy—a negative correlation emerged after conditioning on the grade. As psychological variables can often be transformed such that all correlations are positive (the positive manifold), we can generally also expect many causal relations between variables to be positive (after recoding). As such, the negative edges in the PMRF due to these common effect structures usually stand out. To this end, whenever an edge in the PMRF of an unexpected sign is found, it is advisable to (a) look if the marginal correlation is of the same sign, and (b) look if there is a third variable that strongly links to the two variables of interest, and whether a common effect structure is plausible.

Figure 6.1a shows, for example, a positive link between 'feeling alone' and 'being happy with physical health,' while you might expect to see a negative link there. Indeed, the

---

[2]We do not consider unobserved variables here.

Mixed graphical models (MGMs; Chen et al., 2015; Yang et al., 2014) are network models in which the nodes can be defined on different domains, such as continuous, count, or categorical. Specifically, each node can be associated with a different conditional exponential family distribution. The family of exponential distributions includes many common distributions such as the Gaussian distribution, the Poisson distribution, the exponential distribution, and the multinomial distribution.

MGMs are constructed by factoring n univariate conditional members of the exponential family to a joint distribution (Yang et al., 2014):

$$P_{PL}(\boldsymbol{Y} = \boldsymbol{y}) = \prod_{i=1}^{n} P(Y_i \mid \boldsymbol{Y}_{\backslash i}),$$

where n is the number of nodes and $\boldsymbol{Y}_{\backslash i}$ is the set of nodes without node i. This factorization does not necessarily lead to a well-defined joint probability distribution, and can therefore also be termed a *pseudo-likelihood* function. Only under certain conditions does this factorization give rise to normalizable distributions (for details see Chen et al., 2015).

The Gaussian graphical model in Technical Box 6.2 and the Ising model in Technical Box 6.1 can be constructed by factorizing conditional Gaussian, and conditional Bernoulli distributions, respectively, which are both members of the exponential family. Hence these two distributions are special cases of MGMs.

MGMs are typically estimated via nodewise regression (Meinshausen & Bühlmann, 2006), in which the conditional distribution of each node is estimated separately, and in a second step all parameter estimates are combined into a final model. The R-package *mgm* provides an implementation of this estimation procedure, including functions to summarize the estimates, compute the predictability of nodes, and assess the stability of estimates via resampling (Haslbeck & Fried, 2017; Haslbeck & Waldorp, 2018, 2020).

MGMs do not necessarily have to be pairwise. If they include higher-order interactions, they can be seen as moderated network models (MNMs; Haslbeck et al., 2021), in which pairwise interactions are moderated by other nodes in the model. Here, the moderator variables can again be any member of the exponential family. If moderator variables are categorical, this allows estimating group differences via MNMs (Haslbeck, 2020).

Technical Box 6.3. Explanation of mixed graphical models.

marginal correlation between these variables is $r = -0.10$, revealing that the estimated partial correlation is of a different sign than the marginal correlation. Looking closer at Figure 6.1a, we can see that both nodes are strongly connected to 'being very happy.' As such, we could hypothesize that feeling alone makes one less happy, and being happy with physical health makes one feel happier. Indeed, it seems that after conditioning on 'feeling very happy,' these two nodes become positively correlated, giving some support for this common effect hypothesis.

A note on Berkson's bias. Relationships between variables being changed due to conditioning on a common effect can occur in more ways than by including a common effect in the network model. de Ron et al. (2021) describe a situation in which this effect occurs due to selection of participants used in the analysis: when a network model is based on a subpopulation which itself is based on a function of the items used in the network model. In clinical research, researchers are often interested only in investigating the clinically severe subpopulation, assuming that the underlying model for this subpopulation is structurally different than that of the healthy populations. For example, a researcher might be interested in the network structure of depression symptoms in a clinically depressed subpopulation. Like many other psychological disorders, however, depression cannot be diagnosed independently from its symptoms. Instead, participants are selected if they endorse 5 out of 9 depression symptoms, one of which must be 'depressed mood.' In essence, such a sampling strategy relies on selecting participants based on the sum-score of symptom endorsements—a natural common effect. This procedure leads to a bias in the network structure (termed 'Berkson's bias') as it can be expected that every correlation between variables becomes less strong in the selected subpopulation and can even become negative. For network modeling, this may lead to unexpected negative links in the PMRF structure. While such links would be true for the exact selected subpopulation (i.e., the subpopulation that endorses 5 out of 9 symptoms), they are likely not true for the intended subpopulation: people suffering from depression. Lacking statistical methods to deal with the induced bias, performing any multivariate analysis on the same variables used for selecting participants should generally be avoided, and results from such an analysis should be interpreted with great care.

Generating structures

Undirected network models can also themselves be used as data generating structures. An example of such a generating structure is the dynamic Ising model, which is explained in much more detail in Chapter 13. In short, the Ising model is a model in which variables that are connected to one another aim to be in the same state. For example, the presence of some symptoms increases the probability that other symptoms are or become present as well (Cramer et al., 2016), or that different opinions on an attitude object may keep one another constant (Dalege et al., 2018). As such, under very strong assumptions we can also interpret PMRFs to model genuine symmetric causal model in which nodes in the network can impact one another directly. In the network of Figure 6.1a, it could be that the variables 'being happy with ones love life' and 'feeling alone' directly influence one another: being happy with your love life might make you feel less lonely, and becoming less lonely (for example by starting a relationship) might make you feeling happier in your love life.

Showing latent variables

A final interpretation of the PMRF greatly departs from all four interpretations discussed above, and takes the PMRF merely as a tool to investigate a potentially underlying factor structure in the data set. Edges in a PMRF do not take potential latent variables into account. For example, in Figure 6.1a it could be that the positive edge between 'trying to keep regular sleep patterns' and 'often feel alone' is due to an unobserved cause such as 'having an active social life,' which is especially plausible as many subjects in the data are students. Ever since the first publications in network psychometrics it has been recognized that there are close links between network models and factor models. van der Maas et al. (2006), for example, show that generating data under a mutualism model (a model closely related to a PMRF) leads to data that fit a factor model. Later, a direct equivalence has been established between the Ising model and the multidimensional item-response theory model (Epskamp, Maris, et al., 2018; Kruis & Maris, 2016; Marsman et al., 2018; Marsman et al., 2015). The relationship between factor models for continuous data and the GGM is simpler, as both are models for the variance–covariance structure (Epskamp, Rhemtulla, et al., 2017; Waldorp & Marsman, 2021). In both equivalences, the network structure takes a low-rank structure if the underlying model is actually a factor structure (Marsman et al., 2015). Golino and Epskamp (2017) described this relationship as the "fundamental rule of network psychometrics":

$$\text{clusters in network} = \text{latent variables,}$$

in which the equal sign should be read as a statistical equivalence.

This rule has important consequences. Most notably, if data were generated through a network model with (low-rank) clusters, a factor model will likely fit the data well. Similarly if a factor model generated the data, a resulting estimated network model will show many connections in clusters of nodes. As such, estimating a network model or factor model and obtaining interpretable results does not mean that that model actually underlies the data, as there could be an alternative explanation that would fit equally well. While this argument has often been used to argue that the latent variable model might not underlie psychological data sets even when a latent variable model fits well (e.g., van Bork et al., 2017), the argument could also be reversed (Epskamp, Kruis, et al., 2017). Interestingly, in this way the network models which originated as an alternative to latent variable models can actually be seen as tools augmenting methods for latent variable modeling. This is exactly the line of reasoning taken by Golino and colleagues, who developed *exploratory graph analysis*—a method for determining the number of underlying factors by investigating the clustering in a PMRF (Christensen et al., 2019; Golino & Demetriou, 2017; Golino & Epskamp, 2017). As such, a final interpretation of the PMRF is to reveal underlying factor structures by investigating its clustering.

6.4   Estimating saturated network models

As is common with any (multivariate) statistical model, there is a plethora of manners in which the parameters of PMRFs can be estimated. Table 6.2 gives an overview of R packages that can be used to estimate PMRFs using various estimation routines. These estimation routines can roughly be divided in two categories: *multivariate* and *univariate* estimation. Both these methods allow, in principle, for estimating *saturated* or *unconstrained* networks in which all edges are included, *constrained* estimation in which some edges are included, and *regularized* estimation in which shrinkage is applied to parameter estimation to reduce parameter estimates and select edges. This chapter

We can estimate a Gaussian graphical model (GGM; Epskamp, Waldorp, et al., 2018; Lauritzen, 1996) using the *bootnet* package for R. To use bootnet, we first need to install it as explained in Chapter 2. Next, we can load the package:

```
library("bootnet")
```

The `estimateNetwork` function can be used to estimate a GGM and other network models. The first argument should be a data set (`data frame` in R) with continuous variables. Next, a custom estimation function can be supplied that takes this data set and estimates a network model. Some estimators, such as maximum likelihood estimation of the GGM, are already built in by default, and can be called using the `default` argument. Suppose your data are called `Data`, we can then estimate a GGM using maximum likelihood estimation as follows:

```
network <- estimateNetwork(Data, default = "pcor")
```

We will learn in Chapter 7 about other options for the `default` argument. The object `network` now contains the estimated network structure, but also the original data and the estimator function used. We can retrieve the network structure with `network$graph` to be used for visualization and further analyses. Alternatively, we can use *bootnet*'s plotting function:

```
plot(network)
```

which simply calls the `qgraph` function on the estimated network structure with arguments `layout = "spring"`, `cut = 0`, and `theme = "colorblind"`.

If we would like to exclude edges that are not significant (a process we term *thresholding* in the next chapter), we can use the argument `threshold = "sig"` in the call to `estimateNetwork`:

```
network <- estimateNetwork(Data, default = "pcor",
                           threshold = "sig", alpha = 0.05)
```

Now, edges that are not significant at $\alpha = 0.05$ are removed from the network.

Tutorial Box 6.1. GGM estimation using *bootnet*.

will introduce saturated estimation; Tutorial Box 6.1 highlights the use of the *bootnet* package and Tutorial Box 6.2 highlights the use of the *psychonetrics* package. Chapter 7 will continue this discussion in which constrained estimation and regularization are used to select which edges should be included in the network structure.

In multivariate estimation, the parameters of the PMRF are estimated by optimizing the parameters of a single multivariate statistical model. This is nearly always done by utilizing the joint likelihood distribution. For example, *maximum likelihood estimation* as implemented in the *psychonetrics* package can be used to search for parameters under which the data were most likely, the graphical LASSO algorithm as implemented in the *glasso* package similarly optimizes the joint likelihood but adds a penalty for model complexity, and Bayesian sampling routines as implemented in the *BGGM* package combine the likelihood with prior information, in order to sample from a posterior distribution of the parameters given the data. Multivariate estimation is a powerful

Table 6.2 Software packages that can be used for estimating undirected network models

Software	Models	Univariate	Multivariate	Saturated	Pseudo-constrained	Constrained	Model search	Regularized	Supported by bootnet
qgraph/glasso	GGM	X	✓	✓	✓	✓	✓	✓	✓
psychonetrics	GGM + Ising	X	✓	✓	X	✓	✓	X	X
IsingSampler	Ising	✓	✓	✓	X	X	X	X	✓
IsingFit	Ising	✓	X	X	X	X	X	✓	✓
mgm	MGM	✓	X	✓	X	X	X	✓	✓
BGGM	GGM	X	✓	✓	✓	X	X	X	✓
GGMnonreg	GGM	✓	X	✓	✓	X	✓	X	X
ggm	GGM	X	✓	✓	X	✓	X	X	X

Models can either be estimated through multivariate estimation (e.g., maximum likelihood estimation) or univariate estimation (e.g., pseudo-likelihood estimation). Saturated models contain all edges possible, pseudo-constrained models are saturated models in which some edges are set to equal zero based on some criterion, and constrained models are models in which in which parameters are estimated while constraining other parameters to zero. Model search and regularization are further detailed in Chapter 7.

estimation technique that is often preferred when it can be used, as it estimates all model parameters in one model setup and optimizes the joint likelihood. Maximum likelihood of the PMRF, for example, is exactly the same as multivariate estimation of structural equation models (SEM; Bollen & Stine, 1993), and as a result many extensions from SEM can directly be applied to PMRFs, such as fit indices, multi-group modeling, latent variables, and meta-analytic extensions (Epskamp et al., 2021). Maximum likelihood estimation of the GGM and Ising model are implemented in several software packages.

The alternative to multivariate estimation is to split the problem in several smaller estimation problems and estimate parameters of a series of univariate statistical models instead of parameters from one single multivariate statistical model, as shown in Figure 6.2. Univariate estimation utilizes convenient full conditional distributions of single variables in the PMRF given all other variables in the PMRF: a multiple regression model in the case of the GGM, a logistic regression model in the case of the Ising model, and a generalized linear model in the case of the MGM. For the Ising model and the GGM the parameters of these univariate models can be directly translated to the parameters of the joint multivariate model (MGM models are only estimated using univariate estimation). For the Ising model, the regression parameters from a logistic regression model directly translate to the network parameters from the multivariate Ising model (Epskamp, Maris, et al., 2018), and for the GGM the regression weights can be standardized to partial correlation coefficients by using the residual variances of multiple regression models (Epskamp, Waldorp, et al., 2018; Waldorp & Marsman, 2021). As such, univariate estimation leads to two estimates of each edge in the network. These estimates can be averaged, and if a form of model selection (further detailed in Chapter 7) is used to determine the presence or absence of edges, an AND-rule can be used to retain an edge only if both estimates are non-zero, and an OR-rule can be used to retain an edge if one of the two estimates is non-zero (as a result, the AND-rule is more conservative than the OR-rule). The product of univariate distributions is also termed the *pseudo-likelihood*, and as such univariate estimation typically aims to optimize the pseudo-likelihood of the data.

While multivariate estimation may be preferable over univariate estimation in principle, in practice univariate estimation offers a strong alternative to multivariate estimation. A particularly powerful aspect of univariate estimation is that in the case of the Ising model and MGM, the normalizing constant or partition function does not have to be evaluated. In multivariate estimation, the evaluation of the likelihood used in the optimization routine

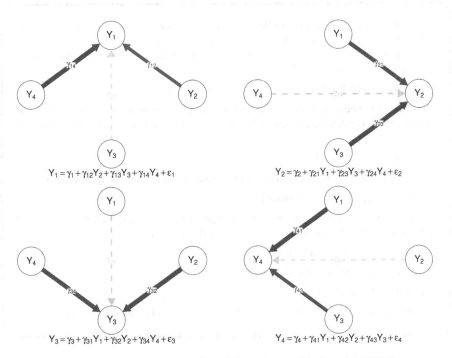

$$Y_1 = \gamma_1 + \gamma_{12}Y_2 + \gamma_{13}Y_3 + \gamma_{14}Y_4 + \varepsilon_1$$

$$Y_2 = \gamma_2 + \gamma_{21}Y_1 + \gamma_{23}Y_3 + \gamma_{24}Y_4 + \varepsilon_2$$

$$Y_3 = \gamma_3 + \gamma_{31}Y_1 + \gamma_{32}Y_2 + \gamma_{34}Y_4 + \varepsilon_3$$

$$Y_4 = \gamma_4 + \gamma_{41}Y_1 + \gamma_{42}Y_2 + \gamma_{43}Y_3 + \varepsilon_4$$

Figure 6.2. Example of univariate estimation of Gaussian graphical model (GGM) parameters (partial correlations). Four separate multiple regression models are performed, each of which uses one of the variables as dependent variables and all other variables as independent variables. The obtained regression-coefficients can be scaled, using the regression parameters (γ) and the variances of the residuals (ε) to the partial correlation coefficients used in the network representation, as $\gamma_{ij} \propto \gamma_{ji} \propto \omega_{ij}$. For the Ising model, logistic regression models can be used to obtain the network edge parameters.

requires to take the sum over all possible outcomes. For binary data, the total number of possible outcomes is 2^n, with n representing the number of nodes. As such, this number grows exponentially and quickly grows beyond the limits of what can conceivably be performed on even the strongest computers available; while with five variables there are only 32 possible outcomes, with 10 variables this number grows to $1,024$, with 20 variables this number grows to $1,048,576$, and with 30 variables this number grows to more than a billion: $1,073,741,824$. Univariate estimation avoids this computationally challenging problem, and is therefore the method of choice for larger Ising models and MGMs. Another benefit of univariate estimation over multivariate estimation is that the estimation procedure is more flexible and stable; relying on relatively simple regression models rather than more complicated multivariate models that, for example, rely on semi-positive definiteness of the variance–covariance structure. As a result, extensions of regression models can readily be applied to estimating more complicated network models, as is done for example in some of the model selection procedures discussed in Chapter 7, multi-level estimation discussed in Chapter 10, and moderated network analysis (Haslbeck et al., 2021).

The Gaussian graphical model (GGM) can also be estimated using maximum likelihood estimation through the *psychonetrics* package. We can load *psychonetrics* coupled with the *dplyr* package for the pipe operator %>% (as described in Chapter 2, the pipe operator can be used to write f(x) as x %>% f):

```
library("psychonetrics"); library("dplyr")
```

The data need to be stored in a data frame containing only continuous variables. Suppose this data frame is called Data, we can then form a *model* using the specific model function ggm:

```
model <- ggm(Data)
```

Next, we can run the parameter estimation procedure on this model using runmodel:

```
model <- model %>% runmodel
```

This performed maximum likelihood estimation of a GGM in which all edges are estimated (saturated model). We can retrieve the network structure with:

```
model %>% getmatrix("omega")
```

Or we can inspect parameter estimates using:

```
model %>% parameters
```

We can then see again that some edges may not be significant at, for example, $\alpha = 0.05$.

Tutorial Box 6.2. Gaussian graphical model estimation using *psychonetrics*.

6.5   Conclusion

This chapter introduced pairwise Markov random fields (PRMFs), which is a class of models that allows for an undirected network representation. Edges in a PRMF indicate the (strength of) conditional association between two variables after controlling for all other variables in the model. For binary data, the appropriate PRMF to use is the Ising model, of which the dynamics will be further explored in Chapter 13. For continuous data, the Gaussian graphical model (GGM) can be used, which quantifies edges with partial correlation coefficients. Finally, for mixed continuous, categorical (including binary) and count data, the mixed graphical model (MGM) can be used. These models can be interpreted in very different ways, ranging from causal interpretations to predictive interpretations to tools in latent variable modeling. To this end, PMRF estimation offers a powerful exploratory data analysis tool that does not necessitate a network perspective. Parameters can be estimated through various estimation routines, which can all be classified as multivariate estimation (estimating all parameters at once) or univariate estimation (estimating parameters in different statistical models and combining these in one network structure). In the next chapter, we will expand on this framework and also discuss methods for determining the presence and absence of edges.

6.6   Exercises

Conceptual

6.1. Suppose we have two variables in a data set that are virtually identical (e.g., they correlate with $r = .95$). Explain why this would be problematic for PMRF estimation.

6.2. Suppose the following causal structure generated the data:

$$\text{coffee} \underset{(+)}{\rightarrow} \text{productive} \underset{(-)}{\leftarrow} \text{procrastinating}.$$

This model states that drinking coffee improves productivity, and procrastinating reduces productivity. Suppose we select an author of this book who wrote a lot of words on one day, and see that they also procrastinated for several hours on that day. Can we then predict that this author drank *less*, *equal*, or *more* coffee on that day?

6.3. Continuing the example from above, in a corresponding PMRF would the nodes 'coffee' and 'procrastinating' be connected? Why?

6.4. Maximum likelihood estimation of a 50-node Gaussian graphical model is doable, but maximum likelihood estimation of a 50-node Ising model is likely not. Describe why this is the case.

6.5. Describe the difference between the OR-rule and the AND-rule. Which rule will result in a sparser network if edges are removed when they are not significant?

True or false

6.6. Maximizing the joint likelihood is a form of univariate network estimation.

6.7. A saturated network has 0 degrees of freedom.

6.8. In an MGM, edges are parameterized with partial correlation coefficients.

6.9. If two nodes do not feature an edge in the PMRF, that means they are uncorrelated (independent).

6.10. Clusters in an estimated network structure could be due to unobserved and unmodeled common causes.

Practical

For practical exercises in R, please navigate to the appropriate folder of this chapter, available on the online *Companion Website*.

References

Agresti, A. (1990). *Categorical data analysis*. John Wiley & Sons.

Bollen, K., & Stine, R. (1993). Bootstrapping goodness-of-fit measures in structural equation models. In K. Bollen & J. Long (Eds.), *Testing structural equation models* (pp. 111–135). Sage.

Chen, S., Witten, D. M., & Shojaie, A. (2015). Selection and estimation for mixed graphical models. *Biometrika, 102*(1), 47–64.

Christensen, A. P., Gross, G. M., Golino, H. F., Silvia, P. J., & Kwapil, T. R. (2019). Exploratory graph analysis of the multidimensional schizotypy scale. *Schizophrenia Research, 206*, 43–51.

Cramer, A. O. J., van Borkulo, C. D., Giltay, E. J., van der Maas, H. L. J., Kendler, K. S., Scheffer, M., & Borsboom, D. (2016). Major depression as a complex dynamic system. *PLoS One, 11*(12), e0167490.

Dalege, J., Borsboom, D., van Harreveld, F., & van der Maas, H. L. J. (2018). The attitudinal entropy (AE) framework as a general theory of individual attitudes. *Psychological Inquiry, 29*(4), 175–193.

de Ron, J., Fried, E. I., & Epskamp, S. (2021). Psychological networks in clinical populations: Investigating the consequences of Berkson's bias. *Psychological Medicine, 51*(1), 168–176.

Epskamp, S., Isvoranu, A. M., & Cheung, M. (2021). Meta-analytic Gaussian network aggregation. *Psychometrika*. https://doi.org/10.1007/s11336-021-09764-3

Epskamp, S., Kruis, J., & Marsman, M. (2017). Estimating psychopathological networks: Be careful what you wish for. *PLoS One, 12*(6), e0179891.

Epskamp, S., Maris, G. K. J., Waldorp, L. J., & Borsboom, D. (2018). Network psychometrics. In P. Irwing, D. Hughes, & T. Booth (Eds.), *The wiley handbook of psychometric testing* (pp. 953–986). John Wiley & Sons, Ltd.

Epskamp, S., Rhemtulla, M., & Borsboom, D. (2017). Generalized network psychometrics: Combining network and latent variable models. *Psychometrika*, *82*(4),
904–927.

Epskamp, S., Waldorp, L. J., Mõttus, R., & Borsboom, D. (2018). The Gaussian graphical
model in cross-sectional and time-series data. *Multivariate Behavioral Research*,
53(4), 453–480.

Golino, H. F., & Demetriou, A. (2017). Estimating the dimensionality of intelligence like
data using exploratory graph analysis. *Intelligence*, *62*, 54–70.

Golino, H. F., & Epskamp, S. (2017). Exploratory graph analysis: A new approach for
estimating the number of dimensions in psychological research. *PLoS One*,
12(6), e0174035.

Haslbeck, J. M. B. (2020). Estimating group differences in network models using moderation analysis. *PsyArXiv*. https://doi.org/10.31234/osf.io/926pv

Haslbeck, J. M. B., & Fried, E. I. I. (2017). How predictable are symptoms in psychopathological networks? A reanalysis of 18 published datasets. *Psychological
Medicine*, *47*(16), 2767–2776.

Haslbeck, J. M. B., & Waldorp, L. J. (2018). How well do network models predict
observations? On the importance of predictability in network models. *Behavior
Research Methods*, *50*(2), 853–861.

Haslbeck, J. M. B., & Waldorp, L. J. (2020). mgm: Estimating time-varying mixed
graphical models in high-dimensional data. *Journal of Statistical Software*,
93(8).

Haslbeck, J. M. B., Borsboom, D., & Waldorp, L. J. (2021). Moderated network models.
Multivariate Behavioral Research, *56*(2), 256–287.

Ising, E. (1925). Beitrag zur theorie des ferromagnetismus. *Zeitschrift für Physik A
Hadrons and Nuclei*, *31*(1), 253–258.

Isvoranu, A. M. (2021). Data: Network analysis course 2020. https://osf.io/45n6d/

Kan, K.-J., de Jonge, H., van der Maas, H. L. J., Levine, S. Z., & Epskamp, S. (2020). How
to compare psychometric factor and network models. *Journal of Intelligence*,
8(4), 35.

Kruis, J., & Maris, G. (2016). Three representations of the Ising model. *Scientific Reports*,
6, 34175.

Lauritzen, S. L. (1996). *Graphical models*. Clarendon Press.

Marsman, M., Borsboom, D., Kruis, J., Epskamp, S., van Bork, R., Waldorp, L., Maas, H.,
Maris, G., Bork, V., Waldorp, L., van der Maas, H. L. J., Maris, G., & Marsman,
M. (2018). An introduction to network psychometrics: Relating ising network
models to item response theory models. *Multivariate Behavioral Research*,
53(1), 15–35.

Marsman, M., Maris, G., Bechger, T., & Glas, C. (2015). Bayesian inference for low-rank
Ising networks. *Scientific Reports*, *5*(9050), 1–7.

Meinshausen, N., & Bühlmann, P. (2006). High-dimensional graphs and variable selection
with the lasso. *The Annals of Statistics*, *34*(3), 1436–1462.

Murphy, K. P. (2012). *Machine learning: A probabilistic perspective*. MIT press.

van Bork, R., Epskamp, S., Rhemtulla, M., Borsboom, D., & van der Maas, H. L. J.
(2017). What is the p-factor of psychopathology? some risks of general factor
modeling. *Theory & Psychology*, *27*(6), 759–773.

van der Maas, H. L. J., Dolan, C. V., Grasman, R. P., Wicherts, J. M., Huizenga, H. M., & Raijmakers, M. E. (2006). A dynamical model of general intelligence: The positive manifold of intelligence by mutualism. *Psychological Review, 113*(4), 842–861.

Waldorp, L. J., & Marsman, M. (2021). Relations between networks, regression, partial correlation, and the latent variable model. *Multivariate Behavioral Research.* https://doi.org/10.1080/00273171.2021.1938959

Waldorp, L. J., Marsman, M., & Maris, G. (2019). Logistic regression and Ising networks: Prediction and estimation when violating lasso assumptions. *Behaviormetrika, 46*(1), 49–72.

Yang, E., Baker, Y., Ravikumar, P., Allen, G., & Liu, Z. (2014). Mixed graphical models via exponential families (S. Kaski & J. Corander, Eds.). In S. Kaski & J. Corander (Eds.), *Proceedings of the seventeenth international conference on artificial intelligence and statistics*, PMLR.

Chapter 7

Estimating Network Structures using Model Selection

Tessa F. Blanken[1], Adela-Maria Isvoranu[1], & Sacha Epskamp[1,2]

1. University of Amsterdam, Department of Psychology

2. University of Amsterdam, Centre for Urban Mental Health

7.1 Introduction

The previous chapter introduced pairwise Markov random fields (PMRFs): undirected network models—such as the model shown in Figure 7.1—in which edges indicate (the strength of) conditional associations. For binary data, the statistical Ising model can be used, which quantifies relationships through log-linear parameters; for continuous data, the Gaussian graphical model (GGM) can be used, which quantifies relationships through partial correlation coefficients; and for mixed data, the mixed graphical model (MGM) can be used, which relies on regression parameters from generalized linear models. Estimation of these models can be done using either *multivariate* (estimating all edge-weights at once) or *univariate* (estimating edge-weights per variable) estimation, and these methods can be used for either *unconstrained* (estimating all possible edges) or *constrained* (estimating edge-weights based on a fixed network structure) estimation. In this chapter we will consider the subsequent problem of model selection: how to determine which edges should be included and which edges can be omitted. This chapter will first discuss the more general problem of model search in multivariate statistics, then discuss four different classes of model search strategies that can be applied to PMRF estimation, and will conclude with recommendations for which of these classes should be used.

Cite this chapter as:

Blanken, T. F., Isvoranu, A. M., & Epskamp, S. (2022). Chapter 7. Estimating network structures using model selection. In Isvoranu, A. M., Epskamp, S., Waldorp, L. J., & Borsboom, D. (Eds.). *Network psychometrics with R: A guide for behavioral and social scientists*. Routledge, Taylor & Francis Group.

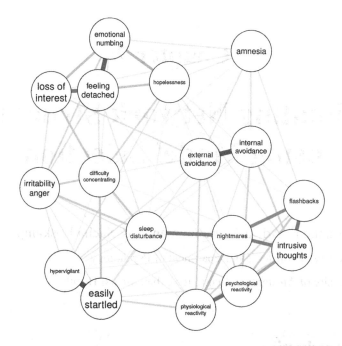

Figure 7.1. Based on a meta-analytic Gaussian graphical model of post-traumatic stress symptoms estimated from 52 samples ($N = 29{,}561$ observations in total) by Isvoranu et al. (2021). The network was estimated using meta-analytic Gaussian network aggregation (MAGNA; Epskamp et al., 2021), and *thresholding* ($\alpha = 0.05$) was used to determine the displayed network. This network contains 78 edges, with weights ranging from 0.02 to 0.36. This model is also used as a true model (generating structure) in a small simulation study reported in Figure 7.7.

7.2   Comparing multivariate statistical models

The PMRF is a multivariate statistical model, and thus must adhere to the same rules as any other (multivariate) statistical model, such as regression analyses or structural equation models. The models that we consider can be seen as lying on a continuum (Figure 7.2) between the independence model, which is the simplest possible model in which we do not include any dependencies (edges), and the saturated model, which is a complicated model including all possible edges. Estimation of the network structures in these extremes is straightforward: the independence model is simply an empty network and therefore does not include any edges, and estimation of the saturated model has already been discussed in Chapter 6. If we assume that one of the models in this continuum is the 'true' model we wish to recover (i.e., the model which generated the data), then neither the independence or the saturated model is likely the preferred model we wish to estimate. This is because the independence model will most likely miss some edges from the true model, and the saturated model will most likely include some spurious edges. Our goal therefore is to select a model somewhere along this continuum where some edges are included and others are put to zero.

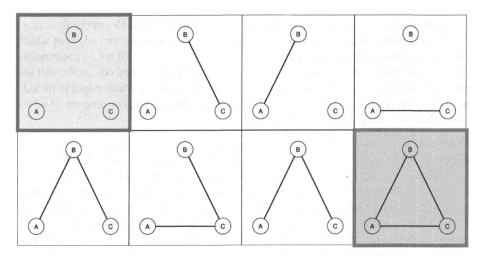

Figure 7.2. The problem of model search: we wish to find a multivariate statistical model that is somewhere in between of the simplest possible model (the independence model shown in blue) and the most complicated possible model (the saturated model shown in red).

Throughout this chapter we will use the term 'true positive' to indicate an edge that was present in the true data generating model and was also included in the estimated model, and 'true negative' to indicate an edge that was absent in the true model and was correctly not included in the estimated model. Likewise, we will use the term 'false positive' to indicate an edge that was absent in the true model and incorrectly included in the estimated network (spurious edge), and the term 'false negative' to indicate an edge that was present in the true model but excluded in the estimated model. Importantly, these terms do not refer to the sign of the edge-weight (positive or negative), merely to the inclusion of these edges in the network regardless of their sign.[1] Referring back to Figure 7.2, assuming the true generating structure was neither the independence nor the saturated model, the independence model features too many false negatives, whereas the saturated model features too many false positives.

Model selection is a fundamental aspect of multivariate statistics and is usually based on the principle of Occam's razor, which is fundamental to science in general: when we have two models (or explanations) that perform equally well, we prefer the simplest one. In psychological networks, based on this principle, we want to remove edges and simplify the network model whenever possible, as long as doing so does not substantially reduce the performance of the model. In other words, this means that we only want to include edges in the network model when there is substantive evidence that the edge is really present. This is especially crucial for PMRFs, as in these network structures edge weights can be subject to sampling variation. Particularly at lower sample sizes (e.g., $N = 300$) this can lead to prominently visible edges that may in fact not be distinguishable

---

[1]Commonly in statistics the probability of obtaining a false positive is also termed the Type 1 error rate (α), whereas the probability of obtaining a false negative is also termed the Type 2 error rate (β). Likewise, *sensitivity* can also be understood as $1 - \beta$ (statistical power) and *specificity* can also be understood as $1 - \alpha$.

from zero statistically and merely reflect sampling variation. At high sample sizes (e.g., $N = 5,000$), edge-weight estimates should be much more accurate, and edges of which the edge weights in the true data generating model are near-zero will not be prominently visible in the estimated network structure under default plotting methods, as we will see below. Nonetheless, we still wish to be conservative in choosing which edges to include in the network structure, especially if the focus is on the presence or absence of edges rather than their weight (Isvoranu et al., 2020).

There are many model selection algorithms available that can be used to select which edges should be included in the network, and there is no golden standard which works best. While there are many criteria for evaluating the performance of a model selection algorithm (Isvoranu & Epskamp, 2021), the most important criteria are *sensitivity* (true positive rate), which quantifies the proportion of true edges that were correctly included in the model; *specificity* (true negative rate), which quantifies the proportion of absent edges in the true model that were also correctly not included in the estimated network; and metrics for evaluating how much the estimated edge weight aligns with the true edge weight (e.g., correlating all edge weights; Epskamp & Fried, 2018). Some algorithms are better in terms of sensitivity (they are less conservative and more lenient to pick up edges, thus minimizing the false negative edges), some are better in terms of specificity (they are more conservative and thus minimize the false positive edges), and some are better in terms of parameter estimation (they present a clearer picture of the network model). Therefore, the algorithm of choice depends both on the available data and on the particular research question. The model selection algorithms can be divided into four general categories: (1) thresholding, (2) pruning, (3) model search, and (4) regularization. Thresholding and pruning first estimate a saturated model, and then remove edges that are not significant or do not meet some other criterion. In pruning, the resulting model in which some edges are put to zero is then refitted to the data. In model search the entire space, from the simple independence to the complex saturated model, is extensively searched for the optimal model. Finally, regularization uses a trick from machine learning to pull or put edges to zero.

The model selection algorithms discussed in this chapter are implemented in various R packages, each with different syntax and different commands. The convenient R package *bootnet* (Epskamp et al., 2018) provides a common framework in which most of these R packages can be called. To this end, many of the methods discussed in this chapter can be constructed via the `estimateNetwork()` function in *bootnet*, using the `default` argument to specify the estimator to be used. Tutorial Box 7.1 describes how networks can be estimated using `estimateNetwork()`, and Table 7.1 lists several of the most commonly used `default` settings. Using the *bootnet* package for network estimation also easily allows for bootstrapping accuracy and stability of the network and comparing networks estimated on different data sets, which is further explained in Chapter 8. In addition to *bootnet*, the *psychonetrics* package (Epskamp, 2021) also contains several estimation algorithms (most notably pruning and stepwise model search). These are explained in more detail in Tutorial Box 7.2. In the following sections we will discuss each of the four model selection algorithm categories in more detail, followed by a set of recommendations for applied researchers on which algorithm to choose in particular settings.

The `estimateNetwork()` function within the *bootnet* package can be used to estimate network models using several of the estimation algorithms discussed in this chapter. Suppose your data are loaded into R in the object Data, we can then estimate a network using a custom estimation function as follows:

```
network <- estimateNetwork(Data, fun = <estimation function>, ...)
```

in which the `fun` argument indicates a custom estimation function that takes a data set as input and returns a network structure, and ... represents any number of arguments used in `fun`. To simplify things, several such functions—also termed *default* functions—are included in the package, as also shown in the help file that you can access in RStudio with `?estimateNetwork`. To use these default functions, the `default` argument should be used instead of the `fun` argument. For example, with `default = "pcor"` a saturated Gaussian graphical model (GGM) is estimated using a predefined estimation function.[a] Any argument listed in the help file for this estimation function can then be used in `estimateNetwork()`. The following code performs *thresholding* at $\alpha = 0.05$:

```
network <- estimateNetwork(Data, default = "pcor",
                           threshold = "sig", alpha = 0.05)
```

If the data are not normally distributed, another common argument for GGM estimation is `corMethod = "spearman"`. Table 7.1 lists some of the most commonly used default functions. For example, the following code estimates a regularized GGM through the graphical LASSO algorithm and EBIC model selection:

```
network <- estimateNetwork(Data, default = "EBICglasso")
```

The `tuning` argument could be used to set the hypertuningparameter γ. Important to note is that *bootnet* does not include any network estimation algorithms itself. It merely includes convenient wrappers around other R packages. To this end, *bootnet* should not be cited alone as the estimation method used, but rather the package should be cited in combination with the other packages used. The output of `estimateNetwork()` provides details on which references should be included to properly reference the estimation method used:

```
print(network)
```

---

[a]In the `?estimateNetwork` help file, this predefined estimation function is referred to as `bootnet_pcor()`. Note that this function should not directly be used, it is only listed in the help file to show which arguments can be used in `estimateNetwork()`.

Tutorial Box 7.1. Network estimation using *bootnet*.

7.3 Thresholding & pruning

Thresholding and pruning are very similar and are among the simplest forms of model selection. The general idea to both approaches, shown also in Figure 7.3, is that we determine whether there is sufficient evidence for edges to be included in the network based on some criterion (such as the *p*-value, false discovery rate, credibility interval, or Bayes' factor). For example, we may omit all edges that are not significant at a chosen

Table 7.1 Most commonly used default methods implemented in *bootnet*

Default	Package	Model	Estimation	Model Selection
pcor	*qgraph*	GGM	multivariate	thresholding
EBICglasso	*qgraph (glasso)*	GGM	multivariate	regularization & EBIC
ggmModSelect	*qgraph (glasso)*	GGM	multivariate	model search
IsingFit	*IsingFit (glmnet)*	Ising	univariate	regularization* & EBIC
IsingSampler	*IsingSampler*	Ising	both	thresholding
mgm	*mgm (glmnet)*	MGM	univariate	regularization* & CV/EBIC

'Default' indicates the value of the `default` argument in `estimateNetwork()`, 'package' indicates the R package which implements the estimation method, 'model' indicates the network model, 'estimation' indicates if univariate or multivariate estimation is used (see Chapter 6), and 'model selection' indicates the variant of model selection used. EBIC is short for model selection by optimizing the extended Bayesian information criterion, and CV is short for model selection by optimizing cross-validation prediction accuracy. Thresholding with `default = "pcor"` requires the `threshold` argument and thresholding with `default = "IsingSampler"` can be done through bootstrapping (`bootInclude` function). An * indicates that the *beta-min condition* is used by default (ensures a low false positive rate (specificity) at the cost of sensitivity in regularized estimation).

significance-level α (i.e., omit all edges for which $p > \alpha$).[2] Instead of *p*-values, Bayesian criteria such as Bayes' factors and Bayesian credibility intervals could also be used to threshold a network. The exact details on how to obtain analytic *p*-values or Bayesian criteria go beyond the scope of this book; for obtaining *p*-values for GGMs and Ising models, we refer to Epskamp et al. (2021), and for Bayesian criteria we refer to Williams et al. (2020).

The difference between thresholding and pruning relates to the handling of edges that do not meet the chosen criterion. In thresholding, we simply remove the edges that do not meet the criterion by fixing them to be equal to zero.[3] While we omit these edges from our network representation, such that they are no longer visible, these edges are still included in the model. As a result, the non-zero edge weights that are included and visualized in the model were estimated assuming that the removed edges were also non-zero. In pruning, on the other hand, we remove the edges that do not meet the criterion, and then we re-estimate the model with those edges fixed to zero. This re-estimation ensures that the edge-weight estimates of the selected edges that we obtain in our final network model are actually based on a model in which these non-substantial edges (as defined by the

---

[2]If desired, a multiple comparison procedure can be used, of which the Bonferroni correction is the most well-known. In Bonferroni the significance level α is divided by the number of tests, which for the complete model of a network with n nodes is $m = n(n-1)/2$ edges, and so each edge is tested at level α/m. Other criteria like the Bonferroni-Holm and false discovery rate have also been developed that are slightly less conservative. Of note, however, is that using corrected *p*-values leads to high specificity but also to low sensitivity. As such, in the exploratory setting of network analysis it is not recommended to use such adjustments by default.

[3]Sometimes, edges that do not meet the criterion are not removed but rather hidden. Hiding or removing thresholded edges leads to the same visual network structure. However, if edges are hidden they are still used in network analyses such as centrality analysis, whereas if they are removed they are not used in such further analyses.

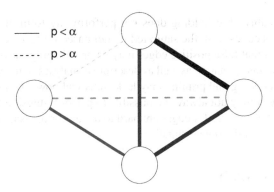

Figure 7.3. An example of thresholding and pruning: edges that do not meet some criterion (in this case, statistical significance at α) can be removed from the network. In the case of thresholding, these edge-weights are put to zero and other edge-weights are not re-estimated. In the case of pruning, other edge-weights are re-estimated using constrained estimation taking into account that the non-significant edges are now set to zero.

criterion) are set to zero. To this end, the edge-weights of the pruned model can be more accurate than the edge-weights of the thresholded model, and statistical fit of the pruned model can also be gauged. Examples of thresholding are the default = "pcor" setting in *bootnet* coupled with significance thresholding, bootstrapped significance thresholding using bootInclude in *bootnet*, and Bayesian estimation routines in the *BGGM* package (Williams & Mulder, 2020). Pruning is implemented in the *psychonetrics* package.

When estimating the network using univariate estimation, two parameter estimates are obtained for each edge (e.g., $A - B$): one for the regression of A on B, and one for the regression of B on A. These parameter estimates can be standardized and averaged to obtain one single estimate of the edge weight, as discussed in Chapter 6. Yet, when applying thresholding or pruning, there is an additional challenge as both parameters underlying each edge weight can be compared to the criterion. You can be more strict or lenient in the criterion you apply. With the AND-rule (usually the default in software), you are more strict, and only include an edge if both regressions meet the criterion (i.e., both regressions need to meet the criterion). Alternatively, using the OR-rule you are more lenient and include an edge if either one of the regressions meet the criterion (i.e., the edge is included as soon as one of the regressions meets the criterion). It should be noted here that in general these univariate edge estimates for GGMs and Ising models are very closely related to each other—they are often either both significant or both not significant. However, this is no longer the case for more advanced univariate estimation techniques, such as multi-level modeling introduced in Chapter 10.

Benefits of thresholding and pruning are that these methods are very fast and, importantly, that the specificity (i.e., the inclusion rate of false positive edges) is very well understood and constant (Williams & Rast, 2020). In addition, sometimes thresholding is the only available model selection method, such as in the meta-analytic network shown in Figure 7.1. There are, however, also several downsides to using thresholding and pruning. Most notably, thresholding does not perform any form of model selection, but merely removes edges from the saturated model based on some criterion. Another potential problem is that false positive edges may be prominently shown, having a large impact on the visual interpretation as well as descriptive analyses of the network structure. Furthermore, thresholding and pruning may lack statistical power (sensitivity) to detect true edges. Finally, it may not always be possible to perform thresholding and pruning. For example, analytic p-values for edges are hard to obtain for the Ising model with more than 20 nodes using multivariate estimation.

7.4   Model search

Another method of PMRF structure estimation is to perform an extensive search through the space of possible models. Pruning, as discussed in the previous section, is already a very basic form of model search: the algorithm simply removes all edges not meeting some criterion in the saturated model and re-evaluates the model. Much more complicated algorithms can be conceived that search through the entire model space (i.e., the range of all possible network structures such as Figure 7.2) in some structured way. Many of these algorithms rely on information criteria to compare competing models, such as the AIC, BIC, and EBIC introduced in Technical Box 7.1. These information criteria can be used to compare two competing models, such as comparing a model with a certain set of edges to a model with one more edge included. This comparison, subsequently, allows for stepwise algorithms that repeatedly add or remove edges—iterating through the model space until the model can no longer be improved (i.e., the information criterion is the lowest). In *step-up* estimation such as shown in Figure 7.4, one or multiple edges are added in each iteration. Which edges to include can for example be determined by using modification indices (indices often used in structural equation modeling to indicate which parameters can be added to improve model fit; Sörbom, 1989). In *step-down* estimation, one or multiple edges are removed from a network in each iteration, for example by removing the weakest edge per iteration. Step-up and step-down estimation can also be combined in algorithms that in each step test every individual edge that can be added or removed, and add or remove edges per iteration until the fit can no longer be optimized.

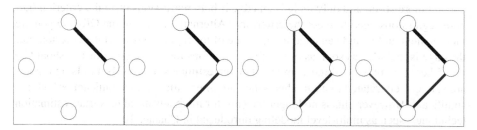

Figure 7.4. An example of model search: in a stepwise fashion (left to right) edges can be added and removed until an optimal network structure is obtained.

When estimating a GGM, a particularly powerful algorithm is the *ggmModSelect* algorithm shown in Figure 7.5. This algorithm first uses regularized estimation (explained in detail in the next section) to perform a fast first search across the model space and to find a network that can subsequently be used as a starting structure in a stepwise model search. Subsequently, the algorithm combines step-up and step-down estimation to investigate all possible models in which one included edge is removed or one absent edge is added. At each iteration the model with the lowest information criterion is selected. This process is repeated until the information criterion can no longer be improved. A method that is comparable to the *ggmModSelect* algorithm is the *modelsearch* algorithm implemented in *psychonetrics* (Epskamp, 2020).

One method for comparing statistical models is through the use of information criteria. These criteria can be evaluated for each model, and typically take the following form:

$$\text{criterion} = \text{model complexity} - \text{model fit}.$$

The criterion becomes lower the better the model fits the data, but is also penalized for models that are very complex (feature many parameters). These criteria can be used for model comparison (provided they are based on the same data): the model with the lower criterion is preferred over models with higher criteria. Let $\mathcal{L}$ represent the log-likelihood of the data (using one of the likelihood distributions discussed in Chapter 6), and q the number of parameters. A common metric for model comparison then is *Akaike's information criterion* (AIC):

$$\text{AIC} = 2q - 2\mathcal{L}.$$

The *Bayesian information criterion* (BIC) also includes the sample size N in the penalty and tends to be more conservative than the AIC:

$$\text{BIC} = q\ln(N) - 2\mathcal{L}.$$

The log-likelihood of the data $\mathcal{L}$ is a sum over log-likelihoods of every case in the data. To this end, $\mathcal{L}$ scales linearly with sample size, whereas the penalty for model complexity scales logistically with sample size. To this end, the larger the sample size, the more important the fit becomes compared to the model complexity. The BIC can be extended with an additional penalty for model complexity controlled through a hypertuningparameter γ, termed the *extended BIC* (EBIC; Chen & Chen, 2008):

$$\text{EBIC}_\gamma = q\ln(N) + 4\gamma\ln(n) - 2\mathcal{L},$$

in which n corresponds to the number of variables. If $\gamma = 0$, the EBIC reduces to the BIC. Of note, some software methods differ in the likelihood computation or how they count the number of parameters. For example, for the GGM, q could only include the network parameters, or also the scaling parameters and means. In addition, it is not uncommon to drop some constant terms from the likelihood computation. To this end, we advise to only use information criteria to compare between models estimated using the same software.

Technical Box 7.1. Information criteria used in model selection.

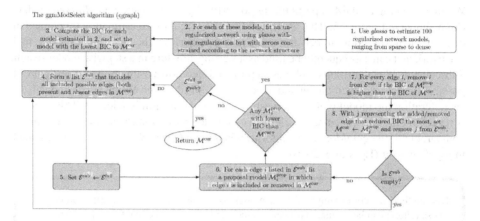

Figure 7.5. The *ggmModSelect* algorithm as implemented in the *qgraph* package. The algorithm starts by using GLASSO to obtain a range of networks such as shown in Figure 7.6. Next, these networks are re-estimated without using regularization, and the best model (typically according to BIC) is selected. Following this first selection, edges are added and removed in a stepwise fashion until an optimal model is found. In this diagram, $\mathcal{M}$ represents a model and $\mathcal{E}$ represents a set of edges.

Model search algorithms can be very powerful and lead to accurate network structures that both feature good sensitivity (ability to detect true edges)—albeit typically lower than in regularization discussed in the next section—and specificity (ability to not include false positive edges). In addition, model search strategies are guaranteed to find a local optimum: a network structure in which no edge can be added or removed (depending on the algorithm used) to improve fit. The main downside, however, is that these algorithms tend to be very slow. While especially with less than 30 nodes the speed of the algorithm is typically acceptable for estimating a single network (e.g., computation can take a few minutes), the speed may be less acceptable for bootstrapping and resampling methods discussed in Chapter 8. Another downside is that, like in thresholding and pruning, false positives may feature prominently in the network, especially at lower sample sizes. Finally, while many model search algorithms converge to a local optimum, they are not guaranteed to converge to a global optimum (the best fitting network model).

7.5 Regularization

Statistical regularization involves estimating edge-weights through penalized maximum (pseudo) likelihood estimation (Hastie et al., 2001), see Technical Box 7.2 for more details. In short, this means that when estimating model parameters, the fit of a model is penalized by the complexity of the parameters in the model (e.g., how many edges are included in the network). One particular variant of regularization that has often been applied to PMRF estimation is the 'least absolute shrinkage and selection operator' (LASSO; Tibshirani, 1996). In LASSO, the added penalty uses the absolute value of the edge-weights, which leads to some edge-weights being estimated to equal exactly zero, thus leading to a sparse model. The amount of penalization has to be chosen, typically through a tuning parameter λ, for which 0 indicates no penalization (i.e., a saturated model is estimated through maximum likelihood estimation) and higher values indicate stronger penalization (i.e., more edge-weights are put to zero). Typically, LASSO estimation requires univariate network estimation, as LASSO has mostly only been implemented for regression models. For the GGM, however, the powerful 'graphical LASSO' (GLASSO; Friedman et al., 2008) algorithm can be used, which takes as input a variance–covariance or correlation matrix and estimates the GGM using regularized multivariate estimation. Regularized regression, used commonly for univariate network estimation, has been implemented in the *glmnet* package (Friedman et al., 2010), and the GLASSO algorithm has been

---

In regularization, parameters of a statistical model are estimated by optimizing a *penalized* likelihood function. Let $\mathcal{L}(\boldsymbol{D}; \boldsymbol{\theta})$ be the log-likelihood of the data $\boldsymbol{D}$ given a set of parameters $\boldsymbol{\theta}$. Typically, parameters are estimated by finding the set of parameters that maximizes this expression—the maximum likelihood estimate $\hat{\boldsymbol{\theta}}$:

$$\hat{\boldsymbol{\theta}} = \operatorname{argmax}_{\boldsymbol{\theta}} [\mathcal{L}(\boldsymbol{D}; \boldsymbol{\theta})].$$

This very generic expression involves the manner in which edge-weights were estimated in Chapter 6, as well as how edge-weights are estimated in many of the nonregularized estimation methods discussed in this chapter (a notable exception is Bayesian estimation, which does not rely on maximizing the likelihood function). For example, $\mathcal{L}$ could indicate the Gaussian log-likelihood, $\boldsymbol{D}$ a data set with continuous variables, and $\boldsymbol{\theta}$ a collection of GGM parameters. In *regularized* estimation, an additional penalty function is added to the expression that is maximized:

$$\hat{\boldsymbol{\theta}} = \operatorname{argmax}_{\boldsymbol{\theta}} [\mathcal{L}(\boldsymbol{D}; \boldsymbol{\theta}) - \lambda \text{Penalty}(\boldsymbol{\theta})].$$

The penalty function returns some positive number based on the value of the parameters. This function is used to add a penalty to the fit of the model (the log-likelihood) based on the *complexity* of the model. The more non-zero parameters and the stronger their absolute values, the more the fit is penalized. Because of this, regularization is also termed *penalized likelihood estimation*. The tuning parameter λ controls the amount of penalization: if $\lambda = 0$ no penalty is added, and the higher λ the more the fit is penalized for model complexity. In LASSO regularization (Tibshirani, 1996), this penalty takes the form of the sum of absolute values over the parameters:

$$\text{Penalty}_{\text{LASSO}}(\boldsymbol{\theta}) = \sum_{i \in S} |\theta_i|,$$

in which S represents the set of parameters that are included in the penalty (for example, for the Ising model the network parameters in $\boldsymbol{\Omega}$ could be included but the thresholds in $\boldsymbol{\tau}$ are typically not penalized). This penalty is also termed the ℓ_1-norm. Because the absolute value used in the LASSO penalty has a sharp peak at 0, parameter estimates can become exactly 0, reducing the number of parameters included. For more information on the LASSO, see Hastie et al. (2015).

Technical Box 7.2. Regularized parameter estimation and the LASSO penalty.

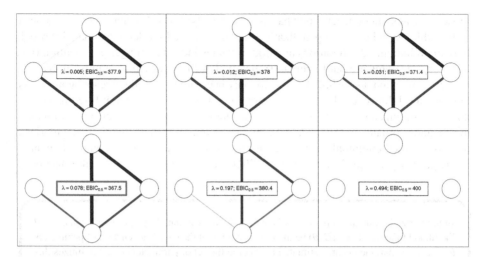

Figure 7.6. An example of the EBICglasso algorithm. Based on data simulated from the right-most panel in Figure 7.4. The GLASSO algorithm is used with six different values for λ (in the software 100 values are used by default) to create a sequence of networks, ranging from dense (many edges included) to sparse (no edges included). The highlighted network is the selected network using EBIC with $\gamma = 0.5$.

implemented in the *glasso* package (Friedman et al., 2008). These packages are used in the most commonly used R packages for network estimation that use regularization (see Table 7.1).

Rather than choosing the tuning parameter λ manually, statistical routines can be used to choose this tuning parameter in an optimal way. For example, cross-validation (CV) prediction accuracy can be used to choose the tuning parameter such that new data are optimally predicted.[4] A more common method, however, is to pick the tuning parameter under which a criterion is optimized. Mainly, the extended Bayesian Information Criterion (EBIC; Chen & Chen, 2008) has been shown to work well for PMRF structure estimation (Foygel & Drton, 2010; van Borkulo et al., 2014), and is implemented in the *EBICglasso* algorithm (*qgraph* package) and the *huge* package (Jiang et al., 2021) for GGM estimation, the *eLasso* (*IsingFit* package) algorithm for Ising model estimation, and MGM estimation using the *mgm* package. The EBIC relies on a *hypertuningparameter* γ that controls the amount of extra penalization (λ) for model complexity. This hypertuningparameter has to be set manually. Intuitively, γ can be thought of as a parameter that tries to constrain estimation by the size of the space of possible models; the more edges the larger the space. Typically, this hypertuningparameter is set between 0 and 0.5 (of note, the EBIC with $\gamma = 0$ is equivalent to the BIC), with higher values of γ leading to sparser networks to be estimated than lower values of γ. Commonly used values for γ are 0.25

---

[4]A typical method is to use k-fold cross-validation. In this procedure, the data are split in k (e.g., 10) parts. Next, for each part a range of networks is estimated by varying λ on the remaining $k-1$ parts of the data. The estimated model is then used to predict the left-out part of the data. This is repeated for each of the k parts. As such, every part of the data is used one time as validation set and $k-1$ times to train a model. Finally, the λ value that led to the best prediction accuracy is chosen for a final model which uses all data.

(default in *mgm* and *IsingFit*) and 0.5 (default in *qgraph* and *huge*). Of note: the same model can be returned under different settings of γ, and γ should not be confused with λ as, for example, $\gamma = 0$ will not lead to a saturated network structure (while $\lambda = 0$ does). Some regularization algorithms (most notably, *IsingFit* and *mgm*), make use of an extra threshold by default for edges with weak weights, termed the *beta-min condition* (Wainwright, 2009), leading to more conservative network estimation (higher specificity, but lower sensitivity).

Regularization, and specifically LASSO regularization, has been extensively applied in the early years of psychological network estimation literature (roughly 2015 to 2020). In more recent years, however, the unregularized estimation procedures described earlier in this chapter (thresholding, pruning and model selection) are also often used, mostly because larger sample sizes are now used to estimate networks models. LASSO regularization has proven a powerful technique in cases where you have few observations and many variables. In fact, in machine learning LASSO regularization is used in situations where the number of variables exceeds the number of observations. In psychological data sets, however, we have seen a shift towards large-scale studies including many more observations than variables. In these cases, LASSO regularization may not be optimal and could actually do more harm than good. Specifically, although at high sample sizes edge-weight estimates obtained through LASSO estimation may be similar to edge-weight estimates obtained through other means, the LASSO may result in the inclusion of false positive edges whereas the other model selection strategies discussed in this chapter may lead to a more predictable level of false positive edges (e.g., with thresholding at $\alpha = 0.05$ we can predict false positive edges to be included with 5% chance).[5] Nonetheless, the use of LASSO regularization is a very powerful method to estimate psychological networks: it is very fast and will result in a clear network picture. The shrinkage to zero has more benefits than merely selecting edges, as this shrinkage also aids the visualization to be much clearer. In addition, when using the *qgraph* package for network visualization, the false positive edges are typically small and faded in the background of the network. Especially at low sample sizes, LASSO regularization can obtain an adequate representation of the overall network structure. This is especially the case in the Ising model, in which parameters are not bounded between -1 and 1 and sampling variation can lead to strong differences in parameter estimates that have a large impact on the visual representation.

7.6 Recommendations for applied researchers

High-dimensional model estimation as described in this chapter is not trivial, and model selection algorithms tend to perform differently in distinct settings, each having pros and cons. Further, psychological research questions pose unique challenges, including placing a strong focus on specific edges (e.g., bridge edges), measuring variables on ordered

---

[5]Especially the *EBICglasso* algorithm has been shown to include many false positive edges in some settings (Williams & Rast, 2020), in part because this algorithm does not use the *beta-min condition*. These falsely included edges typically have an edge-weights close to zero and are not very prominent when the network is visualized using *qgraph*. Some researchers who used the *EBICglasso* algorithm opted for setting the `minimum` argument in *qgraph* to a value between 0.01 and 0.05 to clear up the image and to remove potential false positive edges (e.g., Galderisi et al., 2018; Isvoranu et al., 2016).

scales, and using small sample sizes. As such, recommending one model selection algorithm over another is difficult, as there is no such thing as one "best" algorithm. In general, an exchange between discovery (i.e., sensitivity) and caution (i.e., specificity) should be expected and achieving both good edge inclusion and no false positive edge inclusion is difficult. It is therefore important to consider the aim of the study when choosing an estimation method.

In *psychonetrics*, the `ggm()` function can be used for GGM models, and the `Ising()` function can be used for Ising models. In both functions the `omega` argument controls the initial setup of the network: setting `omega = "full"` (the default) will create a saturated model with all edges included, and setting `omega = "empty"` will create a model with no edges included. After the model is created, the `runmodel()` function needs to be used to estimate the parameters, as also explained in Chapter 6. Following, several functions can be used for model search strategies. The `prune()` function can be used to fix all non-significant edges to zero and re-estimate the non-zero edges (termed *pruning* in this chapter). As such, the following code performs pruning for the GGM, assuming that the data are loaded into R as `Data` and using *dplyr* for the pipe operator `%>%` also introduced in Chapter 2.

```
model <- ggm(Data) %>% runmodel %>% prune(alpha = 0.05)
```

If the data in `Data` are binary, `ggm(Data)` could be replaced by `Ising(Data)` to instead estimate a pruned Ising model. The `stepup()` function can be used to add edges with the strongest modification index until some criterium is optimized. For example, the following code uses step-up GGM estimation to optimize the BIC (see Technical Box 7.1):

```
model <- ggm(Data, omega = "empty") %>% runmodel %>%
            stepup(criterion = "bic")
```

The model search strategies can also be combined. For example, the following code starts with a conservative pruning step (pruning all edges non-significant at a Bonferroni corrected $\alpha = 0.01$) followed by step-up model search:

```
model <- ggm(Data) %>% runmodel %>%
            prune(alpha = 0.01, adjust = "bonferroni") %>%
            stepup(criterion = "bic")
```

A more advanced model search strategy is implemented in the `modelsearch` function, which uses parameter significance and modification indices to stepwise add and remove edges until an optimal model is found (Epskamp, 2020). This can be used following a pruning step:

```
model <- ggm(Data) %>% runmodel %>% prune(alpha = 0.05) %>%
            modelsearch(criterion = "bic")
```

Of note, the `modelsearch()` aflgorithm can be very slow for larger networks (e.g., more than 20 nodes).

Tutorial Box 7.2. Network estimation with model search using *psychonetrics*.

Gaussian graphical model. Recent large-scale simulation studies provide some guidance on GGM estimation for applied researchers as to which estimation method is best chosen in light of the research question(s) of the researcher (Isvoranu & Epskamp, 2021). Figure 7.7 shows an example of networks estimated using the four estimation methods discussed in this chapter on three data sets generated using the network shown in Figure 7.1. This true network contains 78 out of 136 potential edges. Figure 7.7 shows that the lower the sample size, the more the methods diverge. The networks estimated with *EBICglasso* show a structure that is comparable to the true network at all three sample sizes. However, these networks also contain many false positive edges, ranging from 20 (specificity: 0.66) in the $N = 300$ network to 25 (specificity: 0.57) in the $N = 5,000$ network. These false positives are on average very weak (average absolute edge weight is 0.04 in the $N = 300$ network and 0.01 in the $N = 5,000$ network). The other (nonregularized) methods are more conservative and include fewer false positive edges ($1 - 3$ across all nine networks), but also perform much poorer in terms of *sensitivity* (lacking statistical power to detect edges), and especially in the $N = 300$ network provide a poorer visual representation of the network structure. The thresholding and pruning networks show prominent false positive edges (most notably a negative edge in the $N = 300$ thresholded network, that was estimated to be positive in the pruned network). At the high sample size all methods retrieve comparable network structures.

The observations made in Figure 7.7 mirror the observations made in the larger simulation study discussed by Isvoranu and Epskamp (2021), as well as the discussion of pros and cons of each of the methods covered in this chapter. Overall, at high sample size (e.g., $N = 5,000$), most model selection algorithms work well, and unregularized estimators (e.g., the *ggmModSelect* algorithm) are likely preferred as they retrieve networks that resemble the true network, include few false positive edges, and have a high rate of identifying the strongest edges in the network structure. At low sample size (e.g., $N = 300$), however, regularization methods (*EBICglasso* and *mgm* with CV selection) may be preferred as long as the goal is to discover a generalizable network structure and the focus does not fall on each individual edge discovered in the network. In terms of specific research questions, at a medium sample size ($N = 1,000$), if the researcher is interested in the overall structure and strong edges of a network, regularized network estimators may work best, while if interested in particular (bridging) edges, the *ggmModSelect* algorithm and *mgm* (with EBIC selection) estimators could be preferred.

Ordered categorical and non-normal continuous data. An often occurring form of data in psychology is data in which items are measured on a scale with only a limited number of answer categories (i.e., Likert scales). With two answering categories, the statistical Ising model should be used and with five or more categories, the scale can usually be treated as continuous (Rhemtulla et al., 2012). For three and four answering categories, the scale might require more consideration. One solution is to binarize the items if this is sensible to do (for example, symptom data could be binarized into 'endorse' and 'not endorse'). Alternatively, a model could be estimated in which an GGM is assumed to underlie a set of ordered categorical responses. Epskamp and Fried (2018) recommended using polychoric correlations (Olsson, 1979) as input to GGM estimation tools that use a correlation matrix

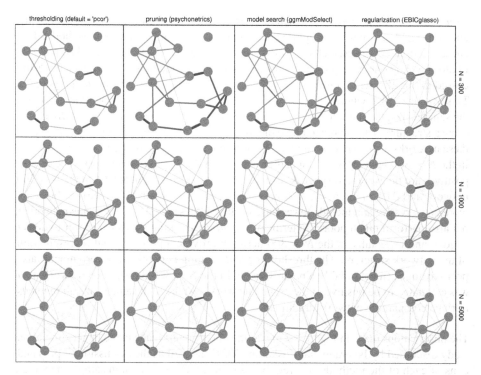

Figure 7.7. Example of simulation results on GGM estimation performance using the network reported in Figure 7.1 as true network structure (generating model). Three data sets were simulated under sample sizes $N = 300$ (a small sample size), $N = 1,000$ (a medium sample size), and $N = 5,000$ (a large sample size). Estimated network structures using thresholding (using `default = "pcor"` in the *bootnet* package), pruning (using the *psychonetrics* package), model search (using `ggmModSelect` in the *qgraph* package), and regularization (using `EBICglasso` in the *qgraph* package). The `maximum` argument was used to make the networks comparable (see Chapter 4). For more extensive simulation results that include these settings, see Isvoranu and Epskamp (2021).

as input (e.g., *EBICglasso* and *ggmModSelect*)[6]. However, it has later been shown that at very low sample sizes, this practice may lead to instability as shown in bootstrapping methods (Chapter 8), possibly due the the likelihood used in these estimators not being correct when polychoric correlations are used. The *psychonetrics* package contains the three-stage weighted least squares estimator (also relying on polychoric correlations, but not on a likelihood expression) as commonly used in structural equation modeling (Muthén, 1984), and the *BGGM* package models ordered categorical data through the use of a semi-parametric Gaussian copula model (Hoff, 2007). Isvoranu and Epskamp (2021) evaluated these methods on 4-point Likert scale data and showed that they adequately recover the network structure at high sample sizes but tend to be conservative at low

---

[6]Note: when using `estimateNetwork` the input correlation matrix is computed from the raw data. As such, the input to `estimateNetwork` should be raw data. If you wish to use a correlation matrix as input to the *EBICglasso* and *ggmModSelect* algorithms, the `EBICglasso` and `ggmModSelect` in the *qgraph* package should be used.

sample sizes. In addition, Isvoranu and Epskamp (2021) show that GGM estimation tools that treat the data as continuous are robust for ordered categorical data.

When the data are continuous but not normally distributed, one strategy is to transform data before estimating a GGM structure. Isvoranu and Epskamp (2021) showed that using a rank-transformation (i.e., using Spearman correlation as input) is recommended.[7] An alternative is the use of the *nonparanormal transformation* (Liu et al., 2009) as implemented in the huge.npn function in the *huge* package (Jiang et al., 2021) to transform data to a normally distributed scale. Importantly, however, the huge.npn function may not handle missing data properly.[8] The rank transformation/Spearman correlations as input and the nonparanormal transformation can also be used in estimating GGM networks from ordered categorical data.

MGM and Ising models. For the MGM and Ising model there are fewer options for estimating model parameters. The MGM has mostly been implemented in the *mgm* package (Haslbeck & Waldorp, 2020), also shown in Tutorial Box 7.3, which uses regularized estimation. The Ising model, on the other hand, can be estimated using regularized (*IsingFit*) and noregularized methods (*IsingSampler* and *psychonetrics*). While both *IsingFit* and *mgm* include LASSO regularization coupled with EBIC model selection, it can also be noted that the behavior of these estimators is different from the *EBICglasso* algorithm used for GGM estimation. This is because *IsingFit* and *mgm* make use of the *beta-min condition* to remove small edges, leading to a much more conservative estimation procedure (Haslbeck & Waldorp, 2020; Hastie et al., 2015).[9] van Borkulo et al. (2014) reported simulation studies for regularized Ising model estimation and showed that this leads to a conservative estimator in which specificity is high. Especially at small and medium sample sizes, we recommend to use regularized estimation for the Ising model, as the regularization also helps returning a clearer visualization. Because Ising model parameters are not bounded, if regularization is not used at lower sample sizes some model parameters can be estimated to be very large, leading to a poor visual representation in which the large edges stand out. At larger sample sizes, the unregularized Ising model estimators can also be used (provided that the number of nodes is not too large for multivariate estimation).

Sample size recommendations and missing data handling. Two final topics which applied researchers frequently wonder about are sample size recommendations and missing data handling. Unfortunately, not very concrete guidelines can be given for these topics. With respect to missing data handling, not much research has been done on this topic for the estimators discussed in this chapter. In univariate estimation, methods for handling missing data in regression models should be applicable to network estimation as well (e.g., Loh & Wainwright, 2012). Multivariate estimators that make use of a correlation matrix as input (*EBICglasso, ggmModSelect, pcor*) can make use of pairwise estimation

---

[7]In *bootnet* the argument corMethod = "spearman" or transform = "rank" can often be used for this purpose.

[8]At the time of writing, package version 1.3.5 of *huge* contains a bug in which missing data are improperly imputed with incorrect values.

[9]Using *mgm* with CV is generally less conservative than using *mgm* with EBIC model selection.

The *mgm* package (Haslbeck & Waldorp, 2020) can be used to estimate a mixed graphical model (MGM) through LASSO regularization. This model allows for the inclusion of different types of variables as nodes. Suppose we have a data set named `Data` with five columns: three continuous columns, a binary column, and a categorical column with four levels. We can then specify the type of variable using a vector:

```
type <- c("g","g","g","c","c")
```

The symbol `"g"` encodes a continuous (Gaussian) variable and the symbol `"c"` encodes a categorical variable (including binary variables). A third symbol, `"p"`, can be used for count variables (Poisson). With this vector specified, we can now estimate an MGM using EBIC model selection as follows:

```
library("mgm")
res <- mgm(Data, type = type, lambdaSel = "EBIC", binarySign = TRUE)
```

The argument `binarySign` can be used to make sure edges connected to binary nodes are colored correctly. The estimated weights matrix can be found in `res$pairwise$wadj`. Importantly, this weights matrix only contains absolute values for the edge weights. The signs of the edges are separately stored in `res$pairwise$signs`. Edges that are 0 or edges connected to categorical variables have no sign. To plot the network using *qgraph*, the edge colors supplied in `res$pairwise$edgecolor_cb` can be used:

```
library("qgraph")
qgraph(res$pairwise$wadj, edge.color = res$pairwise$edgecolor_cb,
       layout = "spring")
```

The *mgm* package can also be used via the `estimateNetwork` function in *bootnet* (see Tutorial Box 7.1), which automatically detects categorical and binary variables and sets `lambdaSel = "EBIC"` and `binarySign = TRUE` by default. The following code will lead to the same network:

```
net_bootnet <- estimateNetwork(data, default = "mgm")
plot(net_bootnet)
```

Tutorial Box 7.3. Introduction to the *mgm* package.

of the input correlation matrix (estimating each correlation separately using cases that are not missing), which is the default in *bootnet*. In *psychonetrics*, full-information maximum likelihood estimation can be used by setting `estimator = "FIML"` (Epskamp et al., 2021). Both these solutions require the assumption that data are missing at random. Many other estimation methods only work when listwise deletion (removing all rows that contain at least one missing data point) of missing data is used, which requires the assumption that data are missing completely at random.

In terms of sample size, the sample size strongly depends on the research question and the expected network structure. To this end, a simulation study can be set up (for example using the `netSimulator` function in *bootnet* as shown in the practical exercises available on the *Companion Website*) given an expected network structure. Obtaining such an expected network structure, however, is very hard, as it would require prior knowledge on $n(n - 1)/2$ parameters (with n being the number of nodes). Alternatively, large-scale simulation studies such as the study by Isvoranu and Epskamp (2021) can be used to provide some pointers on the sample size requirements. In general, we recommend to aim to include no more than 30 nodes in the network to keep the network interpretable and sample size requirements for stable networks manageable. In addition, we recommend to aim to have as large as possible a sample size. At least several hundreds of cases are required for a stable network, and it is not uncommon for sample sizes to be over a thousand or several thousands of cases.[10] Finally, as discussed above the research question is also crucial: a focus on particular (potentially small) edges, such as bridge edges, will require a larger sample size than a focus on the overall network structure. Regardless of the sample size, parameter stability and accuracy should be assess post-hoc through confidence intervals, credibility intervals, or bootstrapping methods, as discussed in the next chapter.

7.7 Exercises

Conceptual

7.1. Suppose we flip three coins 1,000 times, and store the data as (1) if the results were 'heads' and as (0) if the results were 'tails,' aiming to estimate an Ising model. What *structure* would we expect to find?

7.2. Explain the difference between thresholding and pruning.

7.3. Model search strategies can reach a local optimum but not necessarily a global optimum. Explain why.

7.4. Explain the difference between λ and γ when using LASSO regularization coupled with EBIC model selection.

7.5. Think about a research question and include details about your (expected) sample size, number, and type of variables. How would you go about selecting the best estimation algorithm to answer your research question?

True or false

7.6. The sensitivity and specificity of thresholding and pruning should be near identical.

7.7. When comparing two models using BIC, the model with the highest BIC is preferred.

7.8. In LASSO regularization, the likelihood is penalized with the sum of squared parameters.

7.9. At high sample size (e.g., $N = 5,000$), regularized estimators will perform well in retrieving a network structure that features a high specificity.

---

[10]In the case of LASSO regularization, it has been shown that reliably retrieving a network with only a few edges may require quite a large sample size. For example, with 30 nodes and aiming to recover 10 edges, you may need at least $N = 341$ observations.

7.10. At high sample sizes, all model selection algorithms are expected to return similar networks.

Practical

For practical exercises in R, please navigate to the appropriate folder of this chapter, available on the online *Companion Website*.

References

Chen, J., & Chen, Z. (2008). Extended Bayesian information criteria for model selection with large model spaces. *Biometrika*, *95*(3), 759–771.

Epskamp, S. (2021). *psychonetrics: Structural equation modeling and confirmatory network analysis* [R package version 0.10]. R package version 0.10. https: //CRAN.R-project.org/package=psychonetrics

Epskamp, S., & Fried, E. I. (2018). A tutorial on regularized partial correlation networks. *Psychological Methods*, *23*(4), 617–634.

Epskamp, S., Isvoranu, A. M., & Cheung, M. (2021). Meta-analytic Gaussian network aggregation. *Psychometrika*. https://doi.org/10.1007/s11336-021-09764-3

Epskamp, S. (2020). Psychometric network models from time-series and panel data. *Psychometrika*, *85*(1), 206–231.

Epskamp, S., Borsboom, D., & Fried, E. I. (2018). Estimating psychological networks and their accuracy: A tutorial paper. *Behavior Research Methods*, *50*(1), 195–212.

Foygel, R., & Drton, M. (2010). Extended Bayesian information criteria for Gaussian graphical models. *Advances in Neural Information Processing Systems 22 (NIPS 2010)*, *23*, 2020–2028.

Friedman, J. H., Hastie, T., & Tibshirani, R. (2008). Sparse inverse covariance estimation with the graphical lasso. *Biostatistics*, *9*(3), 432–441.

Friedman, J. H., Hastie, T., & Tibshirani, R. (2010). Regularization paths for generalized linear models via coordinate descent. *Journal of Statistical Software*, *33*(1).

Galderisi, S., Rucci, P., Kirkpatrick, B., Mucci, A., Gibertoni, D., Rocca, P., Rossi, A., Bertolino, A., Strauss, G. P., Aguglia, E., et al. (2018). Interplay among psychopathologic variables, personal resources, context-related factors, and real-life functioning in individuals with schizophrenia: A network analysis. *JAMA Psychiatry*, *75*(4), 396–404.

Haslbeck, J. M. B., & Waldorp, L. J. (2020). mgm: Estimating time-varying mixed graphical models in high-dimensional data. *Journal of Statistical Software*, *93*(8).

Hastie, T., Tibshirani, R., & Friedman, J. H. (2001). *The elements of statistical learning*. Springer.

Hastie, T., Tibshirani, R., & Wainwright, M. J. (2015). *Statistical learning with sparsity: The lasso and generalizations*. Taylor & Francis.

Hoff, P. D. (2007). Extending the rank likelihood for semiparametric copula estimation. *The Annals of Applied Statistics*, *1*(1), 265–283.

Isvoranu, A. M., & Epskamp, S. (2021). Which estimation method to choose in network psychometrics? deriving guidelines for applied researchers. *Psychological Methods*. https://doi.org/10.1037/met0000439

Isvoranu, A. M., Epskamp, S., & Cheung, M. (2021). Network models of post-traumatic stress disorder: A meta-analysis. *Journal of Abnormal Psychology, 130*(8), 841–861.

Isvoranu, A. M., Guloksuz, S., Epskamp, S., van Os, J., Borsboom, D., & GROUP Investigators. (2020). Toward incorporating genetic risk scores into symptom networks of psychosis. *Psychological Medicine, 50*(4), 636–643.

Isvoranu, A. M., van Borkulo, C. D., Boyette, L., Wigman, J. T. W., Vinkers, C. H., Borsboom, D., & GROUP Investigators. (2016). A network approach to psychosis: Pathways between childhood trauma and psychotic symptoms. *Schizophrenia Bulletin, 43*(1), 187–196.

Jiang, H., Fei, X., Liu, H., Roeder, K., Lafferty, J., Wasserman, L., Li, X., & Zhao, T. (2021). *Huge: High-dimensional undirected graph estimation* [R package version 1.3.5]. R package version 1.3.5. https://CRAN.R-project.org/package= huge

Liu, H., Lafferty, J., & Wasserman, L. (2009). The nonparanormal: Semiparametric estimation of high dimensional undirected graphs. *Journal of Machine Learning Research, 10*, 2295–2328.

Loh, P.-L., & Wainwright, M. (2012). High-dimensional regression with noisy and missing data: Provable guarantees with nonconvexity. *Annals of Statistics, 40*(3), 1637–1664.

Muthén, B. (1984). A general structural equation model with dichotomous, ordered categorical, and continuous latent variable indicators. *Psychometrika, 49*(1), 115–132.

Olsson, U. (1979). Maximum likelihood estimation of the polychoric correlation coefficient. *Psychometrika, 44*(4), 443–460.

Rhemtulla, M., Brosseau-Liard, P. É., & Savalei, V. (2012). When can categorical variables be treated as continuous? a comparison of robust continuous and categorical sem estimation methods under suboptimal conditions. *Psychological Methods, 17*(3), 354–373.

Sörbom, D. (1989). Model modification. *Psychometrika, 54*(3), 371–384.

Tibshirani, R. (1996). Regression shrinkage and selection via the lasso. *Journal of the Royal Statistical Society: Series B (Methodological), 58*(1), 267–288.

van Borkulo, C. D., Borsboom, D., Epskamp, S., Blanken, T. F., Boschloo, L., Schoevers, R. A., & Waldorp, L. J. (2014). A new method for constructing networks from binary data. *Nature: Scientific Reports, 4*(5918).

Wainwright, M. J. (2009). Sharp thresholds for high-dimensional and noisy sparsity recovery using-constrained quadratic programming (lasso). *IEEE Transactions On Information Theory, 55*(5), 2183–2202.

Williams, D. R., & Mulder, J. (2020). BGGM: Bayesian Gaussian graphical models in R. *Journal of Open Source Software, 5*(51), 2111.

Williams, D. R., & Rast, P. (2020). Back to the basics: Rethinking partial correlation network methodology. *British Journal of Mathematical and Statistical Psychology, 73*(2), 187–212.

Williams, D. R., Rast, P., Pericchi, L. R., & Mulder, J. (2020). Comparing Gaussian
    graphical models with the posterior predictive distribution and Bayesian model
    selection. *Psychological Methods*, 25(5), 653.

Chapter 8

Network Stability, Comparison, and Replicability

Eiko I. Fried[1], Sacha Epskamp[2,3], Myrthe Veenman[1], & Claudia D. van Borkulo[2,3]

1. Leiden University, Department of Psychology

2. University of Amsterdam, Department of Psychology

3. University of Amsterdam, Centre for Urban Mental Health

8.1 Introduction

Statistical parameter estimation (e.g., estimating edge weight parameters) is subject to sampling variation: when estimating the same parameters from different *samples* from the same *population*, there will be variation in the parameter estimates. Because we only observe a small part of the population (i.e., our sample), our estimate of the population value is not perfect, and we will likely obtain a different estimate when analyzing a different sample. As such, there is a level of *uncertainty* that is paired with the estimated parameter. This uncertainty typically becomes lower with larger samples, which is why election polls based on larger (rather than small) representative samples tend to be more accurate. Because of this uncertainty, we (a) cannot assume that an estimated network structure perfectly resembles a hypothetical true generating network structure, and (b) we cannot assume that the exact same network will be obtained when analyzing a new sample. Figure 8.1 shows an example of 12 networks that were estimated on 12 different $N = 500$ samples generated from the same true network model (i.e., from the same population).

Cite this chapter as:

Fried, E. I., Epskamp, S., Veenman, M., & van Borkulo, C. D. (2022). Chapter 8. Network stability, comparison, and replicability. In Isvoranu, A. M., Epskamp, S., Waldorp, L. J., & Borsboom, D. (Eds.). *Network psychometrics with R: A guide for behavioral and social scientists*. Routledge, Taylor & Francis Group.

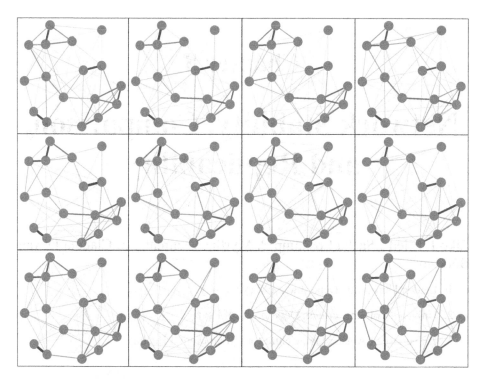

Figure 8.1. Example of 12 networks estimated using the *EBICglasso* algorithm from 12 different $N = 500$ samples generated using a meta-analytic Gaussian graphical model of post-traumatic stress symptoms as generating structure (Isvoranu et al., 2021; see also Figure 7.1).

We can see that while the structure is overall comparable across all networks,[1] there are also differences across the networks in terms of which edges are present or not and how strong these edges are. This is similar to obtaining somewhat different election poll results in different samples. As such, we cannot state based on visual inspection that one particular edge is statistically larger than another edge, the same way we should not conclude that one party has a significant vote advantage over another based on visual inspection of poll graphs.

This chapter will focus on techniques that allow for more insight in this variability due to sampling variation. Mainly, the chapter will focus on two aspects: *stability* and *accuracy* of parameters and descriptive analyses within the same sample, and *network comparison* between samples. In some cases, analytic statistical methods can be used to this end. For example, the uncertainty of parameter estimates can be expressed as a confidence interval (CI; described further in the next section). The poll result of a given party in a sample of people could be 30%, with a 95% CI of 28%–32%. Likewise, poll results of two parties can be compared statistically through the use of a statistical test (see Chapter 5). While

---

[1]Obtaining similar network structures is not guaranteed, of course; here, this happens in part due to the *EBICglasso* algorithm being used for estimation purposes. If a different algorithm is used, the structures may be less similar. See also Figure 7.7.

similar methods can be applied to network models, they come with some complications. For one, they usually require *saturated* network models—networks in which all edges are included (see Chapter 6).[2] Analytic methods designed for saturated models may no longer be valid after model selection methods are used (see Chapter 7), as the model selection procedure itself introduces an extra level of variation that also needs to be taken into account. For example, CIs of parameters in a constrained network obtained using the same data as used for model selection are typically too small.

This chapter discusses these issues, introduces data-driven resampling methods to gauge stability and accuracy of network models using the *bootnet* package, and shows how to perform network comparison tests using the *NetworkComparisonTest* package.

8.2 Stability and accuracy in one sample

In this section we will discuss the stability and accuracy of results obtained from analyzing a single sample. We use the R package *bootnet* and follow routines and recommendations described by Epskamp et al. (2018), including some updates. We focus on the stability of two types of parameters that have been introduced in previous book chapters: edge weights and centrality indices.

Edge weights

Confidence intervals. For typical statistical results, the CIs can be approximated through the use of a non-parametric bootstrap (Efron, 1979). Bootstrapping is a method that re-samples the data with replacement (e.g., 1,000 times) and then uses the parameter estimates obtained from these re-sampled samples to construct, for instance, a 95% CI by recovering the 2.5th and 97.5th quantiles. In the case of 1,000 bootstrap samples, this would entail ordering all estimates and reporting the 25th and 975th values. Typically, CIs constructed this way will adhere to the default interpretation of the 95% CI: In 95% of the times such an interval is created, a hypothetical underlying *true* parameter is expected to lie in the interval. The non-parametric bootstrap can readily be applied to assess the accuracy of edges estimated through the saturated model estimation procedures discussed in Chapter 6.[3] The smaller the estimated CI, the more accurate the parameter estimate. Tutorial Box 8.1 shows how the *bootnet* package can be used to bootstrap CIs.

Bootstrapped CIs are not always CIs. When applying model selection strategies, as introduced in Chapter 7, non-parametric bootstrapping can also readily be used to gain insight in the stability of network estimates (Hastie et al., 2015). This can be referred to as *bootstrapped confidence interval* (BCI), which can be useful to assess the stability of parameter estimation while taking the model selection procedure into account. However, these BCIs may lose the fundamental property of a CI in that these no longer contain

---

[2]For example, the *psychonetrics* package allows for confidence intervals of edges in saturated models to be drawn using the `CIplot` function, and has several methods for multi-group comparison (Epskamp et al., 2021).

[3]CIs can often also be obtained analytically for saturated and constrained network models, for example, through the use of maximum likelihood estimation. However, such CIs are based on an approximation to the normal distribution, which is not required for the bootstrap.

the true value in 95% of intervals constructed this way. This is in part because model selection procedures set the parameter to exactly 0 when there is not enough evidence that the parameter is non-zero. For example, consider a 100-node network which we aim to estimate from an $N = 10$ sample using LASSO regression coupled with EBIC model selection (i.e., a scenario with extremely low power). Suppose the true edge weight A — B is 0.25. From our $N = 10$ regularized network, we would very likely obtain a parameter 'estimate' of 0 for almost every possible bootstrapped $N = 10$ sample. To this end, the BCI would likely have both a lower bound and an upper bound of 0, and as such would never include 0.25. This BCI would therefore not have the property that 95% of such created intervals contain the true value of 0.25. In addition to model selection, LASSO regularization also shrinks parameter estimates to zero, further complicating interpreting a BCI as an analytic CI: even at large sample sizes, the true edge weight of 0.25 might often not be included because parameters are estimated closer to zero.

This is why the BCI obtained by bootstrapping network model selection strategies should not be interpreted as an analytic CI around the true parameter value. Instead, these intervals should solely be interpreted to show the variability in parameter estimates that is to be expected in the data. When using LASSO regularization, such BCIs should often cut off exactly at zero, as LASSO pulls edge estimates towards zero. Signs of instability in such BCIs based on regularized networks are if there are some edges with much larger confidence intervals than others, possibly due to a violation of assumptions, and if many BCIs do not cut off neatly at zero. Although there are methods to obtain confidence intervals when using LASSO type estimators (referred to as debiased or desparsified estimators, see, e.g., van de Geer et al., 2014), they are not (yet) part of the software packages used in this book and therefore we do not discuss them here.

In addition to the BCI not capturing the true parameter, we may also see that the BCI may sometimes not accurately reflect the bootstrap samples at all. Suppose in 1,000 bootstrap samples we obtain parameter values between 0.24 and 0.26 970 times, and fix the edge to 0 in the remaining 30 times. A 95% BCI will then have a lower bound of 0 and an upper bound of 0.26. This interval, however, does not accurately reflect the bootstrap samples, as none of the times the parameter was estimated to be above 0 and below 0.24—a sizeable range of the BCI. This problem does not occur often in BCIs based on regularized networks (as the regularization pulls to zero, avoiding such a gap), but will be prominent in non-regularized model selection strategies. To this end, we recommend using a *split-0* BCI when applying non-regularized model selection (e.g., *ggmModSelect*). In such a *split-0* BCI, the BCI is drawn only using the bootstrap samples in which a parameter was non-zero, and is coupled with a proportion of the times the parameter was put to zero. This way, the information on how often a parameter was included and what parameter values the parameter then obtained is split. A parameter is stable if it is consistently included and if it then also has a relatively small *split-0* BCI, or if it is consistently not included.[4] When visualizing such a *split-0* BCI, it is recommended to visualize the intervals less prominently (e.g., faded) for edges that are not often included (as the *split-0* BCI is then based on only a few samples).

---

[4]Typically the *split-0* BCI of edges that are consistently not included is very large, as it is based only on the few times the parameter is included as non-zero. To this end, *bootnet* will draw this interval with a faded color.

A final important note with regard to using BCIs is that these should never be used for significance testing of individual edges by checking if zero is in the interval or not; BCIs cannot be interpreted in the same manner as CIs. For example, LASSO regularization already controls for sampling error when putting an edge to be non-zero, and pulls edges towards zero in its estimation procedure; additionally checking if zero is in the BCI does not lead to valid inference. Likewise, in the *split-0* BCI used in non-regularized model selection procedures, the intervals are by definition based only on the times a parameter is included (non-zero), and can therefore be very wide and cross zero for small parameters that are put to zero in, for example, 99% of the samples.

Using the *bootnet* package, we can estimate a network using `estimateNetwork` as shown in the previous chapters:

```
library("bootnet")
n1 <- estimateNetwork(Data, default = "...")
```

After estimating a network structure via the `estimateNetwork` function, we can use the following routine to perform a non-parametric bootstrap (resampling cases with the same N and with replacement) using 1,000 bootstrap samples:[a]

```
b1 <- bootnet(n1, nBoots=1000)
```

This process will typically be slow, but can be made faster by using multiple computer threads using the nCores argument.[b] The BCIs around edge weights can be plotted via:

```
plot(b1, order = "sample")
```

Alternatively, the *split-0* BCIs can be plotted with:

```
plot(b1, plot = "interval", order = "sample", split0 = TRUE)
```

If the network contains many nodes, the labels on the y-axis can be turned off with `labels = FALSE`. The edge weights difference plot can be created via:

```
plot(b1, "edge", plot = "difference", order = "sample")
```

The argument `onlyNonZero = TRUE` can also be used to only show edges that were included as non-zero in the sample network. Finally, a similar plot can be made for centrality differences:

```
plot(b1, "strength", order="sample")
```

Many additional arguments are available via `?plot.bootnet`.

---

[a]Given that bootstrapping can be computationally intensive, we save the results with saveRDS(b1, file = "b1.RDS") and load them later with b1 <- readRDS("b1.RDS") so we need not estimate bootstraps again every time we run the R code. Note, however, that this object (and therefore also the stored file) contains the raw data, so do not share these files if you cannot share your data.

[b]Many modern computers support at least nCores = 8. Note, if this leads to an error, try setting nCores = 1 to see if a more informative error is returned.

Tutorial Box 8.1. Investigating accuracy and differences using the non-parametric bootstrap with the *bootnet* package.

Bootstrapped difference tests.   Another way in which bootstrap samples can be used is to assess if two edges are different from one another. This can be done by forming a BCI on the difference of two edge estimates (e.g., the edge weight of $A — B$ minus the edge weight of $B — C$). Unlike edge weights, Epskamp et al. (2018) showed in a simulation study that checking if zero is in the 95% difference BCI does lead to valid inference to reject the null-hypothesis that two edges are equal at at most $\alpha = 0.05$. These results can then be visualized in, for example, a plot showing for each pairwise test if these are significant or not (see Tutorial Box 8.1). Typically, no correction for multiple testing is performed when making such a plot because (1) doing so would require an intolerable number of bootstrap samples[5], (2) the low significance level would likely lead to most tests being non-significant simply due to power, and (3) these analyses are almost always performed exploratory, and as such the substantive drop in sensitivity (power) to detect differences is not worth the improvement in specificity. This means that results from such bootstrapped difference tests should be interpreted with some care: it can show if some edges are consistently stronger than other edges and if there are many differences in edge weights in the network, but one should hesitate to focus interpretation on the difference between two specific edges only unless this can be consistently shown in different samples.

Centrality

Common descriptive statistics that are investigated from network models are centrality measures, such as node strength, closeness, and betweenness that were introduced in Chapter 3. Similar to edge weights, we want to know how precisely centrality measures are estimated. Unfortunately, however, we cannot rely on BCIs when studying the stability of centrality indices (Epskamp et al., 2018). This is because many of the weighted variants of centrality metrics rely on the absolute value of an edge weight (Opsahl et al., 2010). As a result, an edge weight of 0 is at the boundary of the possible parameter range, which is highly problematic for bootstrapping (Davison & Hinkley, 1997). This is especially true for network models, where many edges can be expected to be near or exactly zero in the true model (sparsity assumption).

For example, consider a toy example discussed earlier in Chapter 5 in which our data consist of repeated throws of two coins: Coin A and Coin B. Since the coins are independent, in an underlying true Ising model the edge $A — B$ would be exactly zero. Suppose we would estimate an Ising model using saturated maximum likelihood estimation as described in Chapter 6 and obtain an edge estimate of 0.01. Suppose that subsequently we bootstrap the data five times and obtain the ordered values of –0.15, –0.08, 0.02, 0.04, and 0.12. The largest BCI we could form would range from –0.15 to 0.12, which indeed contains the true parameter of 0. However, given that centrality metrics often utilize the *absolute value* of edge weights, the node strength of these two nodes would be the absolute value of the weight of edge $A — B$. If we would form the BCI on the absolute values, the largest possible interval would be from 0.02 to 0.15, which not only does not include the true value of 0, it does not even contain the sample

---

[5]For a 20-node network there are 19 edges and 17,955 tests to be performed, leading to an adjusted $\alpha = 2.8 \times 10^{-6}$. This would likely require over a million bootstraps at least.

estimate of 0.01! Repeating this with more bootstrap samples, we would never be able to capture the true value of 0 in the BCI unless many parameters are set to be exactly 0. As such, it is exceedingly hard to draw a proper interval on the uncertainty of absolute edge weights. If we now consider that, for example, node strength in networks with more than two nodes is the sum of many absolute edge weights, it is not surprising that it is impossible to draw a proper interval for such a statistic.

Because the non-parametric bootstrap cannot be used to assess accuracy of centrality indices relying on absolute values, we instead introduce the *case-drop bootstrap* procedure to get an idea how accurately the order of centrality is estimated (Costenbader & Valente, 2003; Epskamp et al., 2018). The case-drop bootstrap looks at if the centrality indices obtained from a sample correlate with centrality indices obtained from a subset of that sample. As such, this bootstrap does not actually check for *accuracy* of the centrality estimates, but does check for *stability* in the interpretation of differences between centralities of different nodes. This is because it is conceivable that nodes simply do not differ in their centrality, and as such that any differences in centrality are due to chance and should be different in different subsets of the data. The case-drop bootstrap drops participants iteratively from the data (e.g., 10%, 20%, and so forth), each time estimating a network structure and deriving centrality estimates. We then correlate the rank order of centrality in the original network structure based on the full sample with the rank order of the networks that are based on the subsetted samples. Tutorial Box 8.2 describes how to use the case-drop bootstrap in *bootnet*.

The information of the case-drop bootstrap can be summarized in the *correlation stability* (CS) coefficient, where 'CS(cor = 0.7)' represents the maximum proportion of cases that can be dropped, such that in 95% of the samples the correlation between original centrality indices and centrality of networks based on subsets is 0.7 or higher. Epskamp et al. (2018) simulated data from a network structure in which each node had the same centrality, and showed that in this null-model, the CS-coefficient rarely exceeded 0.25 and almost never exceeded 0.5 regardless of sample size used. To this end, they recommended that to substantively interpret centrality of nodes the CS-coefficient should be at least above 0.25 and preferably above 0.5. Of note, however, is that the CS-coefficient makes several arbitrary choices (i.e., the correlation threshold of 0.7 and the reliance on 95% probability) and that these recommendations are based solely on one single simulation study. To this end, the CS-coefficient can be useful, but should not be the only factor in determining stability of centrality; it may be more fruitful to plot the correlation between centrality in the original sample with centrality in subsamples as a function of sample size, as shown in Tutorial Box 8.2.

Finally, while the non-parametric bootstrap cannot be used to assess accuracy in centrality estimates, Epskamp et al. (2018) show that these bootstraps can be used in testing for differences between centrality indices through the bootstrapped difference test, exactly in the same manner as used to assess differences between edge weights. This does allow for a statistical comparison between centralities of different nodes. Of note, Epskamp et al. (2018) show that such a centrality difference test tends to perform more conservatively than the α-level provided, and as such the test may lack statistical power in detecting true differences between centrality indices.

Using the estimated network from Tutorial Box 8.1, we can perform a case-drop bootstrap (sampling cases without replacement with a lower N than the original sample) with the argument `type = "case"` in `bootnet()`:

```
b2 <- bootnet(n1, nBoots=1000, nCores=8, type="case")
```

We can plot the correlation of centrality rank order in subsetted with centrality rank order in the original network structures via

```
plot(b2)
```

We can also zoom in on specific nodes:

```
plot(b2, perNode=TRUE, "strength")
```

The correlation stability (CS) coefficient can be obtained via

```
corStability(b2)
```

Tutorial Box 8.2. Investigating stability of centrality indices with case-drop bootstrapping in *bootnet*.

8.3 Analyzing and comparing multiple samples

The previous section discussed methods that can be used to assess stability and accuracy of results obtained from a single sample. Often, researchers instead have multiple samples, and may be interested in analyzing results from each of these samples. Broadly, research topics involving two (or more) samples usually can be categorized as one of two classes: studies that aim to compare two samples and test if the underlying network models of these samples are different, and studies that aim to investigate if the results match (replicate) earlier conclusions drawn in a different study. This section will discuss both these topics.

In general, there are several ways to compare network models estimated from different samples: (1) visual comparison, (2) correlating network parameters and descriptive statistics, and (3) performing statistical tests. In this paragraph, we discuss the first two options. To compare networks visually, it is best to plot the networks with a similar layout and similar scaling of the edge weights, which will aid visual comparison (see Chapter 4). Figure 8.2 provides an example: four networks of substance abuse (A1–A4) and dependence (D1–D7) symptoms, adapted from Rhemtulla et al. (2016). These figures were plotted with the same layout and with the scaling of edge weight visualization fixed to be the same across the networks.[6] This figure also reveals the challenge of visual network comparison without statistical tools: how would we determine how much these networks differ from each other, or how similar they are? The networks certainly look somewhat different: network *Opioids*, for example, is sparser than the others. One important consideration when comparing networks is how they were estimated. When

---

[6]This can be achieved by using the `averageLayout` function and the *maximum* argument in the *qgraph* package, as explained in Chapter 4.

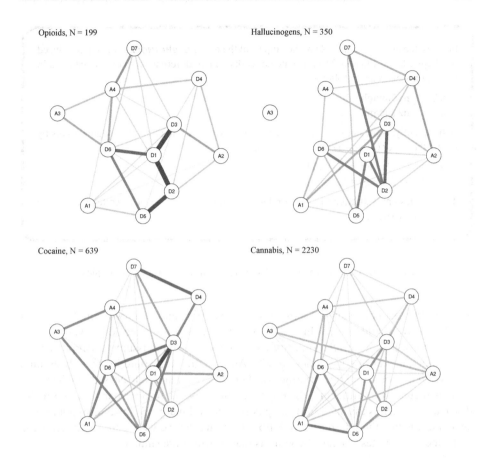

Figure 8.2. Four networks of substance abuse (A1–A4) and dependence (D1–D7) symptoms, adapted from Rhemtulla et al. (2016), estimated via an Ising Model with ℓ_1-regularized logistic regressions.

using regularized estimation, sample size may influence sparsity of network models. As explained in Chapter 7, sensitivity (power) increases with sample size, and more and more edges are estimated with growing sample size. This means that the networks of a smaller and a larger group will show differences in density, and the smallest sample will have the most sparse network structure when the groups come from the same population.

As further explained in Tutorial Box 8.3, network structures can also be compared by correlating all edge weights, and potential similarities can be visualized by plotting both sets of edge weights in a scatter plot. A high correlation would mean that network structures are highly similar. While the edge weights between networks can be correlated, it is important to note that the typical significance tests for correlations should be avoided when investigating this correlation for three reasons. (1) Such a test is based solely on the edge estimates and not on the observations of the subjects used to estimate the edge

Suppose the objects n1 and n2 are the outputs of the `estimateNetwork` function introduced in Chapter 6 and Chapter 7 to estimate networks on two different samples. We can obtain the weights matrices as follows:

```
w1 <- n1$graph
w2 <- n2$graph
```

Subsequently, if the network is an undirected network we can obtain the edge weights by taking the lower (or upper) triangular elements:

```
e1 <- w1[lower.tri(w1)]
e2 <- w2[lower.tri(w2)]
```

These edges can subsequently be correlated using `cor(e1, e2)` or a scatter plot can be made using `plot(e1, e2)`.

Tutorial Box 8.3. Correlating edge weights estimated from two samples.

weights. For example, suppose a three-node network is based on two samples of both $N = 5,000$. We would expect a high level of certainty in the estimated edge weights. The statistical test for the correlation coefficient, however, would assume a sample size of three (total number of edges), not 10,000. As such, the test would incorrectly assume a large amount of sampling variation. (2) For some estimators discussed in Chapter 7, such as regularized estimators, the edge weights may not be approximately normally distributed, which is assumed for testing correlations. Finally, (3) the null-hypothesis in such a test is that there is zero correlation, meaning that networks are vastly different, while the aim is to test the null-hypothesis that networks are similar.

Network comparison

Researchers that apply statistical network models are often interested in comparing groups in their underlying network structures. For example, the subject of study could be to see whether patients who will remit or persist in having a major depressive disorder differ in connectivity of symptom networks (van Borkulo et al., 2015), or whether the network structure of resilience factors differs for adolescents who did and did not experience childhood adversity (Fritz et al., 2018). The aim is then to investigate whether there are differences between network structures in different samples. The first steps in such network comparison studies are to compare the observed sample networks (e.g., visually or by correlating the edge weights). As described above, however, we would expect to find some differences in these networks even if the underlying generating network model was the same. To this end, this research also involves rejecting the null hypothesis that the data generating network structures were equal across the groups—could the data have been generated from the same underlying distribution? We will term these steps *network comparison*.

Beyond comparing the estimated network models visually and by correlating the edge weights, statistical tests can be used to test if the underlying network structure could have been the same for multiple groups. Haslbeck (2020) provides an overview of these methods and assesses their performance in detecting differences between groups. Like the non-parametric bootstrap used above in *bootnet*, a powerful non-parametric method that can be flexibly used with any estimation method (e.g., *IsingFit* or *EBICglasso*) also exists for network comparison: a permutation test. This test, termed the *network comparison test* (NCT; van Borkulo et al., 2021) is implemented in the *NetworkComparisonTest* package, and will be discussed in more detail below, followed by a brief introduction to other (parametric) methods.

The network comparison test (NCT)

The NCT, introduced by van Borkulo et al. (2021), is a permutation test that assesses whether the data of two groups are realizations from the same population network or not. The accompanying null hypothesis is that both samples come from the same population and, therefore, do not have different generating network structures. Comparison of two networks requires a test statistic that expresses the difference in a relevant network characteristic. Before providing details about the specific test statistics that are implemented in NCT, we explain the procedure of this test first. The NCT algorithm can be described in three steps:

1. Estimation of the network structures of both observed samples and calculation of the relevant test statistic (see Figure 8.3, Step 1).

2. Permutation of the data by repeated random rearrangement of group labels in the data and recalculation of the test statistic of each pair of permuted samples (these test statistics form the reference distribution; see Figure 8.3, Step 2).

3. Evaluation of the significance of the observed test statistic (i.e., comparing it to the reference distribution; see Figure 8.3, Step 3).

Tutorial Box 8.4 shows how the NCT can be used in R.

The NCT algorithm. In the first step, the relevant test statistic, called S_0, is calculated for the observed networks. For example, the test statistic could be the difference between the sums of all absolute edge weights between the two networks (see the next subsection for some of the currently implemented test statistics). The test statistic expresses the difference in a certain characteristic of both networks. For example, step one of Figure 8.3 shows that the network estimated from Group A is more connected (denser) than the network estimated from Group B. Now, we wish to know if this difference is significant, or if it is in line with differences that can be expected by chance (given the sample sizes of the groups). In the second step, the null distribution of the test statistic is created, since the null distribution of the test statistic is unknown. This is accomplished by repeated permutations (i.e., random rearrangements) of the data, estimating the network structures according to the permuted groups, and calculating the test statistic for each permutation ($S_1, S_2, \ldots$, see Figure 8.3, Step 2). If there is no difference between the two groups (i.e., participants of both groups come from the same population), then it does not matter to which group each participant is assigned. When the null hypothesis is true (e.g., there is no difference between the networks), the test statistic of the observed data will have a value that is expected under the null hypothesis. If this test statistic exceeds what you would expect under the null hypothesis (i.e., the difference of the observed networks is in the tail), then the difference between the networks is significant.

Using NCT to compare network characteristics.   Networks have various characteristics. The difference in one or more characteristics of two networks can be statistically compared in NCT. Which test statistic to use depends on the research question. Currently, the performance of NCT is validated for three test statistics, which involve hypotheses about the (1) invariance of the network structure, (2) invariance of the strength of an edge, and (3) invariance of global strength. These measures were chosen to capture differences in both global (i.e., invariance of the network structure and of global strength) and local characteristics (i.e., invariance of the strength of an individual edge). While other test statistics, such as common centrality metrics, expected influence (Robinaugh et al., 2016), and bridge centrality measures (Jones, Ma, et al., 2021), have been implemented, their performance has not been investigated. There is, however, no inherent reason to believe that the permutation test would not work well with such alternative statistics.

The first test is an *omnibus* test evaluating whether there is at least one edge that differs across networks by evaluating the null hypothesis that each pair of edges is equal; this test is suitable when a researcher has no prior hypotheses about which edge or edges might differ. This exploratory test is superfluous when the researcher does have hypotheses about specific edges and wants to perform a confirmatory test.

We use the *NetworkComparisonTest* package for R to estimate the precision of edge weights:

```
library("NetworkComparisonTest")
```

Suppose the objects n1 and n2 are the outputs of the `estimateNetwork` function introduced in Chapter 6 and Chapter 7 to estimate networks on two different samples. We can then use the following routine to compare the estimated network structures:[a].

```
resNCT <- NCT(n1, n2, it=1000, test.edges=TRUE,
              edges = "all", p.adjust.methods = "none")
```

The *p*-value of the global strength test can then be obtained via:

```
resNCT$glstrinv.pval
```

The *p*-value of the omnibus test can be obtained via:

```
resNCT$nwinv.pval
```

Finally, the *p*-values of the edge tests can be obtained via:

```
resNCT$einv.pval
```

---

[a]Like with bootstrapping, given that the procedures can be computationally intensive, it may be advisable to store the results with `saveRDS` so that they can be read with `readRDS`

Tutorial Box 8.4. Comparing two network structures via the *NetworkComparisonTest*.

Observed data and networks

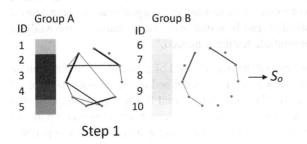

Step 1

- -

Permuted data and networks

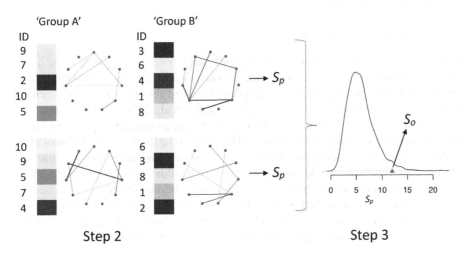

Step 2   Step 3

Figure 8.3. NCT explained in three steps. In Step 1, the network structures of Group A and B are estimated based on the observed data (blue squares); this example has five participants per group (IDs 1–5 and 6–10). A metric of interest, S_0, is calculated. In Step 2, groups are repeatedly, randomly rearranged into 'Group A' and 'Group B.' Based on each of these sets of permuted data, the metric of interest is calculated (i.e., S_p). All S_p values form the reference distribution under the null hypothesis. In Step 3, the p-value is calculated by evaluating the observed S_0 against the reference distribution.

The second test investigates invariance of strength of particular edges, and can be used in two scenarios: (1) when the researcher has a specific hypothesis about one or more edges and, consequently, wants to test these edge(s) confirmatory, and (2) when the omnibus test is significant and the researcher wants to know which edge or edges are different across networks. In the first scenario of confirmatory testing, it might be necessary to control for multiple testing. We want to note that NCT does not correct for multiple testing by default. However, several correction options are available, including Holm-Bonferroni. Although we leave it to the researcher's consideration what the best option for correction is, we suggest Holm-Bonferroni when one has a specific hypothesis about multiple edges (van Borkulo et al., 2021). This step-down procedure corrects the smallest p-value most strictly. In the second scenario of exploratory testing, and a significant omnibus test on network structure invariance, all edges can be tested. Because the nature of the analysis is exploratory, no correction for multiple testing is needed.[7]

The third test is about the invariance of the overall level of connectivity, which can be summarized by *global strength*. Global strength is defined as the absolute sum of all edge weights (Opsahl et al., 2010). This test can be used if a researcher expects that the network of one group is more strongly and/or more densely connected compared to the other group. For example, a researcher may want to compare two groups of patients with depression and expects that the group with a certain risk factor (e.g., genetic and environmental risk factors; van Loo et al., 2018) has a more strongly connected network than the group of patients without this risk factor.

Other methods for network comparison

Beyond the NCT, there are also several other statistical routines for testing if the underlying network structure could be the same for two (or more) groups (Haslbeck, 2020). One method is to use the *psychonetrics* package to test for equivalence between the network structures of two (or more) groups (Epskamp et al., 2021), as further described in Tutorial Box 8.5. Similar tests of equivalence between groups can be performed using Bayesian tests as implemented in the *BGGM* package (Haslbeck, 2020; Williams et al., 2020), or regularized moderated network analysis as implemented in the *mgm* package (Haslbeck et al., 2021). These methods all have in common that they are tied with a certain estimation method (respectively: multivariate maximum likelihood estimation in *psychonetrics*, multivariate Bayesian estimation in *BGGM*, and regularized univariate estimation in *mgm*), and are to this end *parametric* methods. Unlike the NCT, these methods cannot be applied to networks estimated using other estimation tools.

Network replicability and generalizability

A research topic that is related to group comparison is to investigate whether the network structure *replicates* in different samples, or the same sample over time (Fried et al., 2018). This question differs from network comparisons discussed above in that it is concerned with the observed sample networks rather than the presumed underlying generating networks (e.g., investigating the correlation between estimated edge weights). For example, researchers may investigate whether specific edges, or the network topology, replicates in a different sample. Steps for assessing if results from a new sample replicate results from a previous sample can follow the same steps as described above: (1) visual comparison, (2) correlating network parameters and descriptive statistics, and (3) performing statistical tests. With respect to statistical tests, the NCT can also be used to study replicability, although its results should be interpreted with care, as the test is not fully designed for this purpose. A non-significant NCT result might indicate that there is no difference between network structures. However, a non-significant result could also be due to low power, and

---

[7]It is important that such results are presented as exploratory—hypothesis generating—and not confirmatory.

The *psychonetrics* package allows for multiple-group comparisons, which in turn can test for equivalence between certain edges in a network or the entire network structure. Suppose a data set of continuous variables is termed Data, which contains variables v1, v2, and v3, and a column indicating the group membership id. We can then form a saturated multi-group Gaussian graphical model as follows:

```
library("psychonetrics"); library("dplyr")
mod1 <- ggm(Data, vars = c("v1","v2","v3"), groups = "id") %>%
runmodel
```

Next, we can compare this model to a model in which the groups have the same network structure (partial correlations stored in the matrix Ω), but different variances (controlled with the scaling matrix Δ):

```
mod2 <- mod1 %>% groupequal("omega") %>% runmodel
```

Because this model is saturated, this is equivalent to fitting a model in which all marginal correlations are equal across the two groups. Next, we can compare these models:

```
compare(different = mod1, same = mod2)
```

We would prefer the model with the lowest AIC and/or BIC, or we could look at the results of the χ^2 difference test.

Tutorial Box 8.5. Comparing two groups via *psychonetrics*.

as such a non-significant NCT does not entail that a network replicates previous findings. A significant NCT indicates that the underlying networks may be different, and as such is evidence for heterogeneity between the groups. Ultimately, the question of how well a network will replicate rests on precisely the topic of heterogeneity: could the two samples have been generated from the same underlying network model? We will discuss each of these settings below in more detail. Finally, a different form of statistical tests that can be used in replication studies is to perform a confirmatory test: checking if the network obtained in one study fits the data of a second study. This will be discussed at the end of this section.

Network replicability in homogeneous samples

If we assume the generating network structure to be identical for two samples, then the question of network replicability becomes an entirely methodological question.[8] The question of how replicable the network found in a study is depends on the accuracy and stability of the network, as discussed above in this chapter, as well as the estimation method and model selection method used. For example, if the BCIs are small, we would expect to find similar edge weights in networks estimated from new samples (assuming the same estimation routine was used), and if centrality coefficients remain stable under

---

[8]Network replicability cannot be studied by observing differences in networks obtained from individual samples. Merely observing (rather than testing) that edges in two networks differ is similar to observing that two samples of people differ in height. The difference could (or could not) be the result of sampling variation.

subsampling (e.g., high CS-coefficient), we would expect to find similar patterns of centrality indices in new samples. In general, the larger the two samples, and the more both samples are in line with assumptions underlying the statistical model, the better we can expect results to replicate.

When the underlying network is assumed to be the same, we can also readily use simulation studies[9] or even analytical results to derive how much we would expect two estimated network models to align given the sensitivity, specificity and accuracy of network estimation procedures (Isvoranu & Epskamp, 2021; Williams, 2020). Such simulations played a crucial role in several of the recommendations made in Chapter 7 on which model selection procedures should be used. In general, most network estimation methods are conservative, meaning that they may not pick up on all true edges, especially if the true network is dense (contains many edges). In that case, it is not to be expected that all edges included in a network based on one sample will also be included in a network based on another sample (although we would expect the stronger edges to be included in the second sample as well). As discussed in Chapter 7, the *EBICglasso* algorithm is more sensitive than many other algorithms and estimates the network topology well, but also tends to include more false edges that tend to be weak. To this end, an algorithm such as the *EBICglasso* should be used to obtain a more replicable network architecture, but should not be used to zoom in on individual (small) edges—a topic for which unregularized estimation methods are better suited (Isvoranu et al., 2020; Williams & Rast, 2020).

While the above discusses statistical aspects of network estimation, there are also practical methodological issues. The relative flexibility in network estimation routines also means that researchers have many choices to make when estimating network models—so called *researchers degrees of freedom* (Simmons et al., 2011). While network estimation is typically presented as exploratory and therefore not bound to strict pre-defined rules, such researcher degrees of freedom may hamper the replicability of findings in new samples (Epskamp, 2019). They may also inflate replicability, if that is what researchers are interested to find. Preregistration may therefore be a helpful tool, limiting researchers degrees of freedom in obtaining desired results. Preregistration ensures that researchers cannot cherry-pick particular estimation methods or network inference metrics after the fact to support their hypotheses. Faelens et al. (2019) provide an example of how such work can be conducted, in an empirical study on networks of well-being and social media use. Authors analyzed a data set of $N = 219$ to obtain an estimated network structure. They then performed a simulation study, using the `netSimulator` function of the *bootnet* package, to understand how much data would be sufficiently powered to replicate the network structure out of sample if the underlying population network were the same. The simulation suggested the collection of $N = 450$. The authors carried out this data collection, and results indicated that networks were highly similar (e.g., correlation between the two adjacency matrices $r = 0.95$), and the NCT yielded no significant differences regarding structure ($p = 0.8$) or connectivity ($p = 0.7$).

---

[9]The *bootnet* function `replicationSimulator` simplifies this.

Generalizability across heterogeneous samples

If two samples feature different underlying network structures (for example as evidenced by a significant NCT test), then the question of network replicability becomes more complicated, as then we can no longer expect networks based on different samples to converge to the same network structure with increasing data. A better term than replicability then may be *generalizability* (Fried et al., 2018), as it may then be of interest to investigate if the conclusions drawn from one sample generalize to another sample, even though samples come from different populations.

One particular field of interest in which we may assume that there is no single underlying network model is in network modeling of post-traumatic stress disorder (PTSD) symptoms. In the initial take on network replicability, Fried et al. (2018) studied differences and similarities in networks across four different data sets, which has been re-analyzed in subsequent studies on replicability (Forbes et al., 2021, but see also Fried et al., 2021; Jones, Williams, et al., 2021). Recently, Isvoranu et al. (2021) used a meta-analytic procedure termed *meta-analytic Gaussian network aggregation* (MAGNA; Epskamp et al., 2021) to analyze a larger set of data sets used for PTSD symptom networks. Both studies found heterogeneity in the underlying samples, Fried et al. (2018) by using the NCT, and Isvoranu et al. (2021) by estimating large cross-study heterogeneity in the MAGNA model. These results may not be surprising, considering that the analyzed PTSD samples differ in important aspects (e.g., PTSD severity, comorbidities, type of trauma). As such, both studies indicate that perfect replicability between PTSD symptom networks based on different samples is not to be expected. Nonetheless, both studies also show that despite this heterogeneity, some results from one study can be generalizable to results from other studies, as the overall structure of PTSD networks tends to be similar, and networks based on single study data sets lead to similar network structures compared to meta-analytic results.

Confirmatory network modeling

Finally, a topic closely related to replicability is cross-validation of the network structure. That is, how well does the network structure obtained in one data set fit a second data set? This can be done using confirmatory network estimation as exemplified in Tutorial Box 8.6. One way of using cross-validation is to use one data set to train models (e.g., network models, but also factor models) using exploratory methods, and a second data set to compare and evaluate these models using strictly confirmatory methods (Kan et al., 2020). Another use is to replicate the structure obtained from one data set in another data set. This can be a very useful method for studies that aim to replicate a network structure obtained in a previous study. However, these methods may be less ideal when one splits up a data set to obtain two samples to include a replication in the same study, as splitting the available data in two necessarily means that less data are available for network estimation, while generally a lot of data are needed for consistent, accurate and stable network estimation. That is, it may be better to estimate a network structure from a single $N = 1,000$ sample, rather than using only half the data ($N = 500$) to estimate the network structure.

The *psychonetrics* package can also be used for confirmatory network modeling, for example, to check if the structure obtained in one data set fits a new data set well. Suppose we have a weights matrix obtained from a previous analysis or study, termed `weights_matrix`. We first need to transform the weights matrix to a binary adjacency matrix in which 1 indicates the presence of an edge and 0 the absence of an edge:

```
adjacency_matrix <- 1 * (weights_matrix != 0)
diag(adjacency_matrix) <- 0
```

Now we can fit the network structure to a new data set (here termed `Data`):

```
library("psychonetrics")
library("dplyr")
mod <- ggm(Data, omega = adjacency_matrix) %>% runmodel
```

Finally, we can obtain fit measures to assess the fit of this model:

```
mod %>% fit
```

Readers that are familiar with structural equation modeling will know how such fit measures can be interpreted (West et al., 2012). Among others, we prefer the RMSEA to be low (e.g., below 0.08), and incremental fit indices such as the CFI and TLI to be high (e.g., above 0.9).

Tutorial Box 8.6. Performing a confirmatory test in *psychonetrics*.

8.4   Conclusion

This chapter discussed accuracy and stability of parameters in the same sample, comparing networks obtained from different samples, and replicability and generalizability of results in new (or future) samples. The chapter mainly focused on non-parametric flexible methods for investigating stability and accuracy (bootstrap) and comparing samples (permutation tests), as these can be generally applied. Other options exist for these purposes as well. For example, analytic confidence intervals or statistical tests can be used to gain insight in uncertainty around parameter estimates. Whatever method is chosen, it is imperative that reported results are supplemented with procedures investigating the (un)certainty in these results (Burger et al., 2021).

8.5   Exercises

Conceptual

8.1. Figure 8.2 uses the `averageLayout` function to constrain the networks. This ensures nodes are plotted in the same position. What are advantages of this method? Further, why it is important to set the maximum edge to the same value across the four graphs?

8.2. The four networks in Figure 8.2 are estimated on different sample sizes. As a reminder, the estimated structures are regularized networks. Could you tell which network is estimated on the largest sample if we had not plotted the sample sizes? How could you tell, and why does this matter for comparing networks across samples?

8.3. Suppose we estimate a network and assess its stability. We find that the BCI of a specific edge weight is relatively wide and contains 0. What can we conclude?

8.4. We also assess accuracy of the centrality indices. The CS (cor = 0.7) for betweenness equals 0.2. What does that tell you about the accuracy of the estimates? What would you expect to happen if we would increase the sample size?

8.5. If we compare two substance use networks from Figure 8.2 regarding global strength, and our statistic of interest falls in the tail of the reference distribution, above the 97.5th quantile, we conclude that there is a significant difference between the networks regarding global strength. Why?

True or false

8.6. BCI can be used to estimate the variability of parameters that are to be expected in the data.

8.7. Bootstrap confidence intervals can be used for significance testing of individual edges by checking if zero is in the interval or not.

8.8. We cannot use the non-parametric bootstrap to assess the accuracy in centrality indices.

8.9. The null hypothesis when comparing networks via the NCT is that networks are different.

8.10. The NCT for global strength can be used if a researcher expects that the network of one group is more strongly and/or more densely connected compared to the other group.

Practical

For practical exercises in R, please navigate to the appropriate folder of this chapter, available on the online *Companion Website*.

References

Burger, J., Isvoranu, A. M., Lunansky, G., Haslbeck, J. M. B., Epskamp, S., Hoekstra, R. H. A., Fried, E. I. I., Borsboom, D., & Blanken, T. (2021). Reporting standards for psychological network analyses in cross-sectional data. *Psychological Methods*. https://doi.org/10.1037/met0000471
Costenbader, E., & Valente, T. W. (2003). The stability of centrality measures when networks are sampled. *Social Networks*, 25(4), 283–307.

Davison, A., & Hinkley, D. (1997). *Bootstrap methods and their application*. Cambridge University Press.

Efron, B. (1979). Bootstrap methods: Another look at the jackknife. *The Annals of Statistics*, 7(1), 1–26.

Epskamp, S. (2019). Reproducibility and replicability in a fast-paced methodological world. *Advances in Methods and Practices in Psychological Science*, 2(2), 145–155.

Epskamp, S., Isvoranu, A. M., & Cheung, M. (2021). Meta-analytic Gaussian network aggregation. *Psychometrika*. https://doi.org/10.1007/s11336-021-09764-3

Epskamp, S., Borsboom, D., & Fried, E. I. (2018). Estimating psychological networks and their accuracy: A tutorial paper. *Behavior Research Methods*, 50(1), 195–212.

Faelens, L., Hoorelbeke, K., Fried, E. I., De Raedt, R., & Koster, E. H. W. (2019). Negative influences of Facebook use through the lens of network analysis. *Computers in Human Behavior*, 96, 13–22.

Forbes, M. K., Wright, A. G. C., Markon, K. E., & Krueger, R. F. (2021). Quantifying the reliability and replicability of psychopathology network characteristics. *Multivariate Behavioral Research*, 56(2), 224–242.

Fried, E. I., Eidhof, M. B., Palic, S., Costantini, G., Huisman-van Dijk, H. M., Bockting, C. L. H., Engelhard, I., Armour, C., Nielsen, A. B. S., & Karstoft, K.-I. I. (2018). Replicability and generalizability of posttraumatic stress disorder (PTSD) networks: A cross-cultural multisite study of PTSD symptoms in four trauma patient samples. *Clinical Psychological Science*, 6(3), 335–351.

Fried, E. I., van Borkulo, C. D., & Epskamp, S. (2021). On the importance of estimating parameter uncertainty in network psychometrics: A response to Forbes et al. (2019). *Multivariate Behavioral Research*, 56(2), 243–248.

Fritz, J., Fried, E. I., Goodyer, I., & Wilkinson, P. (2018). A network model of resilience factors for adolescents with and without exposure to childhood adversity. *Scientific Reports*, 8, 15774.

Haslbeck, J. M. B. (2020). Estimating group differences in network models using moderation analysis. *PsyArXiv*. https://doi.org/10.31234/osf.io/926pv

Haslbeck, J. M. B., Borsboom, D., & Waldorp, L. J. (2021). Moderated network models. *Multivariate Behavioral Research*, 56(2), 256–287.

Hastie, T., Tibshirani, R., & Wainwright, M. J. (2015). *Statistical learning with sparsity: The lasso and generalizations*. Taylor & Francis.

Isvoranu, A. M., & Epskamp, S. (2021). Which estimation method to choose in network psychometrics? deriving guidelines for applied researchers. *Psychological Methods*. https://doi.org/10.1037/met0000439

Isvoranu, A. M., Epskamp, S., & Cheung, M. (2021). Network models of post-traumatic stress disorder: A meta-analysis. *Journal of Abnormal Psychology*, 130(8), 841–861.

Isvoranu, A. M., Guloksuz, S., Epskamp, S., van Os, J., Borsboom, D., & GROUP Investigators. (2020). Toward incorporating genetic risk scores into symptom networks of psychosis. *Psychological Medicine*, 50(4), 636–643.

Jones, P. J., Ma, R., & McNally, R. J. (2021). Bridge centrality: A network approach to understanding comorbidity. *Multivariate Behavioral Research*, 56(2), 353–367.

Jones, P. J., Williams, D. R., & McNally, R. J. (2021). Sampling variability is not nonreplication: A Bayesian reanalysis of Forbes, Wright, Markon, and Krueger. *Multivariate Behavioral Research*, *56*(2), 249–255.

Kan, K.-J., de Jonge, H., van der Maas, H. L. J., Levine, S. Z., & Epskamp, S. (2020). How to compare psychometric factor and network models. *Journal of Intelligence*, *8*(4), 35.

Opsahl, T., Agneessens, F., & Skvoretz, J. (2010). Node centrality in weighted networks: Generalizing degree and shortest paths. *Social Networks*, *32*(3), 245–251.

Rhemtulla, M., Fried, E. I. I., Aggen, S. H., Tuerlinckx, F., Kendler, K. S., & Borsboom, D. (2016). Network analysis of substance abuse and dependence symptoms. *Drug and Alcohol Dependence*, *161*, 230–237.

Robinaugh, D. J., Millner, A. J., & McNally, R. J. (2016). Identifying highly influential nodes in the complicated grief network. *Journal of Abnormal Psychology*, *125*(6), 747–757.

Simmons, J. P., Nelson, L. D., & Simonsohn, U. (2011). False-positive psychology: Undisclosed flexibility in data collection and analysis allows presenting anything as significant. *Psychological Science*, *22*(11), 1359–1366.

van Borkulo, C. D., Boschloo, L., Borsboom, D., Penninx, B. W. J. H., Waldorp, L. J., & Schoevers, R. A. (2015). Association of symptom network structure with the course of depression. *JAMA Psychiatry*, *72*(12), 1219–1226.

van Borkulo, C. D., Boschloo, L., Kossakowski, J., Tio, P., Schoevers, R., Borsboom, D., & Waldorp, L. (2021). Comparing network structures on three aspects: A permutation test. *Psychological Methods*. https://doi.org/10.13140/RG.2.2.29455.38569

van de Geer, S., Bühlmann, P., Ritov, Y., & Dezeure, R. (2014). On asymptotically optimal confidence regions and tests for high-dimensional models. *The Annals of Statistics*, *42*(3), 1166–1202.

van Loo, H. M., van Borkulo, C. D., Peterson, R. E., Fried, E. I., Aggen, S. H., Borsboom, D., & Kendler, K. S. (2018). Robust symptom networks in recurrent major depression across different levels of genetic and environmental risk. *Journal of Affective Disorders*, *227*, 313–322.

West, S. G., Taylor, A. B., Wu, W., et al. (2012). Model fit and model selection in structural equation modeling. In R. H. Hoyle (Ed.), *Handbook of structural equation modeling* (pp. 209–231). Taylor & Francis.

Williams, D. R. (2020). Learning to live with sampling variability: Expected replicability in partial correlation networks. *PsyArXiv*. https://doi.org/10.31234/osf.io/fb4sa

Williams, D. R., & Rast, P. (2020). Back to the basics: Rethinking partial correlation network methodology. *British Journal of Mathematical and Statistical Psychology*, *73*(2), 187–212.

Williams, D. R., Rast, P., Pericchi, L. R., & Mulder, J. (2020). Comparing Gaussian graphical models with the posterior predictive distribution and Bayesian model selection. *Psychological Methods*, *25*(5), 653.

Part III

Network Models for Longitudinal Data

Chapter 9

Longitudinal Design Choices: Relating Data to Analysis

Sacha Epskamp[1,2], Ria H. A. Hoekstra[1], Julian Burger[1,2,3], & Lourens J. Waldorp[1]

1. University of Amsterdam, Department of Psychology

2. University of Amsterdam, Centre for Urban Mental Health

3. University of Groningen, University Medical Center Groningen

9.1   Introduction

The previous part (Chapters 6, 7, and 8) discussed the interpretation and estimation of pairwise Markov random fields (PMRFs), which can be used to gain insight into the correlational structure of data sets in which a single observation is present per person. In this part (Chapters 9, 10, and 11), we will expand on this framework by analyzing data sets in which not one but several measurements are available per person. By measuring people over time, we can separate within-person from between-person effects and extend the PMRFs to include temporal dynamics. However, before doing so, it is important to clarify several concepts that are often not clearly separated in the literature. For example, authors usually mean different things when describing concepts such as *cross-sectional* and *between-person* analyses. This chapter discusses several concepts and explains seemingly paradoxical differences on different levels of analysis. To simplify matters, we will mainly discuss two-variable models in which we only model a single correlation between

Cite this chapter as:

Epskamp, S., Hoekstra, R. H. A., Burger, J., & Waldorp, L. J. (2022). Chapter 9. Longitudinal design choices: Relating data to analysis. In Isvoranu, A. M., Epskamp, S., Waldorp, L. J., & Borsboom, D. (Eds.). *Network psychometrics with R: A guide for behavioral and social scientists*. Routledge, Taylor & Francis Group.

variables.[1] First, we discuss different types of *data* that can be used for multivariate correlational analysis (such as PMRF estimation or factor analysis). Second, we discuss different types of *analyses* that can be used on these types of data. Finally, we discuss differences between within-person and between-person effects, especially in relation to the time-frame of measurement. The next chapter will continue this discussion and also introduce temporal dynamics through vector-autoregressive modeling, and discuss differences in temporal and contemporaneous results.

9.2   Data designs

Figure 9.1 shows several types of data that can be used for network analysis.[2] So far, we only considered data sets in which we had one particular observation per person, which can be termed *single measurement data*, shown in the top left panel of Figure 9.1. Such a data set is often also termed a *cross-sectional* data set, but this term is incorrect and may potentially be confusing; the term *cross-sectional* refers to a *cross-section* at a particular moment in time, one which could have been different at another moment in time. Single measurement data may also refer to other types of data for which only one observation is available per person. For example, data sets in clinical psychology often involve therapist-rated scores on symptoms that cover a range of time (e.g., depressed mood over a period of several months), and variables that do not vary over time could be included in an analysis (such as experiencing childhood trauma in adults).

All other three types of data introduce a second dimension in the sampling setup: time. The top-right panel of Figure 9.1 shows $N = 1$ data, in which a single individual is measured over time. Such data sets are increasingly common, as technological advances made it possible to store these large data sets and statistical advancements facilitated the analysis of this type of data (Hamaker, 2012). For example, we may measure a patient in clinical practice through the use of experience sampling method (ESM) or ecological momentary assessment (EMA) several times per day over a period of several weeks, leading to many observations of the same person over time.

Single measurement data only involves the people dimension, and $N = 1$ time series data only involves the time dimension. These two dimensions can also both be used in the sampling plan in a setup where multiple people are measured on multiple occasions. While any combination of a number of people and number of measurements per person is possible, typically, data sets can be classified as one of the two bottom panels of Figure 9.1. In panel data designs, many people are measured on relatively few occasions with large differences of time in between. For example, a large sample can be measured yearly for a period of five years. Finally, in $N > 1$ time series data, a smaller set of people (perhaps 50–100 rather than hundreds to thousands often seen in panel data sets) are measured on many measurement occasions, usually with small windows of time in

[1]Of note: a two-variable PMRF is simply a model with two variables with one correlation that is not conditional on any other variable (because there are none).

[2]Of note, while in this book we focus on network analysis, the general description of types of data and types of analyses in this chapter equally applies to other statistical routines, such as regression analysis or factor analysis.

between. As such, panel data could be considered a collection of single measurement data sets, whereas $N > 1$ time series can be considered a collection of $N = 1$ time series data sets. Both types of data, however, allow for some form of separation of within-person and between-person effects, something that is impossible to do in single measurement data and $N = 1$ time series, which brings us to the next topic.

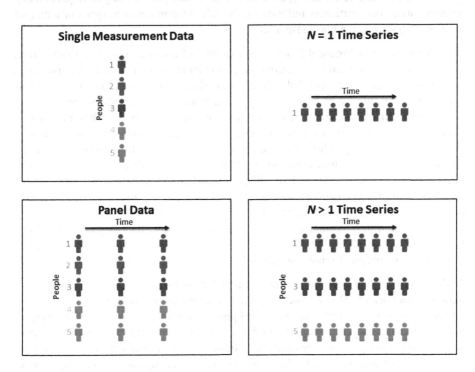

Figure 9.1. Different types of data that can be used for multivariate correlational analyses such as network analysis. In single measurement data only one observation is present per person, in $N = 1$ time series repeated measures of one individual over time are available, in panel data some repeated observations of many people are available, and in $N > 1$ time series many repeated measures are available from, usually, a relatively small set of people.

9.3   Analysis designs

Figure 9.2 shows examples of different types of analysis that could be performed. Such analyses are often confused with the types of data shown in Figure 9.1. While some types of analysis require certain types of data (e.g., within-person analysis requires many observations of one particular individual), the relationship between types of data and types of analysis is often not transparent.

The top left panel of Figure 9.2 shows an example of *cross-sectional analysis*. Here, several people are analyzed on data from one particular moment in time, and, importantly, these people could have responded differently in other moments in time. We can obtain a relationship of interest in such an analysis, such as a correlation between 'drinking coffee' and 'being productive,' or more advanced network structures such as the PMRFs discussed in the previous chapters. Suppose we assessed all authors of this book on a particular day of writing, whether they drank much coffee and whether they wrote many words, and we find a positive correlation between these variables. This correlation is a blend of between- and within-person effects (Hamaker, 2012; Molenaar, 2004): these variables could be correlated because authors who on average drink a lot of coffee on average also write many words (a between-person effect), or because when authors drink more coffee than they normally do, they write more words than they normally do (a within-person effect). This downside of cross-sectional analysis is important to recognize: cross-sectional analysis cannot distinguish between these types of variances.

While cross-sectional analysis is often termed *between-person analysis*, this generalization is not correct. *Between-person analysis* refers to the analysis of relationships between aspects that are stable in the studied people over time. As such, we can interpret between-person analysis to be collapsed over the time dimension, investigating only stable averages per person. For example, a between-person analysis could investigate if the authors of this book that drink much coffee on average, also, on average, write more words per day. The exact term *between-person* then refers to studying individual differences in variables that do not vary within (potential) repeated measures of any particular person. It is important to note that the term does *not* refer to any interactions between people (such as social dynamics). Indeed, we usually assume people in the sample to be statistically independent of one another.[3]

A *within-person* analysis, on the other hand, solely focuses on studying the variance of variables in repeated measures of one particular person. A true within-person analysis always refers to the study of one particular person over time. For example, we can study one particular author of this book, measure their coffee consumption and number of written words per day, and observe that on days this author drank a lot of coffee, they also wrote many words. This relationship is then established purely *within* the observations of one particular person, and this relationship may differ in other people.

---

[3] Statistical independence between cases (subjects) means that the scores of one case cannot be predicted by the scores of another case. With this assumption, the likelihood function required to estimate parameters becomes a product of likelihoods per case, which is a fundamental property in many statistical routines.

Finally, the *fixed-effects* analysis collapses sampling over people rather than time. In such an analysis, within-person relationships of an average person are analyzed. For example, we can find that in general, whenever authors drank more coffee than their average in a day, they also tended to write more words than their average on that day. This marks a distinct difference between true within-person analysis and fixed-effects analysis: a within-person analysis refers to relationships between deviations from the average of a particular person, whereas fixed-effects analysis refers to relationships between deviations from the average of a hypothetical average person. This person, however, does not exist. As such, the fixed-effects results are not established *within* the observations of one particular person. To this end, there is some debate on whether or not a fixed-effects analysis can really be interpreted as a within-person analysis.

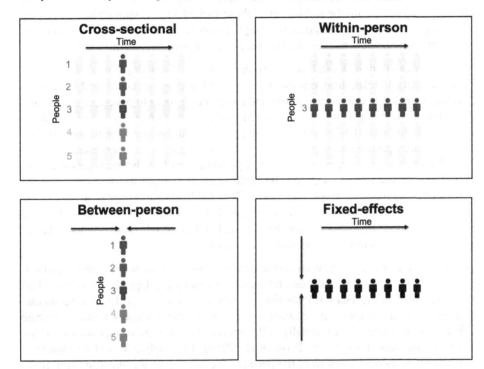

Figure 9.2. Different types of analysis that can be performed. In cross-sectional analysis, only one observation per person is analyzed, which represents a snapshot of those people over time. In between-person analysis, relationships between stable averages or traits are analyzed. In within-person analysis, only repeated measures from one person are considered. In fixed-effects analysis, the within-person effects of the average person are studied.

9.4   Differences between data and analysis

The previous sections introduced several different terms. For data, we can distinguish between four broad categories: (A) single measurement data: data of many subjects with only one observation per subject, (B) panel data: data of many subjects measured on a few occasions, (C) $N = 1$ time series data: data of a single subject measured on many occasions, and (D) $N > 1$ time series: several subjects measured on many occasions. In terms of analyses, we can also distinguish roughly between four categories: (1) cross-sectional analysis: analyzing a relationship between variables across people that can be expected to change on these variables over time, (2) between-person analysis: analyzing a relationship across people on variables/aspects that are not expected to change over time (or on the stable part of these variables), (3) within-person analysis: analyzing a relationship across time in a single individual, and (4) fixed-effects analysis: the within-person relationship of an average person (aggregated over people).

With our vocabulary now established, we can continue discussing how these types of data and analysis relate to one another. In general, a cross-sectional analysis can be performed on single-measurement data and on temporal slices of panel and $N > 1$ time series data. A within-person analysis can be obtained through $N = 1$ time series analysis or in $N > 1$ time series analyses (by analyzing each person separately). A between-person analysis can be performed on panel data and $N > 1$ time series data sets using methods that adequately separate (fixed-effect) within-person effects from between-person effects. A between-person analysis can also be performed on a single measurement data set if it can be assumed that these responses reflect stable averages over time. Finally, a fixed-effects analysis can be performed in panel data and $N > 1$ time series data, or on single measurement data if it can be assumed that the single observations correctly represent deviations from the person-wise averages.

Single-measurement data, therefore, could be used in principle to perform cross-sectional analyses, between-person analyses, and fixed-effect analyses, depending on the content of the variables in the data set. It should be noted, however, that evidence suggests that responses to trait-like questions on stable averages (e.g., 'are you a person that on average drinks a lot of coffee?') are usually still impacted by the state of that person in that particular moment in time (e.g., Brose et al., 2013). In principle, it is also possible to ask questions on deviations from the person-wise average (e.g., 'did you drink more coffee than average today?'), in which case a fixed-effects interpretation can be used in the analysis. Such designs, however, are not common yet. As such, the interpretation of analysis performed on single-measurement data discussed in the previous chapters relies on the question of validity: do the variables measure what they intend to measure? This question goes beyond the scope of this book, but in general shows that considering any analysis on single-measurement data a cross-sectional analysis is incorrect.

Ergodicity and within- and between-person effects

Many authors consider cross-sectional analysis insufficient, as cross-sectional analysis can be considered a blend of within- and between-person effects. Furthermore, they consider the within-person effects to be the general target of inference in psychology—such as establishing that drinking coffee is a useful intervention to improve productivity for one particular author—and that cross-sectional analysis can fail to retrieve these within-person relationships adequately. Taking it one step further, this line of reasoning can also be used to argue against the study of fixed-effects, as these effects model an average person and not actually an effect of the people in the analyzed data set. In his seminal work on this topic, Molenaar (2004) showed that only when a concept known as *ergodicity* holds, cross-sectional and fixed-effects analyses align with within-person analyses for every person in the sample. In the relevant cases for this book, ergodicity mainly entails that it needs to be assumed that every person is a virtual replication of one another. That means: every person has the same means and the same model structure (in our case a network model) that is also stable over time. Each person having the same means also indicates that there should be no between-person relationships (e.g., an empty network at the between-person level). Only in this case will cross-sectional analysis and fixed-effects analysis align with within-person analysis of every individual. These assumptions are so strong that ergodicity is never likely to hold in psychological data.

While this reasoning is undeniably true, it is important to note again here that *within-person* does not refer to things that happen within a person, but rather to relationships that can be established within the potential repeated measures of that person. The term *between-person*, on the other hand, refers to relationships that can only be obtained by investigating individual differences. As such, *between-person* does not solely place the relationship outside of the person, and relationships at the between-person level can also be indicative of dynamics within an individual (potentially over time).

For example, consider the two examples in Figure 9.3, which were first published by Epskamp et al. (2018). Panel 9.3a (based on an example by Hamaker, 2012) shows a positive (fixed-effect) within-person relationship between typing speed and spelling errors, but also a between-person relationship between the same variables. While seemingly paradoxical (the term Simpson's paradox is often used for such a discrepancy), these relationships are not paradoxical and can readily be understood. Whenever a person writes faster than their average, that person also tends to make more spelling errors. However, people that on average write very fast are likely very experienced writers and, therefore, also likely to make fewer spelling errors. Thinking in terms of interventions here: suppose an author of this book wants to make as few as possible spelling errors, then that author would likely consider writing slower than usual.

Now consider Panel 9.3b, which shows the exact same relationships, but between the variables 'physical activity' and 'heart rate' (based on Hoffman, 2015): whenever a person exercises, their heart-rate goes up, and people that on average exercise a lot, on average, have a lower heart-rate. Thinking again in terms of interventions, a medical doctor advising a patient with a high heart-rate would likely not disregard the between-person effects here and advise that patient never to exercise anymore. On the contrary, the doctor may advise exercising more with the aim to obtain a lower average heart rate. Such an effect would ultimately take place within that patient but over a longer time-frame. To this end, the exact same relationships can have entirely different meanings depending on the variables, and evidence for successful interventions may be found in both the within-person and the between-person level.

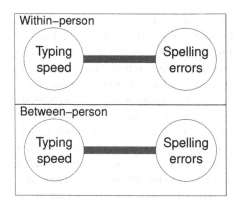

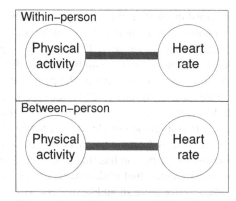

(a) A positive within-person correlation and a negative between-person correlation between typing speed and spelling errors. Based on an example provided by Hamaker (2012).

(b) A positive within-person correlation and a negative between-person correlation between exercising and heart rate. Based on an example provided by Hoffman (2015).

Figure 9.3. Hypothetical examples of within-person (or fixed-effect) and between-person relationships that could be found. Adapted from Epskamp et al. (2018).

The importance of timescales

An important consideration to the interpretation of results is the time-frame in which the study was conducted. For example, Figure 9.4 shows hypothetical data of a person measured over the period of a few weeks or months on 'anxiety' and 'stress.' Using this person's repeated measures, we may establish a within-person correlation between these two variables: whenever this person experienced stress, this person was likely also experiencing anxiety. Figure 9.5, on the other hand, shows an entirely different scenario in which 'lung cancer' and 'smoking' are measured instead. In any time series analysis of only a few weeks or months, we will not establish any within-person correlation for any of the people in the sample, as there is not enough variance for statistical analysis. However, if we perform a $N > 1$ time series analysis over a few weeks or months, or a cross-sectional analysis at any point in time, we may obtain a between-person correlation between these two variables. In a longer panel design, we may even obtain a within-person relationship between these variables, but likely only in fixed-effects, as none of the subjects show enough variation in their scores to warrant statistical analysis.

As such, relationships that are between-person in one study can be within-person in another study, depending on the time-frame over which the study took place. This shows that the argument for within- and between-person effects is not black and white: both levels of analysis are essential for understanding relationships between variables of interest. To this end, it is vital to separate these levels of analysis whenever possible. Beyond separating between-person from within-person effects (at least the fixed effects), the temporal dependency of time series data also allows for further separation of within-person effects: separating effects that take place over time (temporal effects) from effects that take place within the same window of measurement (contemporaneous effects). This separation will be discussed in the next section.

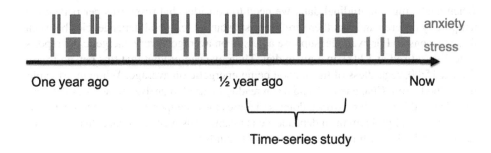

Figure 9.4. Example of $N = 1$ data collected in a relatively short time-frame. Colored boxes indicate times that one of these variables would be endorsed. In this example, we could perhaps establish a within-person relationship between anxiety and stress, potentially even a temporal effect depending on the choice of lag-interval (time between measurements) in a vector auto-regression analysis.

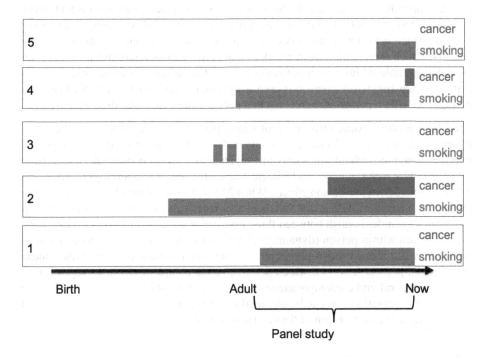

Figure 9.5. Example of $N > 1$ panel data. Colored boxes indicate times that one of these variables would be endorsed. In this case, we would likely not have enough variance to establish a within-person relationship in any person.

9.5   Separating contemporaneous and temporal effects

When analyzing longitudinal data, we need to consider that responses per person are temporally ordered and that there are likely substantial temporal dependencies between these responses. For example, suppose a person on average is very energetic but reports to feel very tired at 12:00 on a given day. Then, we can predict that this person is still tired at 15:00, regardless of this person being energetic on average. While in principle, the methods from Chapters 6, 7, and 8 can readily be used to analyze time series data (we would term this a lag-0 network), doing so ignores these temporal dependencies, which is both a statistical problem (as independence is assumed) as well as a conceptual downside (as temporal relationships can be fascinating to study).

The most commonly used method for handling temporal ordering in data is through the use of the lag-1 (only modeling consecutive measurements) vector auto-regression model (VAR). In VAR, linear regression is used between consecutive time-points to model temporal dependencies, allowing one to gain separate estimates for relationships across time (temporal effects) and relationships in the same window of measurement after controlling for temporal effects (contemporaneous effects). The VAR variant that is the core focus of this part of the book is the *graphical VAR* (GVAR) model in which the contemporaneous effects are further modeled as a Gaussian graphical model (GGM; see Chapter 6). As such, the GVAR model returns two network structures: a *temporal network*, which is a directed network of temporal relationships,[4] and a *contemporaneous network*, which is an undirected network of contemporaneous relationships. Figure 9.6 gives an example of how such networks can lead to different interpretations: these networks show that when a person is exercising, that person is more energetic than their average, but after a person is exercising, that person is less energetic than their average.

The GVAR model separates two levels of within-person variance: temporal and contemporaneous relationships. Important to note is that both of these have a within-person interpretation: these relationships only investigate relationships between deviations from the person-wise mean. It may also be interesting to investigate relationships of the means across people—between-person effects. When $N > 1$ data are available, this can be done by forming a separate GGM on the variance–covariance structure of the means per person. As such, we can distinguish between three network structures: (1) *temporal networks*, which contain within-person (dynamic) relationships over time; (2) *contemporaneous networks*, which contain within-person relationships in the same window of measurement; and *between-person networks*, which describe relationships of stable averages across people. Temporal and contemporaneous networks can be obtained per person if there are enough observations, or can be obtained through a fixed-effects analysis. The next chapter will discuss estimation of the GVAR model in more detail.

---

[4]The temporal network used in GVAR modeling can also be termed a lag-1 network, with the word 'lag' indicating the number of time steps between measurements in an effect. In principle, such a model can be extended with lag-2 effects, lag-3 effects, and so forth, but in practice doing so will likely lead to an intolerable number of parameters that need to be estimated. As such, we only focus here on lag-1 models. A lag-0 model can be seen as a model in which no correction has been performed for temporal effects. Such a network should not be confused with a contemporaneous network, which controls for temporal effects as well.

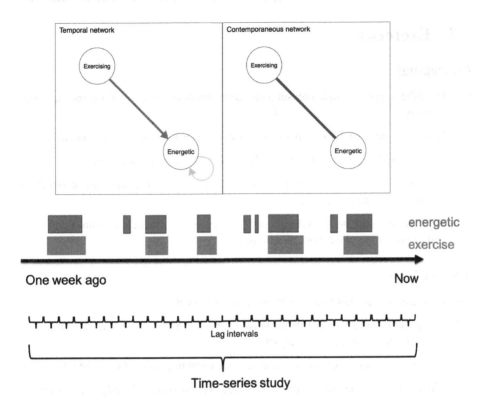

Figure 9.6. A graphical vector auto-regression (GVAR) model with corresponding hypothetical data of two variables: 'exercise' and 'energetic.'

9.6 Conclusion

This chapter discussed challenges that emerge when repeated measures are introduced to the sampling plan. We distinguished four types of data: single measurement data (one measure per person), panel data (many people measured a few times), $N = 1$ time series data (one person measured many times), and $N > 1$ time series data (several people measured many times). We also discussed different analysis options: cross-sectional analysis, between-persons analysis, within-persons analysis, and fixed-effects analysis. The interpretation of results strongly relies on the type of data analyzed as well as the content of the variables included. When longitudinal data are analyzed, the graphical VAR (GVAR) model can be used to separate temporal within-person relationships from contemporaneous within-person relationships. As such, two within-person networks can be obtained: a temporal and a contemporaneous network. In the next chapter, we will discuss the addition of temporal dynamics and the estimation of network models from panel data and time series data in more detail.

9.7 Exercises

Conceptual

9.1. Describe a type of single measurement data that does not allow for cross-sectional analysis.

9.2. Why can it be argued that a fixed-effects analysis is not a within-person analysis?

9.3. What is the difference between panel data and $N > 1$ time series data?

9.4. Describe how the self-loop on the node 'energetic' in the temporal network of Figure 9.6 can be interpreted.

9.5. Suppose we estimate a GVAR model from cross-sectional data. What would you expect the temporal network to look like?

True or false

9.6. In single measurement data, only one person is measured.

9.7. If ergodicity holds, results from between-person analysis are expected to equal results from within-person analysis.

9.8. A between-person effect in one study can be a within-person effect in another study.

9.9. When single-measurement data are analyzed, a cross-sectional analysis is performed.

9.10. Using the GVAR model, contemporaneous and between-person networks can be obtained per person (within-person analysis) or for the average person (fixed-effects analysis).

References

Brose, A., Lindenberger, U., & Schmiedek, F. (2013). Affective states contribute to trait reports of affective well-being. *Emotion, 13*(5), 940–948.

Epskamp, S., Waldorp, L. J., Mõttus, R., & Borsboom, D. (2018). The Gaussian graphical model in cross-sectional and time-series data. *Multivariate Behavioral Research, 53*(4), 453–480.

Hamaker, E. L. (2012). Why researchers should think "within-person": A paradigmatic rationale. In M. R. Mehl & T. S. Conner (Eds.), *Handbook of research methods for studying daily life* (pp. 43–61). The Guilford Press.

Hoffman, L. (2015). *Longitudinal analysis: Modeling within-person fluctuation and change.* Routledge.

Molenaar, P. C. M. (2004). A manifesto on psychology as idiographic science: Bringing the person back into scientific psychology, this time forever. *Measurement: Interdisciplinary Research & Perspective, 2*(4), 201–218.

## Chapter 10

Network Estimation from Time Series and Panel Data

Julian Burger[1,2,3], Ria H. A. Hoekstra[2], Alessandra C. Mansueto[2,3,4], & Sacha Epskamp[2,3]

1. University of Groningen, University Medical Center Groningen

2. University of Amsterdam, Department of Psychology

3. University of Amsterdam, Centre for Urban Mental Health

4. University of Amsterdam, Department of Communication Science

10.1   Introduction

The previous chapter introduced *time* into the sampling design of studies. With the addition of time, longitudinal analysis of multiple measures per person becomes possible. As the previous chapter discussed, this step is vital in separating within- from between-person relationships. Time adds a new level of complexity to the modeling frameworks we have used before: temporal dependencies between observations of the same person over time. This complicates the models—as many more parameters need to be estimated—but also comes with the substantial benefit of allowing researchers to study temporal effects—often termed 'dynamical relationships.' With the advent of modern data collection methodologies, such as electronic diaries or wearables, time series data have become a new data source to estimate networks. For example, in experience sampling method and ecological momentary assessment, a smartphone can be used to query a subject multiple times per day (also termed 'beeps') on a set of questions. Through these advances, the

Cite this chapter as:

Burger, J., Hoekstra, R. H. A., Mansueto, A. C., & Epskamp, S. (2022). Chapter 10. Network estimation from time series and panel data. In Isvoranu, A. M., Epskamp, S., Waldorp, L., J. & Borsboom, D. (Eds.). *Network psychometrics with R: A guide for behavioral and social scientists*. Routledge, Taylor & Francis Group.

use of dynamical network models has grown prominent. This chapter introduces the estimation of dynamical networks from longitudinal data. The chapter begins with a summary of the main modeling framework used, followed by explanations on how to estimate these models from $N = 1$ and $N > 1$ data sets. The chapter will then conclude with an overview of practical and methodological challenges in dynamical network analysis.

10.2   Graphical vector auto-regression

The main model we focus on in this chapter is the (lag-1) graphical vector auto-regression (GVAR; Epskamp, Waldorp, et al., 2018; Wild et al., 2010) model for continuous (and assumed normal) data introduced in Chapter 9 and further detailed in Technical Box 10.1. In this model, a person's responses on a certain measurement are modeled as a Gaussian graphical model (GGM; see Chapter 6) after conditioning on their responses in the previous measurement. Alternatively, the GVAR model can also be interpreted as a multivariate regression on the previous responses, with the residuals (then termed *innovations*) being modeled through a GGM. The GVAR model includes two network structures: a *temporal network* that encodes how well deviations from the person-wise mean in one variable at a certain measurement occasion predict deviations from the person-wise mean in the *next* measurement occasion,[1] and a *contemporaneous network* that encodes relationships between variables within the same measurement occasion and after controlling for temporal effects. These networks allow for a within-person interpretation and can be estimated per person or for the average person (fixed effects). In $N > 1$ data, relationships between the means can further be investigated to construct a GGM termed the *between-person network*.

Figure 10.1 shows an example of these three network structures, estimated from time series data collected by Fried et al. (2021).[2] The temporal network in the left panel of Figure 10.1 contains self-loops (auto-regressions) and edges between nodes (cross-lagged regressions). For example, the self-loop on 'difficulty relax' indicates that when a person had more difficulty relaxing than their average in one measurement occasion, that person likely still had a higher than average difficulty to relax in the next measurement occasion.[3] Edges between nodes indicate similar predictions but then for different nodes. For example, we can see that 'angry' and 'irritable' predict one another well over time. The contemporaneous network in the middle panel of Figure 10.1 indicates, for example, that a person who is currently more 'worried' than their average is likely also more 'nervous' than their average at the same time. Lastly, the between-subjects network in the right panel of Figure 10.1 shows, for example, that individuals who 'worry' a lot on

---

[1]Temporal connections can also be said to encode *Granger causality* (Eichler, 2007; Granger, 1969) as they encode temporal predictions. However, that does not mean the edges necessarily encode *causal* relationships. Ultimately, temporal edges are just partial correlations between a lagged (encoding the previous time point) and a non-lagged variable after controlling for all other lagged variables. As such, similar reservations to causal interpretations in the temporal network should be taken as discussed in Chapter 6.

[2]The data, including a detailed overview of the measures used, are available online at https://osf.io/mvdpe/.

[3]The inverse interpretations are also true: a positive edge also indicates that whenever people experienced *less* difficulty relaxing than their average in one measurement occasion, they likely also experienced *less* difficulty relaxing in the following measurement occasion.

average also tend to be individuals that are 'irritable' on average. The between-person network also shows an interesting negative relationship between feelings of hopelessness[4] and difficulty relaxing. As explained in Chapter 6, this could be due to a common effect structure. For example, perhaps both being a person who often feels hopeless and being a person who often has difficulty relaxing leads one to become a person who often worries.[5] Interestingly, this common effect structure can also be seen at the temporal level. Another explanation is Simpson's paradox, in which an effect becomes different when conditioning on a different level of the data (Hamaker, 2012; Kievit et al., 2013).

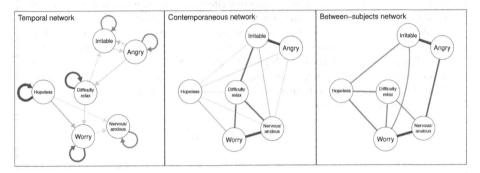

Figure 10.1. Example of a temporal (fixed effects), contemporaneous (fixed effects), and between-subjects network with six nodes based on data collected by Fried et al. (2021). The data consist of four measurements per day for 14 subsequent days, filled in by 80 undergraduate students. Networks were estimated using two-step multi-level estimation with the *mlVAR* package using correlated random effects. The network structure was obtained by thresholding edges at $\alpha = 0.05$ (using an AND-rule for the contemporaneous and between-person networks).

10.3 *N = 1* estimation: personalized network models

The GVAR model can be estimated in various ways from time series data of a single subject ($N = 1$). Doing so will return a temporal and a contemporaneous network.[6] Estimation of the GVAR model from $N = 1$ data mostly follows the same principles as estimating GGMs from single measurement data: the GVAR model can be estimated through multivariate or univariate (nodewise) estimation, using frequentist and Bayesian estimation, and model selection can be performed through regularization or other model search strategies. This section will discuss estimation strategies for the GVAR, followed by model selection strategies.

---

[4]The actual measure used for this node was "I felt that I had nothing to look forward to."

[5]These data were collected during the first weeks of the 2020 COVID-19 pandemic outbreak. As such, any between-person effects could also be due to the general atmosphere of this time.

[6]It is not uncommon that only the temporal network obtained through a (G)VAR analysis is of interest. Not reporting the contemporaneous network, however, is not recommended, as (a) the temporal network is only half the statistical model, (b) the method might lack sensitivity, especially in temporal connections (which are often weak), and (c) relationships in the same window of measurement can be interesting as well (Epskamp, van Borkulo, et al., 2018).

The vector auto-regression (VAR) model is a model that assumes responses from longitudinal data of a single subject to be normally distributed after controlling for the previous
measurement. Let $\mathbf{y}_{p,t}$ represent a set of responses from a subject p measured at time point t
(for simplicity we do not denote random vectors different from realizations here). The VAR
model can then be written as:

$$\mathbf{y}_{p,t} \mid \mathbf{y}_{p,t-1} \sim N\left(\boldsymbol{\mu}_p + \boldsymbol{B}_p\left(\mathbf{y}_{p,t-1} - \boldsymbol{\mu}_p\right), \boldsymbol{\Sigma}_p^{(C)}\right). \tag{10.1}$$

The $\boldsymbol{B}_p$ matrix encodes these temporal regression effects, with element β_{ijp} (row i, column j)
encoding the temporal effect from variable j to variable i for subject p. The transpose of
this matrix therefore encodes a *temporal network*.[a] The matrix $\boldsymbol{\Sigma}_p^{(C)}$ can be interpreted as
the *contemporaneous* variance–covariance matrix: the variance–covariance structure after
controlling for temporal dependencies. The subscript p indicates that these matrices can be
modeled per person. In *graphical* vector auto-regression (GVAR; Epskamp, Waldorp, et al.,
2018; Wild et al., 2010), we further model $\boldsymbol{\Sigma}_p^{(C)}$ through the use of a Gaussian graphical
model (GGM; see Chapter 6):

$$\boldsymbol{\Sigma}_p^{(C)} = \boldsymbol{\Delta}_p^{(C)}\left(\boldsymbol{I} - \boldsymbol{\Omega}_p^{(C)}\right)^{-1}\boldsymbol{\Delta}_p^{(C)}.$$

The matrix $\boldsymbol{\Omega}_p^{(C)}$ encodes a *contemporaneous network*. Finally, in $N > 1$ data, the means can
subsequently be treated as a random variable and also be modeled with a GGM:

$$\boldsymbol{\mu}_p \sim N\left(\mathbf{0}, \boldsymbol{\Sigma}^{(B)}\right); \quad \boldsymbol{\Sigma}^{(B)} = \boldsymbol{\Delta}^{(B)}\left(\boldsymbol{I} - \boldsymbol{\Omega}^{(B)}\right)^{-1}\boldsymbol{\Delta}^{(B)},$$

in which the matrix $\boldsymbol{\Omega}^{(B)}$ encodes the *between-persons network*.

---

[a]Unlike the contemporaneous and between-person networks, the temporal network is not standardized in this notation. Typically, all variables are standardized before analysis to make the $\boldsymbol{B}$ matrices
interpretable (Bulteel et al., 2016). Alternatively, these coefficients can be standardized to *partial
directed correlations* (Wild et al., 2010). Elements from $\boldsymbol{\Omega}_p^{(C)}$ are sometimes termed *partial contemporaneous correlations*, and elements from $\boldsymbol{\Omega}^{(B)}$ are sometimes termed *partial between-person correlations*
(PBC).

Technical Box 10.1. Technical description of the graphical vector auto-regressive model.

Maximum likelihood estimation

Chapter 6 introduced maximum likelihood estimation as an approach to establish multivariate structures: parameters are found under which the data were most likely to occur.
This process requires a *joint likelihood* expression of the entire data. For single measurement data, computing the joint likelihood is relatively straightforward: this quantity
can be computed by multiplying (summing) the (log) likelihoods of every individual
case—the rows in the data set. While proper maximum likelihood estimation of the
GVAR model parameters from time series data is possible in principle as well, it becomes
computationally much more challenging in practice compared to analyzing single measurement data (Ciraki, 2007). This is because an inherent property of time series data
is that cases in the data set are no longer independent. As a result, the likelihood can

no longer be formed easily. To this end, the covariance between every case needs to be modeled, resulting in a covariance matrix that contains a row/column for every variable of every case; in the case of 100 measures on 10 variables, the variance–covariance matrix modeled would be a 1,000 × 1,000 matrix, which is too large for most software packages to handle.

Data augmentation

To overcome the computational challenges of maximum likelihood estimation, GVAR estimation typically relies on a trick that involves augmenting the data (Hamaker et al., 2002; Lane et al., 2019). While this trick no longer results in 'true' maximum likelihood estimation, the resulting parameters and standard errors are comparable to true maximum likelihood estimates, especially at larger sample sizes. Figure 10.2 demonstrates how the data can be augmented: by making a copy of the data, shifting that copy by one row, and appending the shifted data set to the original data set. This way, each row t contains both responses at time t as well as the previous time $t - 1$. If the mean structure is not explicitly modeled, the data can also be centered. The variance–covariance matrix of this augmented data takes the form of a block Toeplitz matrix and can be modeled in the same manner as the variance–covariance matrix of single measurement data (see Technical Box 10.3 at the end of this chapter). Alternatively, regression models can be used on the

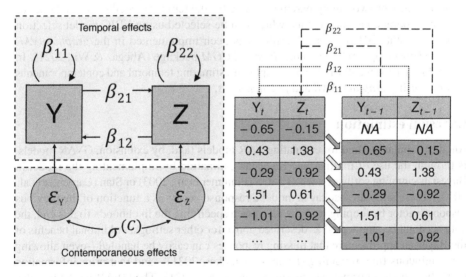

Figure 10.2. Example of a graphical vector auto-regression (GVAR) model (left) and data augmentation usually used to estimate model parameters (right). In the data augmentation, all variables (here Y and Z) are copied and shifted by one row (also termed *lagged*). Rows in the augmented data that cross a night or non-equal measurements can be removed before analysis. The temporal effects (β parameters) encode within-person prediction over time, and the contemporaneous effects (here $\sigma^{(C)}$) can be used to form a GGM encoding relationships in the same window of measurement. For interpretable parameters the data should also be within-person centered or the mean structure should be explicitly modeled.

augmented data: a multivariate regression model can be used with the set of responses at t as dependent variables and the set of responses at $t - 1$ as independent variables, resulting in the parameters of the temporal network. Subsequently, the residuals can be analyzed using the methods discussed in Chapter 6 to obtain the contemporaneous network. Another alternative is to use univariate estimation to obtain all temporal effects by regressing each variable on all lagged variables first, and subsequently, to obtain all contemporaneous effects by using univariate estimation tools on the residuals as discussed in Chapter 6.

Model selection

Model selection can be performed in similar manners as discussed in Chapter 7. For example, edges could be selected based on some threshold or through stepwise model selection search strategies, which has been implemented in the *psychonetrics* package, using mostly the same code as described in Chapter 6 and Chapter 7 except that the gvar model function is used instead of the ggm model function (Epskamp, 2020). A popular way in which the GVAR is estimated is through a regularization procedure closely related to the *EBICglasso* procedure used in GGM models. The multivariate regression with the covariance estimation (MRCE; Rothman et al., 2010) algorithm can be used to sequentially estimate a regularized temporal network (using LASSO regularization) and a contemporaneous network (using the GLASSO algorithm) until convergence. This algorithm utilizes two tuning parameters, one for the temporal coefficients and one for the contemporaneous coefficients, which can be selected using EBIC model selection (Abegaz & Wit, 2013). This algorithm has been implemented in the *graphicalVAR* package (Epskamp, 2021a) and the *SparseTSCGM* package (Abegaz & Wit, 2021). In Tutorial Box 10.1, we illustrate an example for estimating temporal and contemporaneous networks using *graphicalVAR* and *psychonetrics*.

Bayesian estimation

Another popular method for estimating VAR models (and, by extension, GVAR models) is through the use of multivariate Bayesian estimation by implementing the model in Bayesian sampling software such as JAGS (Plummer et al., 2003) or Stan (Carpenter et al., 2017). These software packages model a response vector as a function of the previous response vector by looping over the data when specifying the likelihood. To this end, the data need not be augmented as described above for other settings. Additional benefits of the Bayesian approach are that missing responses can easily be handled—even allowing for continuous time modeling (Ryan & Hamaker, 2021)—and that prior information could be used to improve estimation (Burger et al., 2021). The GVAR model has also been implemented in the BGGM package (Williams & Mulder, 2020).

Suppose a data frame `data` in R has the following form:

subject	day	beep	worry	relax	angry
1	1	1	2	1	2
1	1	2	2	2	2
1	1	3	3	1	1
1	2	1	2	1	1
1	2	2	2	3	1
⋮	⋮	⋮	⋮	⋮	⋮

We can estimate GVAR model parameters from this *N* = 1 data set using the R packages
graphicalVAR (Epskamp, 2021a) for regularized estimation (Abegaz & Wit, 2013; Rothman
et al., 2010) and *psychonetrics* (Epskamp, 2021b) for maximum likelihood estimation. The
input to both packages is comparable, and requires information about the columns in the
data to be stored first:

```
vars <- c("worry","relax","angry") # Variables used in the model
dayvar <- "day" # The day variable, only use with >1 assessment/day
beepvar <- "beep" # The beep variable
```

These objects correspond to argument names in the R packages. The `vars` argument
specifies the variables used in the analysis, the optional `dayvar` argument specifies the days
and is used to cut out pairs of measurements that cross a night[a], and the optional `beepvar`,
corresponding to the measurement number within each day, can be used if the data contain
missing measurements. Now, the *graphicalVAR* package can be used as follows:

```
library("graphicalVAR")
graphicalVAR(data, vars = vars, dayvar = dayvar, beepvar = beepvar)
```

The estimated network structures are stored as *partial directed correlations* (PDC) and
partial contemporaneous correlations (PCC) for the temporal and contemporaneous networks
respectively, and we can visualize the networks using the `plot` function. In *psychonetrics*,
the gvar model function can be used:

```
library("psychonetrics"); library("dplyr")
gvar(data, vars = vars, dayvar = dayvar, beepvar = beepvar,
    estimator = "FIML") %>% runmodel
```

Optionally, further model search functions can be applied such as `prune` and `modelsearch`.
The weights matrices can be obtained using the `getmatrix` function, with `omega_zeta`
indicating the contemporaneous network and PDC the standardized temporal network.

---

[a]Importantly: do not use the `dayvar` argument with only one observation per day, as then all data
will be removed!

Tutorial Box 10.1. Estimating *N* = 1 networks from time series data using *graphicalVAR* and
psychonetrics.

10.4   *N* > 1 estimation: multi-level estimation

If intensive longitudinal data are available from multiple subjects, we might be interested in constructing a network of the average temporal and contemporaneous effects, the *fixed effects* network structures introduced in Chapter 9. A first, intuitive approach to estimating these fixed effects is to compute a network for each subject separately using the methods discussed above and subsequently calculate the averages for each parameter, as well as their variance–covariance structure. This approach of *pooling parameter estimates*, however, discards the nested structure of the data and relies on the—potentially underpowered—estimation of many (*N*) models separately. An alternative to estimating separate models per person is to estimate only one model for all observations. The most straightforward way to do this is to within-person center all variables[7], combine all within-person centered data sets, and estimate a single GVAR model (making sure that responses from one person are not regressed on responses from another person). This process has been automated in the mlGraphicalVAR function in the *graphicalVAR* package[8] and the gvar function in *psychonetrics* (if the idvar argument is used). These methods provide good estimates of the fixed effect structures, but still do not properly take nesting of data points into account. These methods also do not provide insight into the variability of parameters across the sample, as individual networks have to be estimated separately per person.

Multi-level modeling

We can actively incorporate the nested structure of our data by estimating a *multi-level* (G)VAR model (Bringmann et al., 2013; Epskamp, Waldorp, et al., 2018). The term multi-level refers to the data being organized in two levels: within-subject variance on level 1, and between-subject variance on level 2. In this approach, each parameter in the model (e.g., edge weights and means) is assumed to have a distribution over the population. Thus, in the estimation procedure, only these distributions (mean and variance of the parameter, and possibly the covariance between parameters) need to be estimated. The fixed effects can then be obtained from the centers of these distributions. Subsequently, the deviations from this center point—the *random effects*—can be sampled, which, together with the fixed effects, lead to estimates for the personal network models. Figure 10.3 shows how the parameter distributions of a multi-level VAR can inform fixed and random parameters in temporal networks.

Estimating GVAR models through multi-level estimation has four main benefits. First, a single analysis can be performed on the entire data set, leading to a well-powered analysis based on a large sample size, especially for the estimation of fixed effects. Second, the multi-level analysis provides not only insight into the fixed effects structure, but also into the heterogeneity around these fixed effects through the standard errors of the random

---

[7]For each variable removing for each person the mean of that person from the scores of the variable. This step is necessary to ensure that between-person effects are not included in the analysis.

[8]Unlike the name suggests the mlGraphicalVAR function does *not* perform multi-level estimation. The function merely computes a pooled GVAR over all combined within-person centered data sets and runs the graphicalVAR function per person separately for individual networks (Epskamp, Waldorp, et al., 2018).

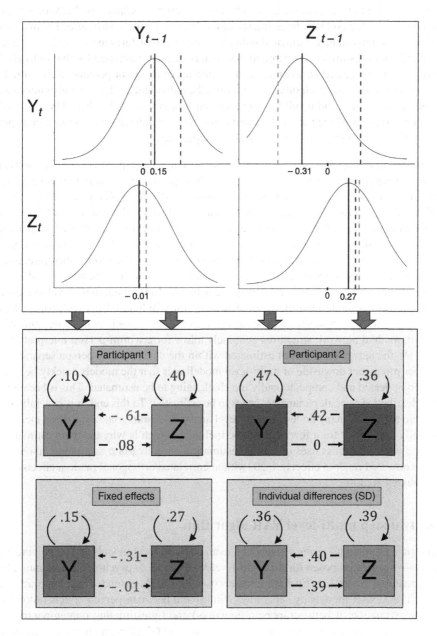

Figure 10.3. Multi-level model for the temporal effects of two variables Y and Z, with data simulated for $N = 150$. The distributions for the temporal effect parameters (top panel) are used to establish the random temporal effects for participant 1 and 2 (bottom panel, top row), as well as fixed temporal effects and the standard deviations of subjects on these effects (bottom panel, bottom row).

effects. Third, multi-level modeling can be used to separate within- and between-person variances, which also leads to estimates of the between-person structure. Finally, and perhaps most importantly, estimated individual network structures are typically closer to the fixed effects estimate compared to parameters that are estimated for that individual directly. This is termed *shrinkage*, as the estimates of different persons in the sample are 'shrunken' towards each other. In other words, individuals' effects are also informed by other individuals and result in estimates that lie close to each other. This can lead to better estimates of the personal network structures, requiring fewer observations per person than performing many $N = 1$ analyses separately.

Multi-level modeling also has some downsides. Assuming a (typical normal) distribution across the population on parameters entails that these parameters do not differ in *structure*, only in weight. For example, suppose that a temporal edge $A \to B$ is modeled with a normal distribution across the population with mean (fixed-effect) 0.2 and standard deviation (of the random-effect) 0.1. This means that we would expect roughly 95% of the population to have individual edge weights for $A \to B$ between 0 and 0.4, with the remaining 5% lower than 0 (negative edge weights) or higher than 0.4. The model, therefore, does not assume that any of these persons have an edge-weight of *exactly* 0, which would lead to the edge not being included in the temporal network. To this end, multi-level modeling does not estimate individual network structures, only individual network parameters. These parameters are also shrunken towards the fixed effect, which makes it questionable if the individual network structures genuinely allow for a within-person interpretation (after all, the networks were not estimated within the data of every person separately). Another prominent downside of multi-level modeling is that the models quickly become very complicated and computationally too challenging to be estimated. This is because a joint distribution over all parameters needs to be estimated. To this end, it is generally not possible to include many nodes in multi-level analyses. Multivariate estimation methods typically only allow for a few nodes to be included, which is why the main estimation method we will discuss uses univariate estimation. In univariate estimation, about six (with correlated random effects) to 20 (with uncorrelated/orthogonal random effects) can be included at most.

The two-step multi-level VAR algorithm

Univariate estimation—using sequential univariate multi-level models and combining the results—was first proposed for the multi-level VAR model in psychological literature by Bringmann et al. (2013). Epskamp, Deserno, et al. (2021) extended this approach for estimating GVAR models by separating within- and between-person effects (allowing for the estimation of between-person networks) and by estimating contemporaneous networks. This extension is termed *two-step multi-level GVAR* estimation (see Technical Box 10.2), and is implemented in the *mlVAR* package (Epskamp, Deserno, et al., 2021), further described in Tutorial Box 10.2. In step 1, the algorithm estimates the temporal and between-subjects networks by performing univariate multi-level modeling, predicting each variable from within-person centered lagged variables and personwise means. In step 2, the estimated residuals of the models run in step 1 are used in a new sequence of univariate multi-level models to estimate the contemporaneous effects. For separating within- and between-person variances, the algorithm makes use of within-person centering: using the sample means from every person separately to center variables. This requires decent estimates of the within-person means, meaning that several (at least about 20) measures have to be available per person.[9] To this end, two-step multi-level GVAR estimation can be used with $N > 1$ time series data, but not with panel data. The *mlVAR* package uses the *lme4* package (Bates et al., 2015) for multi-level estimation of all effects.

The *two-step multi-level* GVAR estimation algorithm, proposed by Epskamp, Waldorp, et al. (2018), is an algorithm for estimating multi-level GVAR models through a series of univariate multi-level regression analyses. First, the entire data set used is standardized to z-scores (subtracting the mean and dividing by the standard deviation). Let $z_{tp}^{(\text{worry})}$, $z_{tp}^{(\text{relax})}$, and $z_{tp}^{(\text{anger})}$ represent three variables answered by person p at measurement occasion t. To separate within- and between-person variances, we within-person center lagged variables as predictors (Hamaker & Grasman, 2014): $\tilde{z}_{t-1,p}^{(\ldots)} = z_{t-1,p}^{(\ldots)} - \bar{z}_p^{(\ldots)}$, in which $\tilde{z}$ represents a within-person centered variable and $\bar{z}$ the person-wise mean. In step 1, for each variable a univariate multi-level regression is performed using that variable as a dependent variable and all within-person centered lagged variables together with the person-wise means as independent variables:

$$z_{t,p}^{(\text{worry})} = \beta_{0p} + \beta_{11p}^{(\text{T})} \cdot \tilde{z}_{t-1,p}^{(\text{worry})} + \beta_{12p}^{(\text{T})} \cdot \tilde{z}_{t-1,p}^{(\text{relax})} + \beta_{13p}^{(\text{T})} \cdot \tilde{z}_{t-1,p}^{(\text{anger})}$$
$$+ \beta_{12}^{(\text{B})} \cdot \bar{z}_p^{(\text{relax})} + \beta_{13}^{(\text{B})} \cdot \bar{z}_p^{(\text{anger})} + \varepsilon_{tp}^{(\text{worry})}.$$

The $\beta^{(\text{T})}$ parameters form the individual temporal networks, and the $\beta^{(\text{B})}$ parameters can be used to form a GGM in the same way univariate regressions in univariate GGM estimation are averaged to partial correlation coefficients (Epskamp, Waldorp, et al., 2018). In the second step, the estimated residuals of the multi-level regression models in step 1 are used in a second round of univariate multi-level models:

$$\hat{\varepsilon}_{tp}^{(\text{worry})} = \beta_{12p}^{(\text{C})} \cdot \hat{\varepsilon}_{tp}^{(\text{relax})} + \beta_{13p}^{(\text{C})} \cdot \hat{\varepsilon}_{tp}^{(\text{anger})} + \zeta_{tp}^{(\text{worry})}.$$

The $\beta^{(\text{C})}$ parameters are subsequently used to form the contemporaneous networks.

Technical Box 10.2. Two-step multi-level graphical vector auto-regression.

---

[9]With too few observations per person, the estimated network structures will likely be biased. This bias is termed *Nickel's bias* (Jordan et al., 2020), and most notably leads to erroneous negative auto-regressions (self-loops in the temporal network).

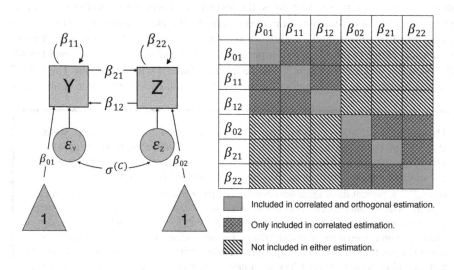

Figure 10.4. Parameter covariation included in *mlVAR* for the estimation of temporal effects. Choosing orthogonal estimation assumes that parameters are independent, whereas correlated estimation considers some (but not all) parameter correlations.

Parameter covariance. A challenging aspect of multi-level modeling is that often covariances between random effects need to be estimated as well. For example, it could be that people that have strong edges between some variables also tend to have strong edges between other variables (Pe et al., 2015). Estimating sequential univariate models, as is done in two-step multi-level GVAR estimation, provides a computationally efficient alternative to estimating the multi-level GVAR model because the univariate multi-level models do not include all parameters; the estimation routine does not have to include all potential covariances between random effects.[10] More specifically, univariate models only include the intercept and (incoming) edge-weights that are connected to the dependent variables. In *mlVAR*, the covariance between these included random effects can be estimated by using the arguments `temporal` and/or `contemporaneous`. The default ("`correlated`") will include correlated random effects, which is feasible for up to about 8 to 10 nodes. For about 10 to 20 nodes, uncorrelated ("`orthogonal`") random effects can be used, which introduces a limitation to the estimation procedure, as random effects can be assumed to be correlated. Figure 10.4 shows that estimating models with no correlated random effects will only assume some random effect covariances to be 0, not all (as not all random effects are included in each model).

---

[10]The upside of not having to estimate covariances between random effects also comes with the downside of not being able to investigate these covariances. This is why the between-person effects are estimated through level 2 predictors rather than by studying the random effects covariances between means.

We can estimate the multi-level VAR model from $N > 1$ time series data using the *mlVAR* package and from panel data using the *psychonetrics* package (fixed effect networks only). Both packages can handle data as structured in Tutorial Box 10.1. The *mlVAR* package uses the mlVAR function, which can be used as follows (assuming a column in the data containing information on the subject id is called subject):

```
library("mlVAR")
mlVAR_results <- mlVAR(data, vars = vars, idvar = "subject",
    temporal = "correlated", contemporaneous = "correlated")
```

Optionally the dayvar and beepvar arguments can be used which work similarly as in Tutorial Box 10.1. For non-correlated random effects, the temporal and contemporaneous arguments can be set to orthogonal. The plot method can be used to threshold and visualize the network. For example, the following command plots the temporal network with non-significant effects hidden:

```
plot(mlVAR_results, "temporal", nonsig = "hide")
```

Replacing plot for getNet will return the weights matrix instead. Networks showing the standard deviation of random effects can be obtained by setting SD = TRUE in plot(...) or getNet(...).

In *psychonetrics* the model can be estimated using the ml_gvar function:

```
library("psychonetrics"); library("dplyr")
ml_gvar(data, vars = vars, idvar = "subject", standardize = "z") %>%
    runmodel
```

Optionally, the beepvar argument can be used (the dayvar argument is not supported because this model is not designed for intensive time series), and further model search functions can be applied such as prune and modelsearch. Standardizing data is recommended to improve estimation. The contemporaneous network is stored as omega_zeta_within and the between persons network is stored as omega_zeta_between. If data are encoded in a wide format (variables encoded as different columns for each measurement), the panelgvar function can be used instead. Both ml_gvar and panelgvar are wrapper functions on the main dlvm1 function used for panel data modeling, which allows for some more options (e.g., modeling between-person effects as a Cholesky decomposition, which can be useful if between-person networks are seemingly not estimated well).

Tutorial Box 10.2. Estimating multi-level GVAR models from $N > 1$ longitudinal data.

Multivariate estimation

Panel data. A considerable downside of the two-step multi-level GVAR estimation algorithm is that due to within-person centering with the person-wise sample means, a decent number of observations per person is required. To this end, it is not recommended to use this algorithm with less than about 20 observations, making it applicable to $N > 1$ time series data but not to panel data. One estimation method for estimating a GVAR model from panel data (also termed *panel GVAR*) has been proposed by Epskamp (2020) and is implemented in the *psychonetrics* package, further described in Tutorial Box 10.2.[11] This model is a multi-level GVAR model with only random intercepts/means. This means that it assumes the same network structure for every person but allows people to differ on their averages. The variance–covariance structure of these random means is used to model the between-person network. The implementation in *psychonetrics* is a full-information implementation, meaning that all covariances between every possible measurement are included in the model. This makes the model computationally challenging to use with many nodes or many time points. It is recommended not to use this model with more than 10 measurements and more than around 10 to 20 nodes.

Bayesian estimation. A final powerful method for multivariate multi-level (G)VAR estimation is Bayesian estimation through sampling procedures. In these frameworks, all effects can be random and are included in the same model. As such, these methods return all possible random effect correlations (e.g., also allowing for between-person networks to contain edges). While it is possible to implement this model manually in software such as JAGS (Plummer et al., 2003) or Stan (Carpenter et al., 2017), doing so is quite challenging, requiring many prior distribution choices and likely leading to long computations if more than a few nodes are modeled. The Mplus software includes a module on dynamic structural equation models from version 8 onwards, which simplifies this process (Asparouhov et al., 2018; McNeish & Hamaker, 2020). This framework accommodates the multi-level VAR model, and while modeling GGMs is not included, partial correlation coefficients can manually be obtained from posterior samples (Epskamp, Waldorp, et al., 2018). The main downside is that even though the implementation in Mplus is very powerful, the number of nodes that can realistically be included in the analyses is still quite limited (about six). Another downside is that Mplus is not open-source and, therefore, not free to use. A more detailed discussion on differences between Bayesian estimation and the two-step multi-level GVAR algorithm can be found in Epskamp, Waldorp, et al. (2018).

10.5   Challenges to GVAR estimation

In this section, we discuss some of the most prominent practical and methodological challenges that researchers may face when estimating GVAR models from data.

Power and feasibility

The required number of observations to estimate reliable networks from time series data of a single subject ($N = 1$) is at least comparable to the number of participants needed to estimate networks from single measurement data. In fact, the required number may even be higher, as the GVAR model includes a temporal network and is estimated from

---

[11]The panel GVAR model is implemented as a special case of a larger modeling framework that also includes latent variables. Epskamp (2020) termed this model the *panel-LVGVAR* model, and the *psychonetrics* package terms this model the dlvm1 (dynamic latent variable model with lag-1) model. The panel GVAR can be obtained by representing each observed variable with a latent variable, setting all factor loadings to 1, and all residual variances to 0. This is done automatically in the *psychonetrics* package if no latent variable structure is assigned.

data with auto-correlated responses (reducing effective sample size). Collecting large time series for a single subject, however, is challenging in most fields of psychological research. Not only can it be burdensome for participants, but extending the measurement to long periods may also hinder the assumption of stationarity (see below). Furthermore, the number of time points needed depends on the estimated network structure and on the number of nodes included. Sparse and well-defined network structures containing a few strong edges can be retrieved with smaller samples than dense networks with fewer strong edges that stand out.

In a series of simulation studies, Epskamp, Waldorp, et al. (2018) showed that reliable estimation of sparse synthetic networks is possible with 100 time points and eight nodes (Epskamp, Waldorp, et al., 2018). However, a recent simulation study by Mansueto et al. (2021) used empirical networks as generating structures and instead found a relatively poor sensitivity (power to detect edges) with around 100 observations. A different generating network with six nodes led to better recovery of the global structure at 100 observations, but weaker edges were still not reliably retrieved. Such weak edges do not necessarily represent small and negligible effects; edges may be weak because of sampling bias or slight variations of the variables in time and may still be relevant for research or clinical purposes. Unfortunately, there is no way to know if the generating structure (assuming data were generated through a GVAR model) was dense or sparse and included strong or weak edges. As such, it is questionable if GVAR estimation is feasible from $N = 1$ data sets that may realistically be obtainable, and this will rely on certain assumptions (notably, that the generating model is sparse). It is advisable to consider that with about 50 to 100 time points, sensitivity likely is low, meaning that only a few edges may be discovered. The best solution to this problem, outside of aiming to collect more data, is to keep the model as small as possible. For $N = 1$ GVAR models, it is generally advisable to include as few nodes as possible (e.g., less than 10).

Heterogeneity

In addition to discovering individual network structures, researchers may also be interested in how much people differ in their network structure (heterogeneity). The detection of heterogeneity between GVAR models is directly related to the reliability of GVAR estimation. If it is not feasible to estimate reliable network structures, visually comparing network structures of individuals may lead to an illusionary sense of heterogeneity. Hoekstra et al. (2021) discuss that even if the generating structure is the same for two people, network structures estimated from their data may differ substantively. For example, suppose that the generating model contains 10 (true) edges, but sensitivity (power) is only 50%, meaning that we only expect to find 5 out of 10 edges in the network of one particular person. Suppose also that the chance of including an edge is the same for all 10 true edges. Then, there is only a 0.000016 probability that the *exact* same edges are detected in two people. As such, even though the generating structure is the same, we would expect to find different networks. This entails high sensitivity (and specificity) are needed to separate true from illusionary heterogeneity when estimating individual network models, and to this end, it is advisable to not interpret differences in personal network models as evidence for heterogeneity, especially when these networks are sparse.

If a large number of people are included in the data set, multi-level modeling can be used to gain insight in the heterogeneity of parameter values. When estimating a multi-level network using the *mlVAR* package, the standard deviations of random effects across the population on the temporal and contemporaneous network parameters are returned and can be visualized as networks (e.g., Figure 10.3). The width of the edges in this network shows the degree to which network parameters exhibit individual differences. Bringmann et al., 2013 recommend using a cut-off score of 0.10 for the edge weights. Alternatively, random effects can in principle be tested statistically by comparing a model with random effects to a fixed effects only model, although this may be hard in practice.[12]

Missing data

In intensive time series designs missing data are very common. Usually, time series data are characterized by wave missingness, where every item at a particular measurement point is missing (McLean et al., 2017; Schafer & Graham, 2002). Many factors can affect missing data, for example, measurement frequency and timing, length of the measurement period, physical activity, substance use, age, and gender (Jones et al., 2019; McLean et al., 2017; Ono et al., 2019; Rintala et al., 2019; Wen et al., 2017). Techniques based on imputation or maximum likelihood can be used to handle data missing completely at random (MCAR) and at random (MAR), while with data missing not at random (MNAR), these may yield biased estimates. For example, Kalman filter imputation (Hamaker & Grasman, 2012; Harvey, 1990) can be applied prior to network estimation with the R package *imputeTS* (Moritz & Bartz-Beielstein, 2017). Alternatively, full information maximum likelihood estimation is implemented in the R package *psychonetrics*, which estimates a model using only observed responses (Epskamp, Isvoranu, et al., 2021). Finally, Bayesian estimation methods are well capable of handling missing data (McNeish & Hamaker, 2020). Mansueto et al. (2021) propose that such methods for handling missing data may lead to promising avenues for reducing participant burden through the use of planned missingness and adaptive testing—only asking a subset of questions in each measurement (Graham et al., 2006).

Stationarity assumption

As any statistical model, (multi-level) GVAR estimation relies on a set of assumptions. A core assumption of the VAR model is *stationarity*. A stationary time series does not indicate changes over time in its defining characteristics, such as the means, variances, and network parameters. Violations of this assumption arise if there are trends in the time series, for example, seasonal or linear trends or changes in volatility. Deviations from the stationarity assumption are not implausible in psychological time series. For example, we might observe mean-shifts in symptoms following certain life events or obtain seasonal patterns for affect variables depending on the time of the year. To understand the dynamic process without such trends, a time series can be broken down into its constituent trend components through a method called *decomposition*, resulting in a trend component, a seasonal/cyclical component, and a residual/regular component. Another scenario

---

[12] A limited implementation for testing random effects of temporal coefficients is implemented in *mlVAR* in the mlVARcompare function.

introducing non-stationarity is the presence of a so-called *unit root*. A unit root is present if the auto-regressive parameter of a time series equals one and can be detected using the (Augmented-)Dickey-Fuller test (Dickey & Fuller, 1979). Figure 10.5 visualizes a stationary distribution, as well as different cases of non-stationarity.

There are several methods of handling non-stationarity. Generally, most of these methods aim to remove existing linear trends or seasonal components. For example, linear trends in the data can be accounted for by performing a regression on time and subsequently modeling the residuals as the time series adjusted for linear changes. Simulation studies showed that it is generally recommended to detrend present linear trends before estimating networks (Epskamp, van Borkulo, et al., 2018). In this study, detrending all versus only significant trends performed comparably, while not detrending led to lower specificity (especially in temporal networks) and lower sensitivity (especially in contemporaneous networks). However, in many situations changing means, variances, or network parameters are of central interest, and therefore removing them from the data through detrending would be detrimental. Instead, these changes over time can be explicitly modeled in time-varying network models, which are further discussed in Chapter 11.

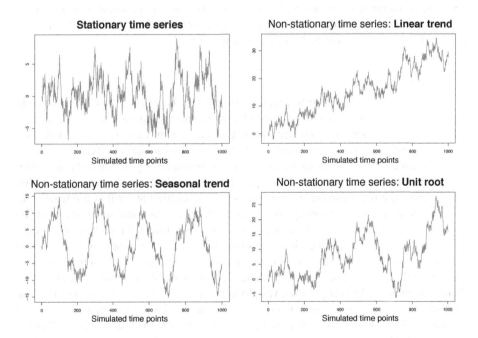

Figure 10.5. Simulated time series data under four conditions. Top left: A stationary time series with auto-regressive effect $\beta = 0.95$. Top right: Non-stationarity, due to a linear trend added to the time series used for the first plot. Bottom left: Non-stationarity due to a seasonal trend added to the time series used for the first plot. Bottom right: Non-stationarity due to the presence of a unit root, time series with auto-regressive effect $\beta = 1$.

Assumption of equidistant measures

The GVAR model establishes temporal dependencies in the form of lagged relationships. In doing so, it treats all lags of the same level as equally distant from one another. In other words, it is assumed that the time difference between any two subsequent assessment points is equal, an assumption referred to as *equidistant measures*. Two primary manners in which this assumption may be violated are (1) when there are multiple measures per day, because there will likely be a larger time difference between the last assessment of a day and the subsequent day's first assessment compared to time differences between other consecutive measurements, and (2) when a participant failed to fill in all measurements, and the data are not properly encoded with missing values on the measurements that were not filled in. These problems can adequately be handled using the software packages discussed in this chapter through the use of the `dayvar` argument (removes pairs of observations that cross a night) and `beepvar` arguments (removes pairs of responses that are not consecutive). Another way this assumption may be violated is (3) when measurement occasions are at random time intervals. While it should not be a big problem if time intervals are roughly equal (e.g., sometimes two hours and sometimes three hours), it may be problematic if time intervals show large differences (e.g., sometimes 10 minutes and sometimes four hours). In this setting, an alternative is to use continuous time modeling, further discussed by Ryan and Hamaker (2021).

Time scales

In the GVAR model, we aim to predict dynamics as lagged relationships, typically including only one time lag. Consequently, to interpret temporal effects, we need to make sure that the time scale chosen for our analysis matches the type of dynamics we want to investigate. For example, if we want to model a temporal effect A → B, we want to ensure that we also capture this effect by appropriately timing our assessment intervals. This, however, is not always possible or feasible; in many cases, we either do not know the true time scale our processes are operating at, or it is not feasible to measure at the desired frequency. A mismatch between true time scale and modeled lags can lead to problematic inferences in two situations: first, the true dynamic process can unfold *faster* than specified in our assessment (e.g., panic symptoms occur within seconds, but we measure every two hours). In this case, the effects will not be captured in the temporal prediction. Such fast effects might be found in the contemporaneous rather than the temporal effects (Epskamp, van Borkulo, et al., 2018). An alternative approach to modeling discrete time lags is to conceptualize dynamics on a continuous level, for example, using continuous structural equation modeling (Driver et al., 2017; Ryan & Hamaker, 2021) or differential equations. Second, the true dynamic process can unfold *slower* than specified in our assessment (e.g., investigating mood dynamics in relation to hormones, but we assess hormone levels every two hours). Such slower effects might be better understood using panel designs (Epskamp, 2020) because they require more distance between assessments.

Epskamp (2020) detail multivariate estimation of the GVAR model from $N = 1$ time series and panel data. To estimate a GVAR model, the data can first be augmented:

$$Y^{(\text{aug})} = \begin{bmatrix} Y^{(\text{lag})} & Y \end{bmatrix},$$

in which $Y^{(\text{aug})}$ represents the augmented data set, Y represents the original data (with measurement t on row t), and $Y^{(\text{lag})}$ the original data set shifted by one row (measurement $t - 1$ on row t). If needed, several rows of $Y^{(\text{aug})}$ can be removed, especially when the pair of measurements $t - 1$ and t feature a large gap in time, such as across a night. The variance–covariance matrix of $Y^{(\text{aug})}$ takes the following form:

$$\Sigma = \begin{matrix} t-1 \\ t \end{matrix} \begin{bmatrix} \overset{t-1}{\Sigma^*} & \overset{t}{\Sigma_1^{\mathsf{T}}} \\ \Sigma_1 & \Sigma_0. \end{bmatrix}$$

Also termed the Toeplitz variance–covariance matrix. The block Σ_0 can be modeled with the following expression:

$$\text{Vec}\,(\Sigma_0) = (I \otimes I - B \otimes B)^{-1}\,\text{Vec}\left(\Sigma^{(\text{C})}\right),$$

in which $\Sigma^{(\text{C})}$ is the innovation variance–covariance matrix that can further be modeled as a GGM (see Technical Box 10.1). The lag-1 variance–covariance matrix can subsequently be modeled as:

$$\Sigma_1 = B\Sigma_0.$$

Finally, with large samples we would expect $\Sigma^* = \Sigma_0$. In the *psychonetrics* package, however, Σ^* is modeled using a Cholesky decomposition instead:

$$\Sigma^* = LL^{\mathsf{T}},$$

such that this block is always positive semi-definite and such that the stationary variance–covariance structure is not modeled twice. This Technical Box explains the main expressions used in maximum likelihood estimation of $N = 1$ GVAR models. The variant for panel data follows mostly the same steps, but creates a larger Toeplitz matrix with all waves of data and models between-person variance in addition to the within-person variances discussed here.

Technical Box 10.3. Toeplitz variance–covariance structure for the graphical VAR model.

10.6   Conclusion

Time series analysis is a fruitful field for constructing dynamical networks. The graphical vector auto-regression (GVAR) model separates longitudinal information in *contemporaneous*, *temporal*, and *between-persons* network structures. This chapter discussed how these networks could be estimated from time series analyses for single subjects and multiple subjects, using intensive longitudinal data collected via novel ambulatory assessment techniques or panel data. Current challenges in estimating time series networks span from a trade-off between power, stationarity, and feasibility to identifying appropriate time scales for lagged relationships.

While this chapter provides an introduction to network analysis from longitudinal data, the topic of longitudinal data analysis itself goes beyond the scope of this book. Indeed, entire textbooks could be written on this topic. Important to note is that the GVAR model, which was the focus of this chapter, is only one of several possible models. Another approach to constructing networks from time series data is the estimation of a structural VAR model (SVAR; Chen et al., 2011; Gates et al., 2010). In contrast to GVAR, the SVAR model uses *directed* effects for the contemporaneous network. Structural VARs can be estimated by transforming (G)VAR results (Lütkepohl, 2005) or through unified structural equation modeling (Beltz & Molenaar, 2016; Gates et al., 2010; Kim et al., 2007), and structure estimation is usually done through stepwise model search. In $N > 1$ data, 'group iterative multiple model estimation' GIMME; (GIMME; Gates & Molenaar, 2012) is an often-used method for estimating structural VAR models for multiple persons. In short, GIMME searches for qualitative similarity across people—using stepwise model search strategies through structural equation models—to find network structures that contain group-level (edges that are included for every person in a group) as well as person-specific temporal and contemporaneous effects. Other variants of network models estimated from time series data are time-varying VAR networks and VAR networks that include non-Gaussian variables. These will be introduced in Chapter 11.

10.7   Exercises

Conceptual

10.1. Explain why pairs of observations that cross a night have to be removed after augmenting the data.

10.2. Suppose you have $N = 1$ data of a person measured once per day on weekdays only for several months. Which argument in *graphicalVAR* or *psychonetrics* can be used to make sure you do not regress the responses from Mondays on the responses from Fridays?

10.3. How can *shrinkage* help in estimating a network for each subject in a data set?

10.4. Describe the difference between *fixed effects* and *random effects*.

10.5. Suppose a researcher has two time series data sets of patients measured in clinical practice, both with 75 measurements in total. The researcher estimates two GVAR models, and finds that these network models are different due to having different edges. Can the researcher conclude that there is *heterogeneity* between these people? Why (not)?

True or false

10.6. In the second step of two-step multi-level GVAR estimation the between-person network parameters are estimated.

10.7. Using multi-level estimation, for every person in the data set, a temporal and contemporaneous network can be estimated but not a between-persons networks.

10.8. It is generally recommended to remove trends (such as linear trends) prior to analyzing your $N = 1$ time series.

10.9. *Correlated* estimation in *mlVAR* includes all parameter correlations.

10.10. Contrary to graphical VAR, structural VAR estimation estimates directed contemporaneous effects.

Practical

For practical exercises in R, please navigate to the appropriate folder of this chapter, available on the online *Companion Website*.

References

Abegaz, F., & Wit, E. (2013). Sparse time series chain graphical models for reconstructing genetic networks. *Biostatistics, 14*(3), 586–599.

Abegaz, F., & Wit, E. (2021). *SparseTSCGM: Sparse time series chain graphical models* [R package version 4.0]. R package version 4.0. https://CRAN.R-project.org/package=SparseTSCGM

Asparouhov, T., Hamaker, E. L., & Muthén, B. (2018). Dynamic structural equation models. *Structural Equation Modeling: A Multidisciplinary Journal, 25*(3), 359–388.

Bates, D., Mächler, M., Bolker, B., & Walker, S. (2015). Fitting linear mixed-effects models using lme4. *Journal of Statistical Software, 67*(1), 1–48.

Beltz, A. M., & Molenaar, P. C. M. (2016). Dealing with multiple solutions in structural vector autoregressive models. *Multivariate Behavioral Research, 51*(2-3), 357–373.

Bringmann, L. F., Vissers, N., Wichers, M., Geschwind, N., Kuppens, P., Peeters, F., Borsboom, D., & Tuerlinckx, F. (2013). A network approach to psychopathology: New insights into clinical longitudinal data. *PLoS One, 8*(4), e60188.

Bulteel, K., Tuerlinckx, F., Brose, A., & Ceulemans, E. (2016). Using raw VAR regression coefficients to build networks can be misleading. *Multivariate Behavioral Research, 51*(2-3), 330–344.

Burger, J., Epskamp, S., van der Veen, D. C., Dablander, F., Schoevers, R. A., Fried, E. I. I., & Riese, H. (2021). A clinical PREMISE for personalized models: Towards a formal integration of case formulations and statistical networks. *PsyArXiv*. https://doi.org/10.31234/osf.io/bdrs7

Carpenter, B., Gelman, A., Hoffman, M. D., Lee, D., Goodrich, B., Betancourt, M., Brubaker, M., Guo, J., Li, P., & Riddell, A. (2017). Stan: A probabilistic programming language. *Journal of Statistical Software*, 76(1), 1–32.

Chen, G., Glen, D. R., Saad, Z. S., Hamilton, J. P., Thomason, M. E., Gotlib, I. H., & Cox, R. W. (2011). Vector autoregression, structural equation modeling, and their synthesis in neuroimaging data analysis. *Computers in Biology and Medicine*, 41(12), 1142–1155.

Ciraki, D. (2007). *Dynamic structural equation models: Estimation and interference*. (Doctoral dissertation). London School of Economics and Political Science (United Kingdom).

Dickey, D. A., & Fuller, W. A. (1979). Distribution of the estimators for autoregressive time series with a unit root. *Journal of the American Statistical Association*, 74(366a), 427–431.

Driver, C. C., Oud, J. H. L., & Voelkle, M. C. (2017). Continuous time structural equation modeling with R package ctsem. *Journal of Statistical Software*, 77(5).

Eichler, M. (2007). Granger causality and path diagrams for multivariate time series. *Journal of Econometrics*, 137(2), 334–353.

Epskamp, S. (2021a). *graphicalVAR: Graphical VAR for experience sampling data* [R package version 0.3]. R package version 0.3. https://CRAN.R-project.org/package=graphicalVAR

Epskamp, S. (2021b). *psychonetrics: Structural equation modeling and confirmatory network analysis* [R package version 0.10]. R package version 0.10. https://CRAN.R-project.org/package=psychonetrics

Epskamp, S., Isvoranu, A. M., & Cheung, M. (2021). Meta-analytic Gaussian network aggregation. *Psychometrika*. https://doi.org/10.1007/s11336-021-09764-3

Epskamp, S., van Borkulo, C. D., van der Veen, D. C., Servaas, M. N., Isvoranu, A. M., Riese, H., & Cramer, A. O. J. (2018). Personalized Network Modeling in Psychopathology: The Importance of Contemporaneous and Temporal Connections. *Clinical Psychological Science*, 6(3), 416–427.

Epskamp, S., Waldorp, L. J., Mõttus, R., & Borsboom, D. (2018). The Gaussian graphical model in cross-sectional and time-series data. *Multivariate Behavioral Research*, 53(4), 453–480.

Epskamp, S. (2020). Psychometric network models from time-series and panel data. *Psychometrika*, 85(1), 206–231.

Epskamp, S., Deserno, M. K., & Bringmann, L. F. (2021). *Mlvar: Multi-level vector autoregression* [R package version 0.5]. R package version 0.5. https://CRAN.R-project.org/package=mlVAR

Fried, E. I., Papanikolaou, F., & Epskamp, S. (2021). Mental health and social contact during the COVID-19 pandemic: An ecological momentary assessment study. *Clinical Psychological Science*. https://doi.org/10.1177/21677026211017839

Gates, K. M., & Molenaar, P. C. (2012). Group search algorithm recovers effective connectivity maps for individuals in homogeneous and heterogeneous samples. *NeuroImage*, *63*(1), 310–319.

Gates, K. M., Molenaar, P. C., Hillary, F. G., Ram, N., & Rovine, M. J. (2010). Automatic search for fMRI connectivity mapping: An alternative to Granger causality testing using formal equivalences among SEM path modeling, VAR, and unified SEM. *NeuroImage*, *50*(3), 1118–1125.

Graham, J. W., Taylor, B. J., Olchowski, A. E., & Cumsille, P. E. (2006). Planned missing data designs in psychological research. *Psychological Methods*, *11*(4), 323–343.

Granger, C. W. J. (1969). Investigating causal relations by econometric models and cross-spectral methods. *Econometrica: Journal of the Econometric Society*, *37*(3), 424–438.

Hamaker, E. L., & Grasman, R. P. P. P. (2014). To center or not to center? investigating inertia with a multilevel autoregressive model. *Frontiers in Psychology*, 5, 1492.

Hamaker, E. L. (2012). Why researchers should think "within-person": A paradigmatic rationale. In M. R. Mehl & T. S. Conner (Eds.), *Handbook of research methods for studying daily life* (pp. 43–61). The Guilford Press.

Hamaker, E. L., Dolan, C. V., & Molenaar, P. C. M. (2002). On the nature of SEM estimates of ARMA parameters. *Structural Equation Modeling*, *9*(3), 347–368.

Hamaker, E. L., & Grasman, R. P. P. P. (2012). Regime switching state-space models applied to psychological processes: Handling missing data and making inferences. *Psychometrika*, *77*(2), 400–422.

Harvey, A. C. (1990). *Forecasting, structural time series models and the Kalman filter*. Cambridge University Press.

Hoekstra, R. H. A., Epskamp, S., & Borsboom, D. (2021). Heterogeneity in individual network analysis: Reality or illusion? *Manuscript in review*.

Jones, A., Remmerswaal, D., Verveer, I., Robinson, E., Franken, I. H., Wen, C. K. F., & Field, M. (2019). Compliance with ecological momentary assessment protocols in substance users: A meta-analysis. *Addiction*, *114*(4), 609–619.

Jordan, D. G., Winer, E. S., & Salem, T. (2020). The current status of temporal network analysis for clinical science: Considerations as the paradigm shifts? *Journal of Clinical Psychology*, *76*(9), 1591–1612.

Kievit, R. A., Frankenhuis, W. E., Waldorp, L. J., & Borsboom, D. (2013). Simpson's paradox in psychological science: A practical guide. *Frontiers in Psychology*, 4, 513.

Kim, J., Zhu, W., Chang, L., Bentler, P. M., & Ernst, T. (2007). Unified structural equation modeling approach for the analysis of multisubject, multivariate functional MRI data. *Human Brain Mapping*, *28*(2), 85–93.

Lane, S. T., Gates, K. M., Pike, H. K., Beltz, A. M., & Wright, A. G. (2019). Uncovering general, shared, and unique temporal patterns in ambulatory assessment data. *Psychological Methods*, *24*(1), 54–69.

Lütkepohl, H. (2005). *New introduction to multiple time series analysis*. Springer Science & Business Media.

Mansueto, A. C., Wiers, R., van Weert, J. C. M., Schouten, B. C., & Epskamp, S. (2021). Investigating the feasibility of idiographic network models. *Psychological Methods*. https://doi.org/10.1037/met0000466

McLean, D. C., Nakamura, J., & Csikszentmihalyi, M. (2017). Explaining system miss-
    ing: Missing data and experience sampling method. *Social Psychological and
    Personality Science*, *8*(4), 434–441.
McNeish, D., & Hamaker, E. L. (2020). A primer on two-level dynamic structural equation
    models for intensive longitudinal data in mplus. *Psychological Methods*, *25*(5),
    610–635.
Moritz, S., & Bartz-Beielstein, T. (2017). imputeTS: Time series missing value imputation
    in R. *R Journal*, *9*(1), 207–218.
Ono, M., Schneider, S., Junghaenel, D. U., & Stone, A. A. (2019). What affects the
    completion of ecological momentary assessments in chronic pain research? an
    individual patient data meta-analysis. *Journal of Medical Internet Research*,
    21(2), e11398.
Pe, M. L., Kircanski, K., Thompson, R. J., Bringmann, L. F., Tuerlinckx, F., Mestdagh,
    M., Mata, J., Jaeggi, S. M., Buschkuehl, M., Jonides, J., et al. (2015). Emotion-
    network density in major depressive disorder. *Clinical Psychological Science*,
    3(2), 292–300.
Plummer, M. et al. (2003). JAGS: A program for analysis of Bayesian graphical models
    using Gibbs sampling, In *Proceedings of the 3rd international workshop on
    distributed statistical computing*.
Rintala, A., Wampers, M., Myin-Germeys, I., & Viechtbauer, W. (2019). Response
    compliance and predictors thereof in studies using the experience sampling
    method. *Psychological Assessment*, *31*(2), 226–235.
Rothman, A. J., Levina, E., & Zhu, J. (2010). Sparse multivariate regression with co-
    variance estimation. *Journal of Computational and Graphical Statistics*, *19*(4),
    947–962.
Ryan, O., & Hamaker, E. L. (2021). Time to intervene: A continuous-time approach to
    network analysis and centrality. *Psychometrika*. https://doi.org/10.1007/s11336-
    021-09767-0
Schafer, J. L., & Graham, J. W. (2002). Missing data: Our view of the state of the art.
    Psychological Methods, *7*(2), 147–177.
Wen, C. K. F., Schneider, S., Stone, A. A., & Spruijt-Metz, D. (2017). Compliance with
    mobile ecological momentary assessment protocols in children and adolescents:
    A systematic review and meta-analysis. *Journal of Medical Internet Research*,
    19(4), e132.
Wild, B., Eichler, M., Friederich, H.-C., Hartmann, M., Zipfel, S., & Herzog, W. (2010). A
    graphical vector autoregressive modelling approach to the analysis of electronic
    diary data. *BMC Medical Research Methodology*, *10*(1), 28.
Williams, D. R., & Mulder, J. (2020). BGGM: Bayesian Gaussian graphical models in R.
    Journal of Open Source Software, *5*(51), 2111.

Chapter 11

Modeling Change in Networks

Jonas M. B. Haslbeck[1], Oisín Ryan[2], Han L. J. van der Maas[1], & Lourens J. Waldorp[1]

1. University of Amsterdam, Department of Psychology

2. Utrecht University, Department of Methodology & Statistics

11.1   Introduction

In the previous two chapters, we considered models for the relationships between variables over time (temporal effects) and within the same measurement occasion (contemporaneous effects). A key assumption of these models is that their parameters do not change across time. If only the means change across time, this problem can in some situations be mitigated by detrending the time series (see also Chapter 10). However, in many situations changes in parameters over time might be the very thing we are interested in. In this chapter we introduce time-varying network models, which allow us to explicitly model such changes.

The difference between parameters that stay the same across time and time-varying parameters is illustrated in Figure 11.1, which displays the (lag-0) partial correlations of a hypothetical time-varying Gaussian graphical model (GGM) capturing the relationships between the variables 'anxious,' 'worried,' and 'irritated' at the same time point in a time series over 100 days. The top panel displays the partial correlations as a function of time. We see that the partial correlation between 'anxious' and 'worried' is 0.4 at the beginning of the time series and monotonically decreases to zero at the end of the time series. In contrast, the partial correlations between 'worried' and 'irritated,' and 'anxious' and 'irritated,' are constant (0.2 and 0) across the entire time series.

Cite this chapter as:

Haslbeck, J. M. B., Ryan, O., van der Maas, H. L. J., & Waldorp, L. J. (2022). Chapter 11. Modeling change in networks. In Isvoranu, A. M., Epskamp, S., Waldorp, L. J., & Borsboom, D. (Eds.). *Network psychometrics with R: A guide for behavioral and social scientists*. Routledge, Taylor & Francis Group.

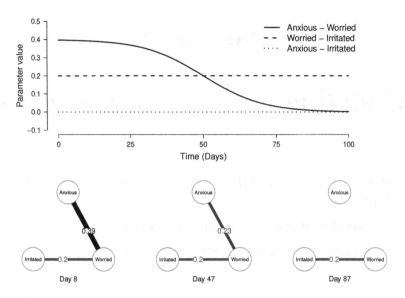

Figure 11.1. Illustration of a time-varying network model over a time period of 100 days. Top panel: The partial correlations between the three variables 'anxious,' 'worried,' and 'irritated' as a function of time. Lower panel: The corresponding partial correlation networks at days 8, 47, and 87.

The lower panel of Figure 11.1 displays the corresponding partial correlation networks on day 8, 47, and 87. Consistent with the top panel, the partial correlation between 'anxious' and 'worried' decreases over the course of the time series, while the other two partial correlations stay the same. This shows that not every parameter in a time-varying model needs to change across time. If the parameters of a model do not change across time, the model is often referred to as a stationary model.[1] Note that in Figure 11.1 we only displayed the three partial correlations as a function of time, and no other parameters of the GGM.

Time-varying analyses are relevant when we are interested in change within an individual. For example, take the transition of an individual into a state in which they are diagnosed with a mental disorder. From the network perspective of psychopathology mental disorders arise from direct interactions between symptoms and vulnerability is closely connected to the nature of these interactions (Borsboom, 2017). For example, it has been suggested that more dense symptom networks are associated with depression diagnoses (e.g., see Cramer et al., 2016; Pe et al., 2015; van Borkulo et al., 2015, but also see Schweren et al., 2018). If this was true, we would expect that the density (or global

---

[1]Technically, a process is stationary if its moments are the same in all parts of the time series. There are some cases in which the parameters of a model do not change across time, but the moments of the distribution are not stationary. An example is a vector auto-regressive (VAR) process with eigenvalues outside the limit circle. However, for the cases discussed in this chapter, non-time-varying parameters and stationarity can be used interchangeably.

strength) of individual symptom networks tends to increase when transitioning from a healthy state to a state with a diagnosis. This prediction could be tested with time-varying models. Time-varying models can also be used to study the impact of unplanned or planned events, such as negative life events or interventions. In addition, time-varying models are central to early warning signals (EWS) of critical transitions, which may allow one to anticipate transitions in alternative states (van de Leemput et al., 2014, however, also see Dablander et al., 2021). The methods to detect EWS currently used in the literature are typically based on univariate measures such as variances and autocorrelations. However, most systems of interest consist of several variables. Time-varying models are the natural multivariate extension of such EWS detection procedures.

Other instructive examples come from the field of developmental psychology. It is possible that a developmental transition, say from non-conserver to conserver as measured by Piaget's conservation task, is solely a change in state and not in the underlying network structure, but developmental theory usually expects that such changes are accompanied by structural changes in the relations between variables. In Dolan and van der Maas (1998) and Schmittmann et al. (2005) it has been shown, with the fit of mixture factor and latent Markov models, that the correlation structure in answers to conservation anticipation items is qualitatively different between non-conservers and conservers. Similar changes in the correlations can be expected for other Piagetian tasks such as the balance scale task (van der Maas & Jansen, 2003). Another example are dyadic interactions such as between parent and child. Such interactions are sometimes time varying (Bringmann et al., 2018). It is interesting to note that the mutualism network model of general intelligence (van der Maas et al., 2006) is a developmental model in which the relations between nodes (cognitive functions) are not varying over time. The main reason for this was that time-invariant relations were sufficient to explain the positive manifold, the main phenomenon to be explained in intelligence research. A newly proposed network model of intelligence is time-varying as it models intelligence as growing networks (Savi et al., 2019).

On a more abstract level, time-varying models allow one to capture the variability of parameters across time. This is important even if the time-varying parameters are initially not related to any events or covariates, because variability is an empirical fact that needs to be explained by a formal theory explaining the phenomenon at hand (Borsboom et al., 2021; Haslbeck, Ryan, et al., 2021). For example, if the relation between 'anxious' and 'worried' fluctuates significantly in depressed individuals, a theory about anxiety and worrying in depressed individuals would need to account for these fluctuations.

11.2 Time-varying network models

A time-varying model is a model that includes parameters that vary across time. This means that we can turn any of the stationary models discussed in the previous chapters such as GGMs, Ising models, mixed graphical models (MGMs) or VAR models into a time-varying model by making its parameters a function of time. For example, for the case of the GGM used above, we would give both the mean vector μ_t and the partial correlation matrix Ω_t an index for time, where t is an ordered variable capturing the time from the start until the end of the time series. That way, we obtain a time-varying

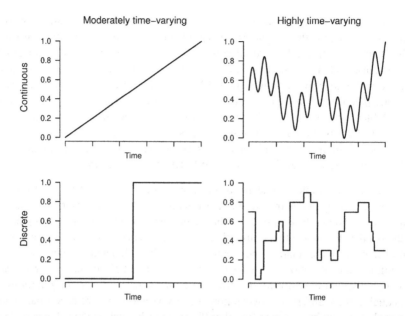

Figure 11.2. Examples of time-varying parameter functions. Top left: moderately time-varying linear function; top right: highly time-varying continuous function; bottom right: highly time-varying step function; bottom left: moderately time-varying function of discrete jumps (with multiple states). The value of the time-varying parameter is on the y-axis.

Gaussian distribution. In such a time-varying network model, each parameter can depend on time in a different way. Some parameters may be constant across time, as we have seen in the example in Figure 11.1, and others may vary in various ways across time. While a time-varying network model always consists of many (time-varying) parameters, we will now focus our discussion on a single parameter. This parameter could be a time-varying partial correlation or mean in a GGM, a time-varying autoregressive or cross-lagged effect in a VAR model, or a time-varying interaction between categorical variables in an MGM. Of course, there is an infinite number of ways in which a parameter can be a function of time. However, in order to develop some intuition for which time-varying models are easier or harder to estimate, we consider four illustrative examples in Figure 11.2 along two dimensions: first, whether the change is continuous (first row) or not (second row), and little change (first column) versus a lot of change (second column) across time.

The top left panel of Figure 11.2 shows a time-varying parameter that is linearly increasing over time, which is the simplest possible time-varying continuous function. But the parameter does not have to follow some simple function. The top right panel displays a parameter that also changes continuously across time, however, this parameter exhibits more change within a particular time interval. Parameters do not have to change continuously, however, but could instead jump between discrete states. The bottom left panel illustrates the simplest case of this type of time-varying model: the parameter stays the same for the first half of the time series, and then jumps to a new value, and remains there for the rest of the time series. Similarly to the continuous case, there can be many more discrete jumps giving rise to a highly time-varying parameter (see bottom right panel). Of course, the true time-varying model could also be a combination of continuous changes and discrete jumps. One's beliefs about whether the changes in parameters across time are best described by continuous or step-functions are important, because they will inform the type of method to be used to estimate the time-varying model. We will return to this question in the next section.

When estimating stationary models, for example a VAR model, a common strategy to obtain more stable estimates is to collect data for a longer period of time, for example three instead of two weeks. However, this strategy does not work for a time-varying model. If we are interested in how the parameters of the VAR model evolve during the first two weeks, then adding a third week does not help. Instead, we need to make sure that enough measurements are available *within* the first two weeks, that is, that the measurement frequency is high enough. How high the sampling frequency needs to be in the interval of interest depends on the form of the time-varying parameters. The simpler time-varying functions on the left of Figure 11.2 require fewer observations than estimating the more complex ones on the right. The exact way to determine how many observations are necessary to estimate the time-varying model with a given accuracy depends on the estimation method at hand. However, across methods the measurements need to be frequent enough to closely follow how the parameter changes across time. For example, it makes sense intuitively that no estimation method can capture the highly time-varying functions in the right panels of Figure 11.2 if there are only a handful of measurements available.

11.3 Estimating time-varying network models

To estimate time-varying network models, we need to make assumptions about how parameters vary across time. This typically involves assuming either that parameters change as a continuous function of time, or that the parameters are piece-wise constant functions across time (see Figure 11.2). If one had infinite data, this choice would not matter too much, because both classes of functions could approximate any function arbitrarily well. However, when estimating time-varying models from empirical data, the choice of assumption makes a big difference. For example, piece-wise constant functions will do poorly in approximating linear relationships, and continuous functions will be a poor approximation of discrete jumps. The choice of assumption therefore has to be carefully considered and should be based on knowledge about the studied phenomenon, either from previous analyses or from theoretical expectations. For example, body weight is probably changing continuously, while the type of errors in a developmental psychology task might jump from one state to another, when a child advances to a new strategy. In the remainder of this section we discuss how a time-varying model could be estimated under these two assumptions.

Methods assuming continuous change

Perhaps the most straightforward method to estimate a time-varying network model with continuously changing parameters is to use a moving window approach. These types of methods move a window with a certain width through the time series and estimate a stationary model in each of the windows. This way one obtains a number of 'local' models throughout the time series which together constitute a time-varying model. Typically, however, one does not use a fixed window, but rather uses all data points for the estimation of all local models and weighs them differently depending on how far away they are from the current 'local' model (e.g., Kolar et al., 2010; Zhou et al., 2010). The key parameter in this method is the width (or bandwidth) of the kernel-function that determines the weights for each data point for a given 'local' model. Similar to the window width in the moving window approach, if the bandwidth is high, many observations around to the time point at which we estimate the model receive a high weight. This has the upside that we use more data and the estimates are less affected by sampling variance. However, it has the downside that we have less sensitivity to detect variations in parameters over time, since we aggregate larger parts of the time series together. Conversely, a low bandwidth offers a high sensitivity to detecting variations in parameters over time, however, the estimates will be affected more by sampling variance. It is thus important to strike a good balance between the two by selecting an appropriate bandwidth parameter for a given time series. Note that selecting an extremely large bandwidth will not allow any variation of parameters across time. Therefore, determining an appropriate bandwidth can also be seen as determining how time-varying (if at all) the parameters of the data generating model are. For a detailed explanation of this method we refer the reader to Haslbeck and Waldorp (2020) and Haslbeck, Bringmann, et al. (2021). Selecting the bandwidth is a model selection problem, which can be tackled with information criteria or data-driven approaches such as cross-validation (see also Chapter 7).

Another approach based on the assumption of continuity is to use a parametric model to explicitly model the time-varying parameters as a function of time. In order to allow for sufficient flexibility, this can be done using the generalized additive modeling (GAM) framework (Wood, 2006). This approach is easiest to imagine for a univariate model consisting only of a single intercept (here the mean of a variable). The GAM-based approach then finds the combination of functions that best fits the time-varying mean of this univariate time series. This idea can be extended to network models including several variables and interaction parameters. Bringmann et al. (2017) used this approach to estimate VAR models. Similar to the bandwidth in the kernel-method described above, the GAM-based method also requires a model selection procedure to determine the extent to which the parameters are time-varying. In this method, this is achieved by a penalized likelihood approach (Wood, 2006), in which increased complexity of the time-varying functions leads to a higher penalty. The penalty parameter in this procedure is selected using generalized cross-validation (Golub et al., 1979). Haslbeck, Bringmann, et al. (2021) provide an overview of the kernel-method and the GAM-based method, including a simulation study evaluating their performance in estimating time-varying VAR models in situations that are typical for psychological research.

Yet another way of estimating time-varying parameters using the assumption of continuity is by using the fused lasso (Hastie et al., 2015), which puts a penalty on differences in parameters in subsequent time points. This approach is implemented for the GGM in the SINGLE algorithm (Monti et al., 2014; Monti, 2014), and Gibbert (2017) provides an implementation of the (group) fused-lasso based method as presented by Gibberd and Nelson (2017).

If all parameters in the true time-varying model are continuous functions of time, and if we have enough measurements in the time interval of interest, we can estimate the time-varying model consistently (Robinson, 1989). However, if the time-varying parameters in the true model exhibit discrete jumps, the above methods will estimate the model incorrectly around those jumps. Thus, if we expect that the parameters are largely changing in discrete jumps across time, we should use this as our assumption to estimate the time-varying model.

Methods assuming discrete change

Many methods that model time-varying parameters which change in a discrete way over time do so using a discrete-valued 'state' or 'regime' variable. The simplest case is when we have an a-priori expectation that changes in parameter values will coincide with changes in the value of some observed (time-varying) variable. For instance, Bringmann et al. (2013) use a multilevel VAR model to analyze experience sampling data collected both before and after participants take part in a treatment program. To test whether the parameters of the VAR network change after treatment, they created a dummy state variable indicating whether observations were pre- or post-treatment, and include this as a moderator in their VAR model. If the regression coefficients for any of the dummy product terms are non-zero, then we have modeled a discrete change in those parameter values. Of course this general procedure can be extended to include multiple different states (for example, each with its own dummy variable).

The more general case is when we are unsure when or if a discrete change in parameters occurs over our window of observation. Although these methods are a little bit more complex than above, they typically also involve modeling a time-varying discrete 'state.' One popular class of models used for this purpose are hidden Markov models (HMM, e.g., Zucchini et al., 2017). HMMs model a system which changes between multiple states (also known as *components*), each with its own set of parameters, but where the state variable is unobserved and must be inferred from the data. As well as obtaining the parameters which describe the K different states, HMMs yield a simple so-called *Markov* model of how the state-switching behavior evolves over time in the form of transition probabilities, specifying how probable it is to switch from one state to the other (or remain at the current state) at the next time point. This allows one to obtain a time-varying model of the form displayed in the bottom row of Figure 11.2. In the classic form of the model, the HMM components represent Gaussian distributions, with each component having a potentially different (and so, time-varying) mean and covariance matrix. The HMM has also been extended such that the components themselves are time series models, often known as *Markov-Switching* time series models (Chow et al., 2018; Hamaker et al., 2010, 2016; Lu et al., 2019).

In the time series literature, models whose parameters change in a discrete fashion over time are often referred to as *regime-switching models* (Hamilton, 1989; Kim & Nelson, 1999) and this class of models includes many different ways of modeling the unobserved state/regime variable. One simple but popular method is to model the state of the system as determined by a threshold variable: the parameters of the time series model change in a discrete manner depending on whether the threshold variable falls above or below a threshold value at a given point in time (Tong & Lim, 1980). The threshold variable itself can be anything but must be specified by the researcher, while the threshold value is estimated from the data. Haslbeck, Ryan, et al. (2021) illustrate the application of threshold-VAR models to estimate time-varying VAR networks, where the threshold variable is one of the four variables included in the VAR model itself. See also Hamaker et al. (2010).

The appropriateness of these models depends on the assumptions we are willing to make about the mechanisms by which the parameters of our network model change over time. For example, threshold-based regime-switching models may be most appropriate when the researcher has some knowledge about which variable(s) determine the state of the system, or when sufficient data are available to reliably test multiple alternatives. HMMs and Markov-Switching models may be more appropriate when we believe the state-switching behavior to be governed by an unobserved variable, or by some unknown function of the observed variables. For an extended discussion and illustrative comparison of univariate HMM and threshold-based models fit to psychological time series data, we refer readers to Hamaker et al. (2010, 2016). Although many of the approaches mentioned here were originally developed for single-subject data, many multiple-subjects and multilevel extensions to these models also exist (Asparouhov et al., 2017; Chow et al., 2018; De Haan-Rietdijk et al., 2016; Ou et al., 2019).

Testing stationary vs. time-varying models

All method discussed above have some sort of mechanism built in that selects an optimal level of variation of parameters across time. The kernel-based approach accomplishes that by using a bandwidth that controls to what extent parameters can vary across time, and selects this hypertuningparameter with a cross-validation scheme. The GAM-based approach uses penalty for more complex models (i.e., more time-varying parameters), and selects the hypertuningparameter for this penalty using generalized cross-validation. And in the case of HMMs we perform model selection between different numbers of components, for example, using an information criterion.

In some situations, one might be interested in performing a formal test of whether a parameter or an entire model is stationary or time-varying. In the GAM-based method, it is possible to perform a significance test on individual parameters, however, there is no global test. For the HMMs, one selects the number of components, often with an information criterion like the Bayesian Information Criterion (BIC, Schwarz et al., 1978). If a single component is selected, we conclude that the time series is stationary, if there are two or more components, we conclude that it is time-varying. For all methods, including the kernel-based method, one can perform a hypothesis test on single parameters or the entire model with the null hypothesis that the population model is stationary. The sampling distribution under the null hypothesis can be constructed by repeatedly reshuffling the ordering of the data and estimate time-varying networks on them.

11.4 Estimating time-varying GGMs from time series of mood measurements

We now apply the ideas from above to estimate a time-varying network model on a time series of a single individual. We use a time series that contains a large variety of measurements of psychological, contextual, and symptom variables on 1,476 occasions on 238 consecutive days with up to ten measurements on each day. The measurements were taken from an individual diagnosed with major depression during a double-blind medication reduction period, which took place in two steps (day 42 and 98). To keep the present illustration simple, we focus on the six mood-related variables 'anxious,' 'lonely,' 'ashamed,' 'guilty,' 'worried,' and 'irritated,' which were measured on a 7-point Likert scale. For further details on this time series, see Kossakowski et al. (2017).

The goal of the analysis is to explore how the dependencies between variables change over the course of the time series. Similar to the example in the introduction, we are interested in the pairwise relations between variables at the same time point and how these relations may change over time. In addition, we assume that those relations are linear and that treating the ordered categorical variables as continuous will not distort the relationships between variables too much. Consequently, we can use the multivariate Gaussian distribution as our network model and therefore need a method that allows one to estimate a time-varying Gaussian distribution. In the interest of keeping the example simple, we model the time-varying lag-0 relationships between variables with a time-varying Gaussian distributions. However, for the reasons outlined in Chapter 9, it may often be advantageous to decompose the lag-0 relationships in temporal and contemporaneous relationships, for example with the graphical VAR (GVAR) model and the method presented here also works for the GVAR model.

As discussed in Section 11.3, the way in which parameters change over time can take many forms, and the estimation method should match our expectations about this form. In the present exploratory analysis, however, we have no expectations about the functional form and we choose a method that allows us to estimate parameters as continuous functions of time. Specifically, we choose the kernel-based method described in Section 11.3 which obtains a time-varying model by estimating a series of 'local' models across the time series. As discussed above, this method requires us to specify a bandwidth which we here set to 0.1. In addition, we provide the time stamps of all measurements, which allows us to take unequal intervals of measurements into account. We estimate the model using an unregularized nodewise regression scheme that combines estimates by averaging them, and we standardize all variables such that the final estimates can be interpreted as partial correlations (for details see Haslbeck & Waldorp, 2020). Finally we need to specify the number of local models to be estimated across the time series. The larger the number of local models, the more similar adjacent local models will be, and the only downside of choosing more is that estimation takes longer. Here, we choose 30

local models. Consequently, the estimated time-varying Gaussian distribution consists of
$6(6-1)/2 \times 30 = 450$ partial correlations and 6×30 intercepts. The large numbers of
parameters in time-varying models make it challenging to report all of them, which means
that in practice one only reports the parameters that are of central interest. However,
for the purpose of illustration, we consider several different visualizations. The Tutorial
Box 11.1 shows how to estimate this model using the R-package *mgm*.

The time-varying Gaussian graphical model (GGM) was estimated with the function
tvmgm() from the R-package *mgm*:

```
library("mgm")
output <- tvmgm(data = data,
               type = rep("g", 8),
               level = rep(1, 8),
               timepoints = timestamps,
               estpoints = seq(0, 1, length=30),
               bandwidth = 0.1,
               lambdaSeq = 0,
               threshold="none")
```

Next to the data, tvmgm() requires specification of the types of variables (here we create a
vector with eight times "g" for our eight Gaussian variables) and the number of categories
for each variable in case they are categorical. For continuous variables the number of
categories is defined by convention as 1. This specification is necessary, because tvmgm()
is also able to estimate time-varying models involving mixed variables.

Next, we specify the time stamps of each measurement in the data matrix via the
timepoints argument. If this argument is not provided, the estimation algorithm assumes equidistant measurements. This is used by the weighting function to make sure that
the time scale of the measurements corresponds to the time scale of the time-varying model.
This can be a problem, for example, if a time series spans over a few weeks, but in one week
measurements are missing for a few days. Next, we specify the estimation points with the
estpoints argument as 30 points from the beginning (0) to the end (1) of the time series.

The argument bandwidth specifies the bandwidth parameter that should be used for estimation. Here, we specify the parameter to 0.1, however, in practice it should be selected using
model selection. This can be done with the cross-validation scheme implemented in the
function bwSelect(), which takes the same input as tvmgm() plus a sequence of candidate
bandwidth values and specifications for the cross-validation scheme.

Finally, lambdaSeq = 0 specifies that the estimation should be unregularized, and that no
additional thresholding should be performed on the estimates (threshold="none").

Tutorial Box 11.1. Estimating time-varying GGM using the kernel-weighting method assuming
continuously time-varying parameters.

A natural choice of presenting the estimates in the network context would be to visualize the parameters of the time-varying Gaussian distribution by displaying its partial correlation matrix at different points in the time series. Figure 11.3 displays those networks at days 32, 66, 151, and 194 of the time series spanning 238 days.

Inspecting the partial correlations at those four time points shows us that the networks are changing across time and that different parameters seem to be changing more than others. For example, the partial correlation between 'anxious' and 'guilty' is relatively stable at around 0.40 and the partial correlation between 'lonely' and 'irritated' is relatively stable around 0. On the other hand, the partial correlation between 'anxious' and 'ashamed' is

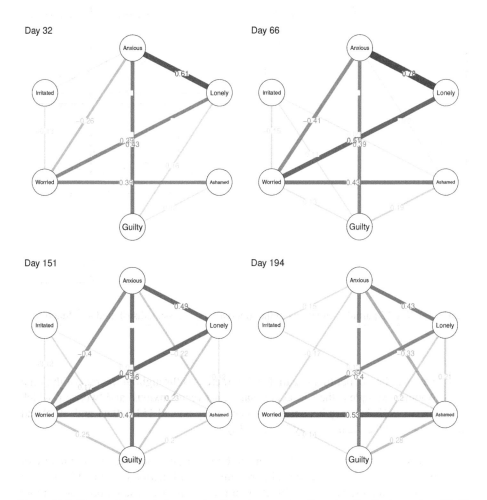

Figure 11.3. The partial correlation matrix of the time-varying Gaussian distribution at days 32, 66, 151 and 194 in the time series spanning 238 days. Blue edges indicate positive partial correlations, red edges indicate negative partial correlations, and the width of edges is a function of the absolute value of the partial correlation.

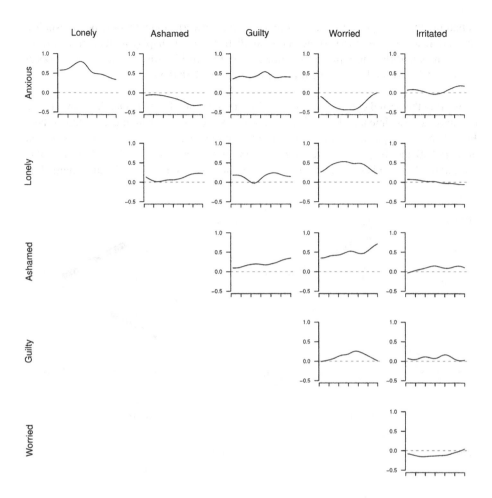

Figure 11.4. The 15 partial correlations in the time-varying Gaussian distributed as a function of time.

close to zero at day 32 but this negative effect increases throughout the rest of the time series. Another example is the partial correlation between 'anxious' and 'worried' which is −0.26 on day 32, but then becomes stronger on day 66 and 151 (−0.41 and −0.4) and then becomes weaker again on day 194 (−0.33).

An alternative visualization that allows one to better inspect the time-varying nature of single parameters is to plot the partial correlations as a function of time. Figure 11.4 displays all partial correlations as a function of time. This visualization provides a more complete view of the time-varying model since it displays all its parameters except the time-varying intercepts. Consistent with the visualization in Figure 11.3 we see that the partial correlation between 'anxious' and 'guilty' stays largely the same, however, we now also see that the partial correlation increase up to 0.50, which we might have missed when only inspecting the four network snapshots. Similarly, we get a better picture of the U-shaped function in which the partial correlation between 'anxious' and 'worried' changes across time.

Finally, Figure 11.5 displays the six time-varying intercepts of the model. We see that the intercepts of 'anxious,' 'lonely,' 'ashamed,' and 'guilty' stay largely the same across the time series. The intercepts of 'worried' and 'irritated,' however, seem to be increasing.

How could these types of results be interesting for empirical research? First of all, the time-varying analysis established that there is some variation in parameters across time, and that this variation differs across parameters. In a second step, we can go about explaining this variation. This could be done by relating changes in parameters to additional observational variables, for example capturing changes in the social or work environment of the individual. Another possible way to explain changes in parameters are interventions, as in the present case with the double-blind medication reduction scheme.

In this application we kept the analysis as simple as possible to focus on the estimation, visualization and interpretation of time-varying parameters. In this process we ignored several crucial questions, such as whether a partial correlation at a given point in time is actually different from zero in the population or only different from zero due to sampling variation. As in non-time-varying analyses, this problem can be addressed by performing significance tests or by using regularization (for details see Haslbeck & Waldorp, 2020). Another question we ignored is how to select the bandwidth parameter which controls how time-varying parameters can be. One way to select the bandwidth is to use a cross-validation scheme in which time-varying models are fit on training sets and their prediction errors are evaluated on hold out sets. Related to the selection of the bandwidth parameter is the question of whether the entire model or individual parameters

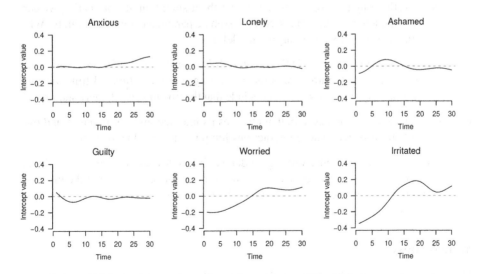

Figure 11.5. The six intercepts in the time-varying Gaussian as a function of time.

are actually time-varying in the population, or whether the observed time-varyingness is merely a function of sampling variation. For the method used here, these questions can be answered by a hypothesis test that simulates data under the null hypothesis that the model is stationary.

11.5   Conclusion

In this chapter we considered time-varying network models, which are models in which parameters can change across time. These models are always relevant when we are interested in how individuals change across time based on intensive longitudinal data. We discussed the difficulties involved in estimating time-varying models and presented a number of estimation methods that make different assumptions about the way in which the parameters change across time. Finally, we illustrated the use of time-varying network models by estimating a time-varying GGM to a $N = 1$ time series of mood measurements.

11.6   Exercises

Conceptual

11.1. I am fitting a stationary VAR model to experience sampling method (ESM) data collected over three weeks, which requires the assumption that the data generating mechanism is also stationary over those three weeks. Now I add measurements of another two weeks to obtain more stable estimates. How does this affect the assumption of stationary? Does this assumption become stronger, weaker, or is it unaffected by adding time points from subsequent weeks?

11.2. When estimating time series models under the assumption of stationarity, we can increase the length of the time series to estimate parameters more accurately. Why does this not work for time-varying models?

11.3. I estimate a time-varying VAR model with five variables and 50 observations. I obtain a high bandwidth parameter, indicating that the estimated time-varying model is largely stationary. Can I conclude that the true model is largely stationary?

11.4. Give an example for a system that changes its interactions continuously, and one example for a system whose interactions jump from one value to another.

11.5. Assume that the true time-varying model exhibits a discrete jump in the middle of the time series. Now, you estimate the time-varying model with one of the methods assuming continuous change. Describe the error you expect from this estimation procedure.

True or false

11.6. Increasing the window width in the moving-window approach increases the sensitivity to detect time-varying parameters.

11.7. The time-varying GAM method uses a weighting approach to estimate time-varying parameters.

11.8. A HMM with a single component is a stationary model.

11.9. In a time-varying model, all parameters are time-varying.

11.10. The bandwidth parameter in the kernel-weighting method can be selected using cross-validation.

References

Asparouhov, T., Hamaker, E. L., & Muthén, B. (2017). Dynamic latent class analysis. *Structural Equation Modeling: A Multidisciplinary Journal, 24*(2), 257–269.

Borsboom, D. (2017). A network theory of mental disorders. *World Psychiatry, 16*(1), 5–13.

Borsboom, D., van der Maas, H. L. J., Dalege, J., Kievit, R. A., & Haig, B. D. (2021). Theory construction methodology: A practical framework for building theories in psychology. *Perspectives on Psychological Science, 16*(4), 756–766.

Bringmann, L. F., Ferrer, E., Hamaker, E. L., Borsboom, D., & Tuerlinckx, F. (2018). Modeling nonstationary emotion dynamics in dyads using a time-varying vector-autoregressive model. *Multivariate Behavioral Research, 53*(3), 293–314.

Bringmann, L. F., Hamaker, E. L., Vigo, D. E., Aubert, A., Borsboom, D., & Tuerlinckx, F. (2017). Changing dynamics: Time-varying autoregressive models using generalized additive modeling. *Psychological Methods, 22*(3), 409–425.

Bringmann, L. F., Vissers, N., Wichers, M., Geschwind, N., Kuppens, P., Peeters, F., Borsboom, D., & Tuerlinckx, F. (2013). A network approach to psychopathology: New insights into clinical longitudinal data. *PLoS One, 8*(4), e60188.

Chow, S.-M., Ou, L., Ciptadi, A., Prince, E. B., You, D., Hunter, M. D., Rehg, J. M., Rozga, A., & Messinger, D. S. (2018). Representing sudden shifts in intensive dyadic interaction data using differential equation models with regime switching. *Psychometrika, 83*(2), 476–510.

Cramer, A. O. J., van Borkulo, C. D., Giltay, E. J., van der Maas, H. L. J., Kendler, K. S., Scheffer, M., & Borsboom, D. (2016). Major depression as a complex dynamic system. *PLoS One, 11*(12), e0167490.

Dablander, F., Pichler, A., Cika, A., & Bacilieri, A. (2021). Anticipating critical transitions in psychological systems using early warning signals: Theoretical and practical considerations. *Psychological Methods.* https://doi.org/10.1037/met0000450

De Haan-Rietdijk, S., Gottman, J. M., Bergeman, C. S., & Hamaker, E. L. (2016). Get over it! a multilevel threshold autoregressive model for state-dependent affect regulation. *Psychometrika, 81*(1), 217–241.

Dolan, C. V., & van der Maas, H. L. J. (1998). Fitting multivariage normal finite mixtures subject to structural equation modeling. *Psychometrika, 63*(3), 227–253.

Gibberd, A. J., & Nelson, J. D. B. (2017). Regularized estimation of piecewise constant Gaussian graphical models: The group-fused graphical lasso. *Journal of Computational and Graphical Statistics, 26*(3), 623–634.

Gibbert, A. (2017). Graphtime. GitHub. https://github.com/GlooperLabs/GraphTime

Golub, G. H., Heath, M., & Wahba, G. (1979). Generalized cross-validation as a method for choosing a good ridge parameter. *Technometrics, 21*(2), 215–223.

Hamaker, E. L., Grasman, R. P. P. P., & Kamphuis, J. H. (2010). Regime-switching models to study psychological processes. In P. C. M. Molenaar & K. M. Newell (Eds.), *Individual pathways of change: Statistical models for analyzing learning and development* (pp. 155–168). American Psychological Association.

Hamaker, E. L., Grasman, R. P., & Kamphuis, J. H. (2016). Modeling BAS dysregulation in bipolar disorder: Illustrating the potential of time series analysis. *Assessment, 23*(4), 436–446.

Hamilton, J. D. (1989). A new approach to the economic analysis of nonstationary time series and the business cycle. *Econometrica: Journal of the Econometric Society, 57*(2), 357–384.

Haslbeck, J. M. B., Bringmann, L. F., & Waldorp, L. J. (2021). A tutorial on estimating time-varying vector autoregressive models. *Multivariate Behavioral Research, 56*(1), 120–149.

Haslbeck, J. M. B., Ryan, O., Robinaugh, D. J., Waldorp, L., & Borsboom, D. (2021). Modeling psychopathology: From data models to formal theories. *Psychological Methods*. https://doi.org/10.1037/met0000303

Haslbeck, J. M. B., & Waldorp, L. J. (2020). mgm: Estimating time-varying mixed graphical models in high-dimensional data. *Journal of Statistical Software, 93*(8).

Hastie, T., Tibshirani, R., & Wainwright, M. J. (2015). *Statistical learning with sparsity: The lasso and generalizations.* Taylor & Francis.

Kim, C.-J., & Nelson, C. R. (1999). *State-space models with regime switching: Classical and Gibbs-sampling approaches with applications.* The MIT press.

Kolar, M., Song, L., Ahmed, A., Xing, E. P., et al. (2010). Estimating time-varying networks. *Annals of Applied Statistics, 4*(1), 94–123.

Kossakowski, J., Groot, P., Haslbeck, J. M. B., Borsboom, D., & Wichers, M. (2017). Data from 'critical slowing down as a personalized early warning signal for depression'. *Journal of Open Psychology Data, 5*(1), 1.

Lu, Z.-H., Chow, S.-M., Ram, N., & Cole, P. M. (2019). Zero-inflated regime-switching stochastic differential equation models for highly unbalanced multivariate, multi-subject time-series data. *Psychometrika, 84*(2), 611–645.

Monti, R. P., Hellyer, P., Sharp, D., Leech, R., Anagnostopoulos, C., & Montana, G. (2014). Estimating time-varying brain connectivity networks from functional MRI time series. *Neuroimage, 103*, 427–443.

Monti, R. (2014). pySINGLE. GitHub. github.com/piomonti/pySINGLE

Ou, L., Hunter, M. D., & Chow, S.-M. (2019). What's for dynr: A package for linear and nonlinear dynamic modeling in R. *R Journal, 11*(1), 91–111.

Pe, M. L., Kircanski, K., Thompson, R. J., Bringmann, L. F., Tuerlinckx, F., Mestdagh, M., Mata, J., Jaeggi, S. M., Buschkuehl, M., Jonides, J., et al. (2015). Emotion-network density in major depressive disorder. *Clinical Psychological Science, 3*(2), 292–300.

Robinson, P. M. (1989). Nonparametric estimation of time-varying parameters. In H. P. (Ed.), *Statistical analysis and forecasting of economic structural change* (pp. 253–264). Springer.

Savi, A. O., Marsman, M., van der Maas, H. L. J., & Maris, G. K. J. (2019). The wiring of intelligence. *Perspectives on Psychological Science, 16*(6), 1034–1061.

Schmittmann, V. D., Dolan, C. V., van der Maas, H. L. J., & Neale, M. C. (2005). Discrete latent Markov models for normally distributed response data. *Multivariate Behavioral Research, 40*(4), 461–488.

Schwarz, G. et al. (1978). Estimating the dimension of a model. *The Annals of Statistics, 6*(2), 461–464.

Schweren, L., van Borkulo, C. D., Fried, E. I., & Goodyer, I. M. (2018). Assessment of symptom network density as a prognostic marker of treatment response in adolescent depression. *JAMA Psychiatry, 75*(1), 98–100.

Tong, H., & Lim, K. (1980). Threshold autoregression, limit cycles and cyclical data. *Journal of the Royal Statistical Society. Series B (Methodological), 42*(3), 245–292.

van Borkulo, C. D., Boschloo, L., Borsboom, D., Penninx, B. W. J. H., Waldorp, L. J., & Schoevers, R. A. (2015). Association of symptom network structure with the course of depression. *JAMA Psychiatry, 72*(12), 1219–1226.

van de Leemput, I. A., Wichers, M., Cramer, A. O. J., Borsboom, D., Tuerlinckx, F., Kuppens, P., van Nes, E. H., Viechtbauer, W., Giltay, E. J., Aggen, S. H., Derom, C., Jacobs, N., Kendler, K. S., van der Maas, H. L. J., Neale, M. C., Peeters, F., Thiery, E., Zachar, P., & Scheffer, M. (2014). Critical slowing down as early warning for the onset and termination of depression. *Proceedings of the National Academy of Sciences, 111*(1), 87–92.

van der Maas, H. L. J., Dolan, C. V., Grasman, R. P., Wicherts, J. M., Huizenga, H. M., & Raijmakers, M. E. (2006). A dynamical model of general intelligence: The positive manifold of intelligence by mutualism. *Psychological Review, 113*(4), 842–861.

van der Maas, H. L. J., & Jansen, B. R. J. (2003). What response times tell of children's behavior on the balance scale task. *Journal of Experimental Child Psychology, 85*(2), 141–177.

Wood, S. N. (2006). *Generalized additive models: An introduction with R*. Chapman; Hall/CRC.

Zhou, S., Lafferty, J., & Wasserman, L. (2010). Time varying undirected graphs. *Machine Learning, 80*(2), 295–319.

Zucchini, W., MacDonald, I. L., & Langrock, R. (2017). *Hidden Markov models for time series: An introduction using R*. CRC press.

Part IV

Theory and Causality

Chapter 12

Causal Inference

Fabian Dablander[1] & Riet van Bork[2]

1. University of Amsterdam, Department of Psychology

2. University of Pittsburgh, Center for Philosophy of Science

12.1 Introduction

> *"The philosophers have only interpreted the world in various ways;*
> *the point, however, is to change it."*
>
> —Karl Marx

The statistical techniques you encounter throughout this book allow us to shed light on the web of associations between a set of variables. They help us interpret the world, allowing us to make statements such as "people with high levels of X are likely to also show high levels of Y." But, as Karl Marx put it, our goal is not to merely interpret the world—we also want to change it.

Causal inference goes beyond statistical inference by modeling the outcome of interventions. Instead of restricting us to statements of associations, causal inference allows us to make statements such as "if we were to increase X, then people would show higher levels in Y." The royal road to such causal statements is a randomized experiment, a tool psychologists are intimately familiar with. However, experiments are often difficult to conduct, unethical, or impossible. Tools from the field of causal inference can help us understand under what conditions it is possible to draw causal conclusions from observational data.

Cite this chapter as:

Dablander, F., & van Bork, R. (2022). Chapter 12. Causal inference. In Isvoranu, A. M., Epskamp, S., Waldorp, L. J., & Borsboom, D. (Eds.). *Network psychometrics with R: A guide for behavioral and social scientists*. Routledge, Taylor & Francis Group.

Causal models provide an intermediate step between purely statistical models and mechanistic models. They go beyond associations by allowing us to answer questions about interventions, but they do not necessarily provide a mechanistic account of cause-effect relationships. For example, while a statistical model may tell us that smoking and lung cancer are associated in the population, a causal model may tell us that, if we were to increase the number of smokers, there would be a corresponding increase in the number of lung cancer patients in the population; a causal model does not necessarily, however, shed light on the mechanism by which smoking causes lung cancer.

Because causal models go beyond probabilistic associations in data, they are not fully constrained by them. In other words, there may exist many causal models that are consistent with the particular associations in the data. As this chapter will show, this added complexity complicates causal inference. In order to infer causality in non-experimental settings, strong assumptions are required. However, we ultimately want to uncover causal—not merely statistical—relationships between variables of interest, and making causal talk a taboo does not advance that goal (Grosz et al., 2020; Hernán, 2018). Instead, this chapter invites you to be explicit about the desire to uncover causal relations, and provides tools that can help you achieve it.

We hope that you will take away the following points from reading this chapter. First, as we explain in Section 12.2, formulating causal effects requires a language that goes beyond probabilistic associations. This makes clear that modeling for prediction and modeling for intervention are fundamentally different things. Second, using this language, you should be able to assess, given a causal model, whether a particular association between two variables is causal or spurious. This requires a link between causal and statistical relations, which is discussed in Section 12.3. Third, as discussed in Section 12.4, you should understand that causal inference from observational data is hard, and requires strong assumptions—but that it is also a brimming field with many important advances.

12.2   A language for expressing causal relations

The study of causality has a long history in philosophy. In this chapter, we focus on the interventionist account of causality, where causal effects are formalized as changes in the distribution of an outcome under different interventions (e.g., Hernán & Robins, 2020; Pearl, 2000; Peters et al., 2017). This is a probabilistic account, in which the cause (e.g., smoking) is not always followed by the effect (e.g., lung cancer), but does increase its probability.

The language of statistics can be used to express *probabilistic dependence* between variables. For example, the association between two random variables X and Y can be expressed using conditional probabilities: $P(Y \mid X = x) \neq P(Y)$ (i.e., the probability of Y conditional on the realization $X = x$ is different from the marginal probability of Y) implies that X and Y are associated. That is, learning that variable $X = x$ provides information about variable Y. While we expect an association between variables that are causally related (learning about the cause provides information about the effect), probabilistic dependence is not sufficient for a causal relation. Associations or correlations are symmetric, whereas causal relations are frequently asymmetric (X is a cause of Y but Y is not a cause of X). For example, $P(Y \mid X = x) \neq P(Y)$ cannot express that X is the cause of Y, because if $P(Y \mid X = x) \neq P(Y)$ then $P(X \mid Y = y) \neq P(X)$ and thus it would be impossible to express that X causes Y, but Y does *not* cause X.[1]

How, then, can we express causal relations? The graphical approach to causal inference, pioneered by Wright (1921) and developed into a full-fledged formal framework by Spirtes et al. (1993) and Pearl (2000), uses directed acyclic graphs (DAGs) to depict causal relations. A graph G is a mathematical object that consists of nodes and edges. In the case of DAGs, these edges are directed, and cycles are not allowed. We take our variables to be nodes in such a DAG, and we draw an arrow between two nodes if there is a direct causal relationship between them. That is, we write $X \rightarrow Y$ if X is a direct cause of Y. Whether $X \rightarrow Y$ or $Y \rightarrow X$ has consequences for the outcome of interventions. In particular, if $X \rightarrow Y$, then we expect that interventions on X change the distribution of Y. Conversely, we expect that interventions on Y *do not* change the distribution of X.

To formalize the notion of an intervention, Judea Pearl (2000) introduced the *do*-operator. The expression $P(Y \mid X = x)$ describes what values Y is likely to take if X *happened to be* x, and is known as an *observational* distribution. In contrast, the expression $P(Y \mid do(X = x))$ describes what values Y is likely to take if X *were set to* x, and is known as an *interventional* distribution. We say that X has a causal effect on Y if $P(Y \mid do(X = x)) \neq P(Y)$. In contrast to the observational setting we have discussed above, if $P(Y \mid do(X = x)) \neq P(Y)$ then it does not necessarily follow that $P(X \mid do(Y = y)) \neq P(X)$.

A key insight that follows from causal inference is that modeling with the goal of prediction is not the same as modeling with the goal of intervention. In other words, the fact that X correlates strongly with variable Y—and hence can be used to predict Y well—does not imply that if we intervene on X, Y changes. Figure 12.1 illustrates this difference by contrasting the DAG $X \rightarrow Y$ (top panels) with the DAG $Y \rightarrow X$ (bottom panels). As shown in the left panels, both DAGs generate the exact same data, and so in both cases X is a good predictor of Y: we know that if X happens to be high, Y will likely also be high—this is what a positive correlation entails. But, as the saying goes, correlation is not causation. If the data come from the causal DAG $X \rightarrow Y$, the distribution of the values that Y likely takes if X *happens to be* 2 (i.e., the observational distribution $P(Y \mid X = 2)$) is the same as the distribution of the values that Y likely takes if X *is set to* 2 (i.e., the interventional distribution $P(Y \mid do(X = 2))$; see the top right panel of Figure 12.1. In general, however, they are not the same. The bottom left panel in 12.1 shows the exact same data as in the top left panel (showing the same correlation), but generated from the DAG $Y \rightarrow X$. In this case, setting X to some value does not change the likely values of Y. The bottom right panel shows that, indeed, the observational distribution is not the same as the interventional distribution.

---

[1]More generally, probabilistic (in)dependence of a set of random variables refers to the factorization of their joint distribution. As also discussed in Chapter 5, X and Y are *independent* if $P(X, Y) = P(X)P(Y)$, which we write as $X \perp\!\!\!\perp Y$, and they are *dependent* if $P(X, Y) \neq P(X)P(Y)$, which we write as $X \not\!\perp\!\!\!\perp Y$ (Dawid, 1979). In case of dependence, it follows that $P(X, Y) = P(X \mid Y)P(Y) = P(Y \mid X)P(X)$, stressing again the symmetry of probabilistic associations.

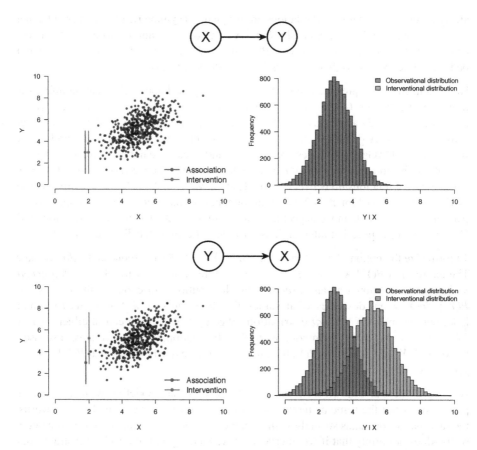

Figure 12.1. Top left: Data generated from the DAG $X \to Y$. The red point and line indicate the mean and 95% interval of the distribution of Y given that X *happens to be* 2. The blue point and line indicate the same quantities given that X *is set to* 2. Top right: The observational distribution equals the interventional distribution. Bottom left: The exact same data generated from the DAG $Y \to X$. Bottom right: The observational distribution and the interventional distribution differ.

This simple example shows that for two variables, observational data are insufficient to identify the causal direction: both the causal models $X \to Y$ and $Y \to X$ are able to generate the exact same data. However, if X and Y were statistically independent, we would be able to conclude that they are also causally independent. This hints at a deep relationship between statistical and causal dependence, which becomes more apparent from looking at more than two variables. We do this in the next section.

12.3   Statistical and causal relations

While correlation is not causation, causal relations do imply probabilistic associations. This is the core of Reichenbach's *common cause principle*, which underlies much of causal inference (Peters et al., 2017; Reichenbach, 1956). In Section 12.3, we discuss three fundamental causal graph structures and the probabilistic associations they imply. In Section 12.3, we discuss how to algorithmically derive such probabilistic associations for graphs of any size. In Section 12.3, we illustrate how these tools help us distinguish spurious (non-causal) from non-spurious (causal) associations in practice.

Three fundamental structures

Real-world systems are usually comprised of more than two variables. We complicate the picture slowly, adding a third variable Z. Suppose that we observe that X and Y are correlated. What causal models can bring about such a fact? In contrast to the scenario with only two variables X and Y, more possibilities should exist now. Indeed, Reichenbach's *common cause principle* states that, in addition to a direct causal relation between X and Y, the correlation between X and Y can be the result of a third variable Z that causes both X and Y (Reichenbach, 1956):

> If two random variables X and Y are statistically dependent ($X \not\perp Y$), then either (a) X causes Y, (b) Y causes X, or (c) there exists a third variable Z that causes both X and Y. Further, X and Y become independent given Z, i.e., $X \perp Y \mid Z$.

Option (a) implies that the underlying DAG has an arrow $X \to Y$ and / or an arrow $X \to Z \to Y$. Option (b) implies that the underlying DAG has an arrow $Y \to X$ and / or an arrow $Y \to Z \to X$. Option (c) implies that $X \leftarrow Z \to Y$, that is, Z is a common cause of both X and Y. The three variable graph structures in options (a) and (b) are known as a *chain*, while the graph structure in option (c) is known as a *common cause*. To understand the differences and similarities between these structures, the top left panel in Figure 12.2 shows a positive association between X and Y that could have been generated by three distinct DAGs. There are more DAGs that could have generated these data, but we focus on these three for now. The DAG $X \to Z \to Y$ could describe the fact that smoking cigarettes does not directly cause cancer (there is no direct arrow from X to Y), but that smoking X means inhalation of smoke that is full of cancer-causing substances such as tar Z that cause cancer Y. In the DAG $X \leftarrow Z \to Y$, Z is a confounder that explains the association between X and Y. For example, the positive association between the number of Nobel laureates per country (X) and the consumption of chocolate per capita in that country (Y) is likely due to a confounder Z such as economic development (Dablander, 2020; Messerli, 2012).

In all three DAGs, X and Y are *marginally dependent*, as shown in the top left panel in Figure 12.2. As before, we denote this as $X \not\perp Y$. In the context of our examples, this means that smoking (X) and cancer (Y) are associated, just as the number of Nobel laureates and the consumption of chocolate per capita are. For all three graphs, if we *condition* on the variable Z, X and Y become *conditionally independent*, as the top right panel in Figure 12.2 shows. We denote this as $X \perp Y \mid Z$. For example, if we look at the association between smoking and cancer in a population that inhales a substantial fixed amount of tar ($Z = 1$) *or* in a population that inhales no tar at all ($Z = 0$), then the association between smoking and cancer would vanish. This is because there is no variation in tar in the respective groups—it is a large but fixed amount in one group and zero in the other group— and so within these populations, variations in the amount of smoking (X) do not correspond to changes in tar intake, which would increase the chances of getting cancer (Y). Similarly, if we would look at countries with low ($Z = 0$) or high ($Z = 1$) economic development *separately*, the association between chocolate consumption and the number of Nobel laureates would vanish. While the causal role of Z is different in the DAGs—it plays a causal mediative role in the DAG $X \rightarrow Z \rightarrow Y$ but a confounding role in the DAG $X \leftarrow Z \rightarrow Y$—these DAGs imply the same (conditional) associations between variables, and we can therefore not distinguish between them using observational data. Note that, if there were a directed path from X to Y or from Y to X, then X and Y would be associated even after conditioning on Z.

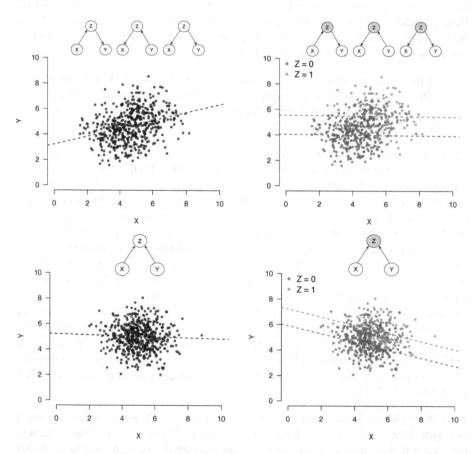

Figure 12.2. Top left: three selected DAGs that can generate a positive marginal association between X and Y ($X \not\perp\!\!\!\perp Y$). Top right: under all these three DAGs, X and Y become independent given Z ($X \perp\!\!\!\perp Y \mid Z$). Bottom left: a DAG that can generate marginal independence between X and Y ($X \perp\!\!\!\perp Y$). Bottom right: X and Y become dependent given Z ($X \not\perp\!\!\!\perp Y \mid Z$).

There is a third type of structure given by $X \to Z \leftarrow Y$ that implies a different set of probabilistic (in)dependencies: a *collider* structure. Instead of Z being a common cause or a mediator, Z is now a common effect of X and Y. The bottom left panel in Figure 12.2 illustrates that X and Y are *marginally independent*—$X \perp\!\!\!\perp Y$—reflecting the fact that they are not causally related in the underlying DAG. However, X and Y become associated when conditioning on Z; we denote this as $X \not\!\perp\!\!\!\perp Y \mid Z$. This can easily happen. A famous example is due to Berkson, who observed that patients in a particular hospital ($Z = 1$) who had diabetes (X) where less likely to also have an inflammation of the gall bladder (Y) (Berkson, 1946; Snoep et al., 2014). This negative association vanishes, however, when we look at the general population, that is, when ignoring the hospital variable Z. This is illustrated in the bottom left panel in Figure 12.2. The association is due to the fact that both diabetes and an inflamed gall bladder cause one to go to the hospital ($Z = 1$). Looking at the population of patients in the hospital—which amounts to conditioning on Z—one sees that X and Y are negatively associated; after all, finding out that a person in the hospital has diabetes indicates that that person is likely in the hospital because of diabetes and not (also) because of an inflamed gall bladder. Note that if X and Y were causally related, then they would be marginally associated. Another example of a collider structure is the following: assuming that both innovative scientific practice and sound statistical reasoning have a positive causal effect on whether a paper gets published, if we look only at the published literature we will find that innovative papers tend to use unsound statistical reasoning.

We have seen that an underlying causal DAG implies a set of statistical relationships in the form of marginal and conditional (in)dependencies between variables. The set of DAGs $\mathcal{D} = \{X \to Z \to Y, X \leftarrow Z \leftarrow Y, X \leftarrow Z \to Y\}$ imply that X and Y are marginally dependent ($X \not\!\perp\!\!\!\perp Y$), but conditionally independent ($X \perp\!\!\!\perp Y \mid Z$), as shown in Figure 12.2. DAGs that imply the same (conditional) (in)dependence structure are called *Markov equivalent* (Verma & Pearl, 1990). The DAG $X \to Z \leftarrow Y$, on the other hand, implies that X and Y are marginally independent ($X \perp\!\!\!\perp Y$), but conditionally dependent ($X \not\!\perp\!\!\!\perp Y \mid Z$). Thus, with three variables, the marginal and conditional dependencies already make it possible to disentangle colliders from chains and common causes.[2]

We have seen that different causal graphs can be consistent or inconsistent with conditional dependencies in the data. For example, both a chain and common cause structure are consistent with the finding that X and Y are marginally dependent but are conditionally independent given Z, while a collider structure is inconsistent with such a finding. It turns out that for larger DAGs, the implied conditional independencies can help in a similar way to infer which DAGs are (in)consistent with the conditional independencies in the data. While it may not be immediately obvious what marginal and conditional (in)dependencies are implied by a large causal DAG, there luckily exists a tool to derive these implied (in)dependencies. We discuss it in the next section.

---

[2] Assuming that X and Y are not directly connected. If that were the case, there would be no marginal nor conditional independencies.

Algorithmic assessment of dependence

For large graphs, it is not obvious how to conclude that two nodes are (conditionally) independent. d-separation is a tool that allows us to check this algorithmically (Geiger et al., 1990). To be able to use this tool, we need to define the following concepts:

- A *path* from X to Y is a sequence of nodes and edges such that the start and end nodes are X and Y, respectively.

- A conditioning set $\mathcal{L}$ is the set of nodes we condition on (it can be empty).

- Conditioning on a non-collider along a path *blocks* that path.

- A collider along a path blocks that path. However, conditioning on that collider (or any of its descendants, that is, variables that are caused by it) unblocks that path.

With these definitions out of the way, we call two nodes X and Y d-separated by $\mathcal{L}$ if and only if conditioning on all members in $\mathcal{L}$ blocks all paths between the two nodes. To illustrate how d-separation works in practice, we apply it to the DAG shown in Figure 12.3.

There are a number of *marginal* independencies in the DAG. For example, T is marginally independent of X. This is because any path from T to X must go through W, but W is a collider on any such path, thereby blocking it. There are many more marginal dependencies, however. For example, there is an unblocked path from X to Y through Z, implying that X and Y are marginally associated. Similarly, there is a path from V to U going through Y and W, implying that V and U are marginally associated.

There are also a number of *conditional* independencies. For example, X and Y are conditionally independent given Z. Why? There are two paths from X to Y: one through Z and one through W. However, since W is a collider on the path from X to Y, the path is already blocked. The only unblocked path from X to Y is through Z, and conditioning on it therefore blocks all remaining open paths. Additionally conditioning on W would unblock one path, and X and Y would again be associated.

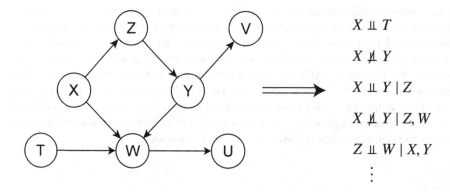

Figure 12.3. Shows a DAG and selected marginal and conditional (in)dependencies that it implies, see main text.

So far, we have implicitly assumed that conditional (in)dependencies in the graph correspond to conditional (in)dependencies between variables. We make this assumption explicit now. In particular, note that d-separation provides us with an independence model $\perp\!\!\!\perp_G$ defined on graphs. To connect this to our standard probabilistic independence model $\perp\!\!\!\perp_P$ defined on random variables, we assume the following *causal Markov property*:

$$X \perp\!\!\!\perp_G Y \mid Z \implies X \perp\!\!\!\perp_P Y \mid Z .$$

In words, we assume that if the nodes X and Y are d-separated by Z in the graph G, the corresponding random variables X and Y are conditionally independent given Z (Lauritzen et al., 1990). This implies that all conditional independencies in the data are represented in the graph. For example, the graph $X \to Y \to Z$ combined with the Markov property implies that the variables X, Y, and Z are all marginally dependent, but that X is conditionally independent of Y given Z.

The ability to derive probabilistic (in)dependence statements from causal models is an important step towards testing them. DAGs enable us to draw our causal assumptions, and d-separation allows us to derive statistical associations that we would expect in data, given our causal assumptions. If these associations are not found in the data we observe, we would need to go back to the drawing board. Finding the statistical associations implied by the causal model does not, however, imply that the causal model is correct. This is because, as we have seen in Section 12.3, there exist many causal models that can lead to the same set of statistical relationships (MacCallum et al., 1993; Raykov & Marcoulides, 2001; Verma & Pearl, 1990).

Causal effects and confounding

While different causal models can imply the same set of probabilistic associations, their causal implications differ. As an example, take the chain and the common cause structures discussed in Section 12.3. Both d-separation and the top left panel in Figure 12.2 show that X and Y are marginally associated given all three DAGs, yet their causal implications differ. To see this, suppose we intervene on X and set it to 2. The chain $X \to Z \to Y$ has a directed path from X to Y, and so under this DAG X has a causal effect on Y. In contrast, in the DAGs $X \leftarrow Z \leftarrow Y$ and $X \leftarrow Z \to Y$ there is no directed path from X to Y, and hence X does not have a causal effect on Y. The probabilistic association between X and Y under these DAGs is non-causal or *spurious* (Aldrich, 1995).

Spurious associations between X and Y bias the estimate of the causal effect of X on Y, in which case the estimate is said to be *confounded*. Confounding occurs when—using the language of graphs—there exists an unblocked path between X and Y that has an arrow into X (see also Greenland et al., 1999). In that case, the estimate is a combination of the causal effect of X on Y and effects due to these other unblocked paths. For example, in the DAG shown in Figure 12.3, the causal effect of Z on W is confounded because of the common cause X. Conversely, the causal effect of X on Y is not confounded, because there exist no unblocked paths between X and Y that contain an arrow into X. (Note that this assumes that we observe all relevant variables; see also Section 12.4.) If we were to condition on W, however, we would unblock a non-causal path from X to Y, resulting in confounding. Confounding due to conditioning on a collider is known as *collider bias* or as *endogenous selection bias* if it is done inadvertently, for example when failing to collect a representative sample as in the hospital example in Section 12.3. The fact that this bias can create spurious associations and the fact that adjusting for variables may block causal paths—known as *overcontrol bias* (Elwert & Winship, 2014)—makes clear that simply adjusting for all variables in a statistical analysis in the hope of removing confounding is misguided.

What variables, then, should we condition on to remove confounding? If we know the causal structure—an assumption we relax in Section 12.4—the set of variables we should condition on is the set that fulfills the *backdoor criterion* (Pearl, 1995; Pearl et al., 2016, p. 61). Given two nodes X and Y, an adjustment set $\mathcal{L}$ fulfills the backdoor criterion if and only if no member in $\mathcal{L}$ is a descendant of X and members in $\mathcal{L}$ block all paths between X and Y that contain an arrow into X. Adjusting for $\mathcal{L}$ thus results in the unconfounded causal effect of X on Y. Formally, we have that

$$P(Y = y \mid do(X = x)) = \sum_{\ell \in \mathcal{L}} P(Y = y \mid X = x, \mathcal{L} = \ell) P(\mathcal{L} = \ell) \, ,$$

which translates the interventional distribution $P(Y = y \mid do(X = x))$ into an observational distribution where we have conditioned on the variables in the adjustment set $\mathcal{L}$. The backdoor criterion works because it (a) blocks all non-causal paths between X and Y, (b) leaves all directed paths between X and Y open, and (c) creates no new spurious paths. While there exist causal effects which the backdoor criterion fails to identify (see for example the *front-door criterion*; Pearl, 1995; Pearl et al., 2016, pp. 85–86) the *do*-calculus provides a full account of whether causal effects can be estimated (Pearl, 1995; Pearl, 2000, pp. 85–86). For an example of estimating a causal effect, see Tutorial Box 12.1.

As an aside, note that the statistical network estimation techniques described in other chapters of this book estimate conditional (in)dependencies, drawing an undirected edge between two nodes in case they are dependent conditional on all other nodes in the network (see Chapter 6). One frequent motivation for conditioning on all other nodes in the network is to remove spurious relationships. Yet as we have seen in this chapter, 'spurious relations' and 'confounding' are causal terms, and statistical network models by themselves do not allow for causal inference (see also Dablander & Hinne, 2019; Ryan et al., 2021). Instead, they are tools to explore the multivariate statistical (in)dependencies present in data. In case one uses a statistical network model with the goal of identifying causal paths, however, it is important to be aware of the assumptions that are required for causal inference.

Suppose we wish to compare two treatments ($T = A$ and $T = B$) for kidney stones, which can either be small ($S = 0$) or large ($S = 1$). The data showing the proportions of treatments that lead to successful recovery ($R = 1$) seem puzzling: While A outperforms B for both small (0.93 vs 0.87) and large (0.73 vs 0.69) kidney stones, overall it leads to fewer recoveries (0.78 vs 0.83). Which outcome should we use to compare the two treatments?

	Treatment A	Treatment B
Small Stones $\left(\frac{357}{700} = 0.51\right)$	$\frac{81}{87} = 0.93$	$\frac{234}{270} = 0.87$
Large Stones $\left(\frac{343}{700} = 0.49\right)$	$\frac{192}{263} = 0.73$	$\frac{55}{80} = 0.69$
	$\frac{273}{350} = 0.78$	$\frac{289}{350} = 0.83$

This type of puzzle is known as *Simpson's paradox*, and the answer requires a causal analysis (e.g., Hernán et al., 2011; Pearl, 2014). We know that treatment does not cause the size of the kidney stones, but that the size of the kidney stones affects the choice of treatment. Hence the size of the kidney stones S is a *common cause* (see Section 12.3), resulting in confounding. (If these were data from an experiment where treatment was randomly assigned, confounding would not exist.) To estimate the causal effect of treatment on recovery, we therefore have to adjust for S. The causal effect of treatment A on recovery is given by:

$$P(R = 1 \mid do(T = A)) = \sum_S P(R = 1 \mid T = A, S = s)P(S = s)$$

$$= \frac{81}{87} \times \frac{357}{700} + \frac{192}{263} \times \frac{343}{700}$$

$$= 0.83 \ .$$

Similarly, the causal effect of treatment B on recovery is given by:

$$P(R = 1 \mid do(T = B)) = \sum_S P(R = 1 \mid T = B, S = s)P(S = s)$$

$$= \frac{234}{270} \times \frac{357}{700} + \frac{55}{80} \times \frac{343}{700}$$

$$= 0.78 \ .$$

This indicates that treatment A is superior to treatment B.

Tutorial Box 12.1. Simpson's Paradox and estimating causal effects.

12.4   Structural causal models

In the previous sections, we have seen how DAGs express a set of causal relations. We have also seen that these causal relations imply certain statistical relationships in the form of marginal and conditional (in)dependencies. DAGs do not, however, tell us how to test for these (in)dependencies. DAGs are nonparametric and do not specify the distributional form of and functional form between variables depicted (Pearl, 2000). For example, a DAG alone does not specify whether the variables should follow a Gaussian distribution, or whether nonlinear relationships between variables are allowed.

The core of the graphical approach to causal inference are not DAGs, but so-called *structural causal models* (SCMs; Peters et al., 2017). These are very similar to structural equation models (Bollen, 1989; Bollen & Pearl, 2013). An SCM that gives rise to the DAG $X \rightarrow Z \rightarrow Y$ may be written as:

$$X := \varepsilon_x$$
$$Z := f(X, \varepsilon_z)$$
$$Y := g(Z, \varepsilon_y) \ .$$

In contrast to purely statistical models such as regression, we use $:=$ to denote causal relations. A complete model specification requires assigning a distribution to the error terms $(\varepsilon_x, \varepsilon_z, \varepsilon_y)$ and specifying the functional forms of f and g. Frequently, researchers assume independent Gaussian error terms and restrict the relationships to be linear, which markedly simplifies analysis (see e.g., Pearl, 2013). In our example, this would lead to:

$$X := \varepsilon_x$$
$$Z := \beta_1 \cdot X + \varepsilon_z$$
$$Y := \beta_2 \cdot Z + \varepsilon_y \ ,$$

where β_1 and β_2 are the causal effects of X on Z and Z on Y, respectively, and where $(\varepsilon_x, \varepsilon_z, \varepsilon_y)$ follow independent zero-mean Gaussian distributions.

Using a DAG to visualize causal relations is a useful first step, but it is a comparatively small step given that DAGs are completely nonparametric. While one can use very general conditional independence tests to assess whether the probabilistic implications of any DAG are apparent in data (e.g., Gretton et al., 2007; Shah & Peters, 2020), more powerful tests result with stronger assumptions. For example, in case of linearity and Gaussian noise, a partial correlation of zero implies conditional independence. The flipside, of course, is that more stringent assumptions about the functional form of the relationships between variables or their distributional form may turn out to be incorrect. The equivalence of causal models in terms of their probabilistic implications again rears its ugly head (e.g., MacCallum et al., 1993; Raykov & Marcoulides, 2001), and choosing between causal models requires theoretical in addition to merely statistical considerations.

Quantifying causal effects

Given a SCM, we can compute causal effects straightforwardly. To illustrate this, suppose the SCM underlying the DAG in Figure 12.3 is given by:

$$X := \varepsilon_X$$
$$T := \varepsilon_T$$
$$Z := 1.25 \cdot X + \varepsilon_Z$$
$$Y := -0.75 \cdot Z + \varepsilon_Y$$
$$V := 0.50 \cdot Y + \varepsilon_U$$
$$W := 0.25 \cdot X + 0.50 \cdot Y + 0.75 \cdot T + \varepsilon_W$$
$$U := 1 \cdot W + \varepsilon_V \ ,$$

where $(\varepsilon_X, \varepsilon_T, \varepsilon_Z, \varepsilon_Y, \varepsilon_U, \varepsilon_W, \varepsilon_V) \sim \mathcal{N}(0, 1)$. Using this SCM, we can compute causal effects by simply changing variables in the SCM. For example, Figure 12.4 shows how the variables in the SCM change under $do(X = 2)$.

We see that while X has a strong causal effect on Z, Y, and U, it has a comparatively weaker effect on W and V and no effect on T. The distributions can be summarized in various ways; for example, we could study how the means change, which gives the *average causal effect* (e.g., Pearl et al., 2016, p. 56). However, we could also study how the variance of the variables in the system would change. We can also go beyond

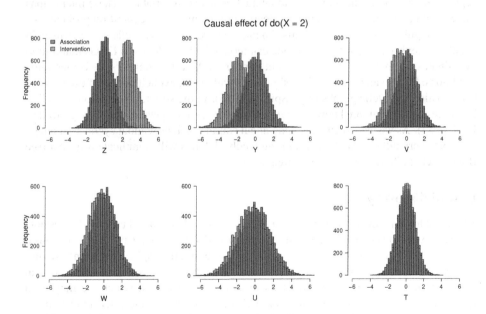

Figure 12.4. Contrasts the observational distributions of the variables in the structural causal model (red) with the interventional distributions under $do(X = x)$ (blue), using $N = 1000$ simulated data points.

so-called 'hard' interventions, where we set X to a particular value and which might be difficult to achieve in practice, to so-called 'soft' interventions, where we change the distribution of X, for example, by changing its mean (Eberhardt & Scheines, 2007).

Assumptions of causal inference

Causal inference requires a number of strong assumptions. First, in order to interpret a DAG causally, we have to assume that there is no unobserved confounding, an assumption called *causal sufficiency* (Dawid, 2010; Peters et al., 2017), and that there is no selection bias. The former is extremely difficult to rule out in practice, and unobserved confounding is the main obstacle to causal inference in observational data analysis (see also Rohrer, 2018). Second, in order to make sense of the interventionist definition of causal effects, we assume that we can intervene on single variables precisely like a surgeon. The extent to which this makes sense depends on the variable, but it is safe to say that in psychology interventions are usually so-called 'fat-hand' interventions in which we inadvertently target other variables as well (Eronen, 2020). Moreover, while there are conceptual issues with manipulating non-manipulable causes such as ethnicity (but see Pearl, 2019, for an upbeat discussion), there are additional issues when intervening on psychological variables (for a discussion, see Eronen, 2020). We agree with Hernán (2016) that the harder it is to think about a 'well-defined' intervention, the more difficult it is to interpret the putative causal effect.

The network perspective holds that psychological phenomena such as intelligence or depression arise out of the direct causal interaction between variables. These interactions can constitute feedback loops, such as sleeping problems → concentration problems → feelings of guilt → sleeping problems. So far, we have assumed acyclic graphs which do not allow feedback loops. However, one can model feedback loops as DAGs that unfold over time, such that $X \to Y$ at time point t and $Y \to X$ at time point $t + 1$. Under some conditions, SCMs can allow cyclic assignments without an explicit notion of time, which leads to directed cyclic graphs (e.g., Spirtes, 1995). In the structural equation modeling literature, such models are known as *nonrecursive* structural equation models (e.g., Bollen, 1989, p. 83). As we have seen, reasoning about causal relations without cyclic assignment is already very difficult, and incorporating feedback loops will complicate it further (see Bongers et al., 2021, for a thorough treatment).

Causal discovery

So far, we have assumed knowledge of a causal model. This allowed us to derive testable predictions about statistical relationships, and provided us with a way to identify causal effects and mitigate confounding—assuming that certain (strong) assumptions are met. We may call this approach *confirmatory*. The more difficult task is to learn the causal model from data, an enterprise referred to as causal discovery, which we may term *exploratory*. We provide a few pointers below, but refer the interested reader to the excellent overviews by Eberhardt (2017), Spirtes and Zhang (2016), and Heinze-Deml, Maathuis, et al. (2018).

The *PC* algorithm (after its inventors **P**eter Spirtes and **C**lark Glymour) is a classic algorithm that, assuming faithfulness,[3] uses observational data to learn the set of DAGs that imply the same probabilistic dependencies (Kalisch & Bühlmann, 2007; Spirtes et al., 1993). The PC algorithm, together with many other algorithms, is implemented in the R packages *pcalg* (Kalisch et al., 2012) and *bnlearn* (Scutari, 2010). The *bnlearn* package also includes a host of similar algorithms for discovering DAGs from observational data, as well as methods for assessing the stability of results through bootstrapping, similar to the methods discussed in Chapter 8.

Learning the full causal structure from purely observational data is extremely ambitious. If one has data from different settings, more promising routes become possible. The method of invariant causal prediction uses data from different environments together with the assumption that direct causal effects are invariant across environments to discover causal effects (Bühlmann et al., 2020; Peters et al., 2016; Weichwald & Peters, 2021). This has been applied to, among others, gene perturbation experiments (Meinshausen et al., 2016) and obsessive compulsive disorder (Kossakowski et al., 2019), and has been generalized to nonlinear settings (Heinze-Deml, Peters, et al., 2018) and to time series data (Pfister et al., 2019). Mooij et al. (2020) propose a 'Joint Causal Inference' framework that unifies causal discovery from multiple contexts. Invariant causal prediction methods are implemented in the R packages *InvariantCausalPrediction*, *nonlinearICP*, and *seqICP*.

Causal discovery methods based on (conditional) independence tests cannot uncover the causal direction for the case of two variables. This is because, as we have seen in Section 12.2, both $X \rightarrow Y$ and $Y \rightarrow X$ imply $X \not\perp Y$. By restricting the underlying SCM, however, one can in fact learn the causal direction. Shimizu et al. (2006) show that restricting the SCM to linear relationships with non-Gaussian noise makes this possible, and even allows learning the causal structure exactly for p variables. Hoyer et al. (2009) show that restricting the SCM instead to nonlinear relationships with Gaussian noise also allows for discovering the direction of the causal relations. Mooij et al. (2016) provide a data set of cause and effect pairs where the direction is known and validate these and other methods. These methods are implemented in the R package *CompareCausalNetworks* (Heinze-Deml, Maathuis, et al., 2018).

While the methods mentioned above come primarily from computer science and machine learning, inferring causal effects from observational data has a long history in a range of fields, including economics, psychology, and public health. Researchers from these domains frequently exploit so-called natural experiments or quasi-experimental designs to draw causal conclusions. Examples include regression discontinuity designs (e.g., Cook, 2008; Marinescu et al., 2018), instrumental variables (e.g., Angrist & Krueger, 2001), interrupted time series (e.g., Bernal et al., 2017; Leeftink & Hinne, 2020), and synthetic control methods (e.g., Abadie et al., 2010). For the latter method, we refer the interested reader to the R package *CausalImpact* developed by Brodersen et al. (2015). Lastly, Sugihara et al. (2012) proposed a method for identifying causal direction using results from dynamical systems theory (see Bradley & Kantz, 2015, for an excellent overview) that is implemented in the R package *rEDM* (Chang et al., 2017).

12.5   Conclusion

This chapter discussed a number of core tenets of causal inference. We have seen that DAGs provide a language to reason about causal effects and the outcome of interventions; how probabilistic relations follow from causal assumptions, and that the same probabilistic relations can arise from different causal models, complicating inference; how DAGs provide us with a way to reason about confounding; and how SCMs parameterize DAGs and formalize causal relations. We have also touched on a number of (strong) assumptions required to draw causal conclusions from observational data, and briefly reviewed the nascent and vibrant field of causal discovery. While causal inference is difficult, it is also necessary. The point, after all, is to change the world—not to merely look at it.

12.6   Exercises

Conceptual

12.1. Suppose we observe that an increase in variable X is always followed by an increase in variable Y. Is this enough to conclude that X causes Y? Why / why not?

12.2. Come up with a real-life example that could be represented as a *chain*, *common cause*, or *collider* structure, respectively. Then search online for cases of collider bias. You will find that it occurs uncannily often!

For the remaining conceptual questions, consider the DAG shown in Figure 12.3.

12.3. Which variables d-separate X and T?

12.4. List all the unblocked paths between Z and T.

12.5. For every path between X and V, list the variables that would block that path. What is the smallest set of variables that blocks all paths?

True or false

12.6. Statistical network models allow us to make statements about the outcome of interventions.

12.7. DAGs assume that the data follow a Gaussian distribution.

12.8. Given a DAG, d-separation allows us to read off all (conditional) independencies that we expect to find in the data.

12.9. Conditioning on a collider or any of its children blocks a path.

12.10. In order to assess the effect of an intervention, we simply adjust the structural assignment (for example, setting $X = 2$) and see what effect this has on the other variables in the SCM.

---

[3]Faithfulness is the assumption that all probabilistic independencies one finds in the data correspond to independencies in the graph, that is, $X \perp\!\!\!\perp_p Y \mid Z \implies X \perp\!\!\!\perp_g Y \mid Z$. Faithfulness is the converse of the Markov condition discussed in Section 12.3.

Additional

These two exercises are included for interested readers.

12.11. Reflect on the possibility of precise interventions in your field. List examples where precise interventions would be possible, and examples were interventions are necessarily fat-handed. There is no correct answer to this question, as your answer entirely depends on your field of study.

12.12. List all marginal and conditional independencies that can be derived from the DAG shown in Figure 12.3.

Practical

For practical exercises in R, please navigate to the appropriate folder of this chapter, available on the online *Companion Website*.

References

Abadie, A., Diamond, A., & Hainmueller, J. (2010). Synthetic control methods for comparative case studies: Estimating the effect of California's tobacco control program. *Journal of the American Statistical Association, 105*(490), 493–505.

Aldrich, J. (1995). Correlations genuine and spurious in Pearson and Yule. *Statistical Science, 10*(4), 364–376.

Angrist, J. D., & Krueger, A. B. (2001). Instrumental variables and the search for identification: From supply and demand to natural experiments. *Journal of Economic Perspectives, 15*(4), 69–85.

Berkson, J. (1946). Limitations of the application of fourfold table analysis to hospital data. *Biometrics Bulletin, 2*(3), 47–53.

Bernal, J. L., Cummins, S., & Gasparrini, A. (2017). Interrupted time series regression for the evaluation of public health interventions: A tutorial. *International Journal of Epidemiology, 46*(1), 348–355.

Bollen, K. A. (1989). *Structural equations with latent variables.* Wiley.

Bollen, K. A., & Pearl, J. (2013). Eight myths about causality and structural equation models. In S. Morgan (Ed.), *Handbook of causal analysis for social research* (pp. 301–328). Springer.

Bongers, S., Forré, P., Peters, J., & Mooij, J. M. (2021). Foundations of structural causal models with cycles and latent variables. *The Annals of Statistics, 49*(5), 2885–2915.

Bradley, E., & Kantz, H. (2015). Nonlinear time-series analysis revisited. *Chaos: An Interdisciplinary Journal of Nonlinear Science, 25*(9), 097610.

Brodersen, K. H., Gallusser, F., Koehler, J., Remy, N., Scott, S. L., et al. (2015). Inferring causal impact using Bayesian structural time-series models. *Annals of Applied Statistics, 9*(1), 247–274.

Bühlmann, P. et al. (2020). Invariance, causality and robustness. *Statistical Science, 35*(3), 404–426.

Chang, C.-W., Ushio, M., & Hsieh, C. (2017). Empirical dynamic modeling for beginners. *Ecological Research*, *32*(6), 785–796.

Cook, T. D. (2008). "waiting for life to arrive": A history of the regression-discontinuity design in psychology, statistics and economics. *Journal of Econometrics*, *142*(2), 636–654.

Dablander, F. (2020). An introduction to causal inference. *PsyArXiv*. https://doi.org/10. 31234/osf.io/b3fkw

Dablander, F., & Hinne, M. (2019). Node centrality measures are a poor substitute for causal inference. *Scientific Reports*, *9*(1), 1–13.

Dawid, A. P. (1979). Conditional independence in statistical theory. *Journal of the Royal Statistical Society: Series B (Methodological)*, *41*(1), 1–15.

Dawid, A. P. (2010). Beware of the DAG! (I. Guyon, D. Janzing, & B. Schölkopf, Eds.). In I. Guyon, D. Janzing, & B. Schölkopf (Eds.), *Proceedings of workshop on causality: Objectives and assessment at nips 2008*, PMLR.

Eberhardt, F. (2017). Introduction to the foundations of causal discovery. *International Journal of Data Science and Analytics*, *3*(2), 81–91.

Eberhardt, F., & Scheines, R. (2007). Interventions and causal inference. *Philosophy of Science*, *74*(5), 981–995.

Elwert, F., & Winship, C. (2014). Endogenous selection bias: The problem of conditioning on a collider variable. *Annual Review of Sociology*, *40*, 31–53.

Eronen, M. I. (2020). Causal discovery and the problem of psychological interventions. *New Ideas in Psychology*, *59*, 100785.

Geiger, D., Verma, T., & Pearl, J. (1990). Identifying independence in Bayesian networks. *Networks*, *20*(5), 507–534.

Greenland, S., Pearl, J., & Robins, J. M. (1999). Causal diagrams for epidemiologic research. *Epidemiology*, *10*(1), 37–48.

Gretton, A., Fukumizu, K., Teo, C., Song, L., Schölkopf, B., & Smola, A. (2007). A kernel statistical test of independence. *Advances in Neural Information Processing Systems*, *20*, 585–592.

Grosz, M. P., Rohrer, J. M., & Thoemmes, F. (2020). The taboo against explicit causal inference in nonexperimental psychology. *Perspectives on Psychological Science*, *15*(5), 1243–1255.

Heinze-Deml, C., Maathuis, M. H., & Meinshausen, N. (2018). Causal structure learning. *Annual Review of Statistics and Its Application*, *5*, 371–391.

Heinze-Deml, C., Peters, J., & Meinshausen, N. (2018). Invariant causal prediction for nonlinear models. *Journal of Causal Inference*, *6*(2).

Hernán, M. A. (2016). Does water kill? a call for less casual causal inferences. *Annals of Epidemiology*, *26*(10), 674–680.

Hernán, M. A. (2018). The C-word: Scientific euphemisms do not improve causal inference from observational data. *American Journal of Public Health*, *108*(5), 616–619.

Hernán, M. A., Clayton, D., & Keiding, N. (2011). The Simpson's paradox unraveled. *International Journal of Epidemiology*, *40*(3), 780–785.

Hernán, M. A., & Robins, J. M. (2020). *Causal inference: What if.* Chapman & Hill/CRC.

Hoyer, P. O., Janzing, D., Mooij, J. M., Peters, J., & Schölkopf, B. (2009). Nonlinear causal discovery with additive noise models.

Kalisch, M., & Bühlmann, P. (2007). Estimating high-dimensional directed acyclic graphs with the PC-algorithm. *Journal of Machine Learning Research, 8*(3), 613–636.

Kalisch, M., Martin, M., Colombo, D., Hauser, A., Maathuis, M. H., & Bühlmann, P. (2012). Causal inference using graphical models with the R package pcalg. *Journal of Statistical Software, 47*(11).

Kossakowski, J., Oudheusden, L. J. B., McNally, R. J., Riemann, B. C., Waldorp, L., & van der Maas, H. L. J. (2019). Introducing the causal graph approach to psychopathology: An illustration in patients with obsessive-compulsive disorder. *PsyArXiv.* https://doi.org/10.31234/osf.io/ed2v5

Lauritzen, S. L., Dawid, A. P., Larsen, B. N., & Leimer, H.-G. (1990). Independence properties of directed Markov fields. *Networks, 20*(5), 491–505.

Leeftink, D., & Hinne, M. (2020). Spectral discontinuity design: Interrupted time series with spectral mixture kernels, In *Proceedings of the machine learning for health neurips workshop*, PMLR. PMLR.

MacCallum, R. C., Wegener, D. T., Uchino, B. N., & Fabrigar, L. R. (1993). The problem of equivalent models in applications of covariance structure analysis. *Psychological Bulletin, 114*(1), 185–199.

Marinescu, I. E., Lawlor, P. N., & Kording, K. P. (2018). Quasi-experimental causality in neuroscience and behavioural research. *Nature Human Behaviour, 2*(12), 891–898.

Meinshausen, N., Hauser, A., Mooij, J. M., Peters, J., Versteeg, P., & Bühlmann, P. (2016). Methods for causal inference from gene perturbation experiments and validation. *Proceedings of the National Academy of Sciences, 113*(27), 7361–7368.

Messerli, F. (2012). Chocolate consumption, cognitive function, and Nobel laureates. *The New England Journal of Medicine, 367*(16), 1562–1564.

Mooij, J. M., Magliacane, S., & Claassen, T. (2020). Joint causal inference from multiple contexts. *Journal of Machine Learning Research, 21*(99), 1–108.

Mooij, J. M., Peters, J., Janzing, D., Zscheischler, J., & Schölkopf, B. (2016). Distinguishing cause from effect using observational data: Methods and benchmarks. *The Journal of Machine Learning Research, 17*(1), 1103–1204.

Pearl, J. (1995). Causal diagrams for empirical research. *Biometrika, 82*(4), 669–688.

Pearl, J. (2000). *Causality: Models, reasoning and inference.* Cambridge University Press.

Pearl, J. (2013). Linear models: A useful "microscope" for causal analysis. *Journal of Causal Inference, 1*(1), 155–170.

Pearl, J. (2014). Comment: Understanding Simpson's paradox. *The American Statistician, 68*(1), 8–13.

Pearl, J. (2019). On the interpretation of do(x). *Journal of Causal Inference, 7*(1).

Pearl, J., Glymour, M., & Jewell, N. P. (2016). *Causal inference in statistics: A primer.* John Wiley & Sons.

Peters, J., Bühlmann, P., & Meinshausen, N. (2016). Causal inference by using invariant prediction: Identification and confidence intervals. *Journal of the Royal Statistical Society. Series B (Statistical Methodology), 78*(5), 947–1012.

Peters, J., Janzing, D., & Schölkopf, B. (2017). *Elements of causal inference: Foundations and learning algorithms.* MIT press.

Pfister, N., Bühlmann, P., & Peters, J. (2019). Invariant causal prediction for sequential data. *Journal of the American Statistical Association, 114*(527), 1264–1276.

Raykov, T., & Marcoulides, G. A. (2001). Can there be infinitely many models equivalent to a given covariance structure model? *Structural Equation Modeling*, *8*(1), 142–149.

Reichenbach, H. (1956). *The direction of time*. University of California Press.

Rohrer, J. M. (2018). Thinking clearly about correlations and causation: Graphical causal models for observational data. *Advances in Methods and Practices in Psychological Science*, *1*(1), 27–42.

Ryan, O., Bringmann, L., & Schuurman, N. K. (2021). The challenge of generating causal hypotheses using network models. *PsyArXiv*. https://doi.org/10.31234/osf.io/ryg69

Scutari, M. (2010). Learning Bayesian networks with the bnlearn R package. *Journal of Statistical Software*, *35*(3), 1–22.

Shah, R. D., & Peters, J. (2020). The hardness of conditional independence testing and the generalised covariance measure. *Annals of Statistics*, *48*(3), 1514–1538.

Shimizu, S., Hoyer, P. O., Hyvärinen, A., & Kerminen, A. (2006). A linear non-gaussian acyclic model for causal discovery. *Journal of Machine Learning Research*, *7*, 2003–2030.

Snoep, J. D., Morabia, A., Hernández-Díaz, S., Hernán, M. A., & Vandenbroucke, J. P. (2014). Commentary: A structural approach to Berkson's fallacy and a guide to a history of opinions about it. *International Journal of Epidemiology*, *43*(2), 515–521.

Spirtes, P. (1995). Directed cyclic graphical representations of feedback models, In *Proceedings of the 11th conference on uncertainty in artificial intelligence*.

Spirtes, P., Glymour, C. N., & Scheines, R. (1993). *Causation, prediction, and search*. MIT Press.

Spirtes, P., & Zhang, K. (2016). Causal discovery and inference: Concepts and recent methodological advances. *Applied informatics*, *3*(1), 1–28.

Sugihara, G., May, R., Ye, H., Hsieh, C.-h., Deyle, E., Fogarty, M., & Munch, S. (2012). Detecting causality in complex ecosystems. *Science*, *338*(6106), 496–500.

Verma, T., & Pearl, J. (1990). Equivalence and synthesis of causal models, In *Proceedings of the sixth annual conference on uncertainty in artificial intelligence*.

Weichwald, S., & Peters, J. (2021). Causality in cognitive neuroscience: Concepts, challenges, and distributional robustness. *Journal of Cognitive Neuroscience*, *33*(2), 226–247.

Wright, S. (1921). Correlation and causation. *Journal of Agricultural Research*, *20*(7), 557–585.

Chapter 13

Idealized Modeling of Psychological Dynamics

Jonas Dalege[1], Jonas M. B. Haslbeck[2], & Maarten Marsman[2]

1. Santa Fe Institute

2. University of Amsterdam: Department of Psychology

13.1 Introduction

Formal theories are among the greatest accomplishments of science. Such theories have ample advantages—they make unambiguous predictions, provide insights on how to influence the system under study, and their strength and weaknesses are easier to analyze than is the case for verbal models. In addition to being useful as data-analytical models, network models can also provide good starting points for the development of formal theories as they can also be used as data-generating models. Using such models, we can investigate dynamics by varying relevant parameters in the network. In this chapter, we introduce the Ising model (Ising, 1925) as such a data-generating model and discuss dynamics that are captured by the Ising model.

The Ising model is a simple model of interactions between nodes in a network and has been originally developed for the study of magnets. Due to its simplicity and hence broad applicability, the Ising model has become one of the most well-known models in statistical physics, which studies the behavior of higher-level (or macroscopic) properties emerging from local interactions of lower-level (or microscopic) properties. Since its conception it has been applied to many different areas where we can make a distinction between micro- and macroscopic properties, such as predator-prey dynamics (Kim et al., 2005),

Cite this chapter as:

Dalege, J., Haslbeck, J. M. B., & Marsman, M. (2022). Chapter 13. Idealized modeling of psychological dynamics. In Isvoranu, A. M., Epskamp, S., Waldorp, L. J., & Borsboom, D. (Eds.). *Network psychometrics with R: A guide for behavioral and social scientists*. Routledge, Taylor & Francis Group.

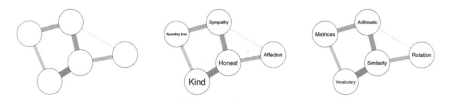

Figure 13.1. Illustration of the difference between the general Ising model and specific theories using the Ising model. The left network represents the general Ising model and the middle and right networks represent specific theories on attitudes and intelligence, respectively.

population dynamics (Galam et al., 1982), opinion dynamics (Vazquez et al., 2003), and neuroscience (Fraiman et al., 2009). For example, in Ising models of opinion dynamics, one studies how societal trends emerge at the macroscopic level from local interactions between individuals at the microscopic level. Due to its simplicity on the one hand and its richness for modeling dynamics, the Ising model has proven to be extremely useful to generate insights across many different areas. As illustrated by these applications, the Ising model is a general 'content-free' model. The dynamics of a network are specified by the Ising model but the content of the nodes are not. To turn the Ising model into a formalized theory in a given area, one needs to specify what the different nodes represent and the connections between them. This difference between the general Ising model and specific theories is illustrated in Figure 13.1. The left plot shows a network with unspecified nodes, representing the general Ising model. The middle and right plots show an attitude network and an intelligence network, respectively, which can be modeled using the dynamics specified by the Ising model.

The outline for this chapter is the following: First, we discuss the basics of the Ising model. Second, we illustrate emerging dynamics of the Ising model using the example of attitudes. Third, we illustrate how the Ising model can be utilized to model cross-sectional phenomena like positive manifolds using the example of general intelligence.

13.2   Basics of the Ising model

The Ising model set the stage for the general development of Markov random field models, and it is likely still the most used Markov random field model for binary variables (Kindermann, Snell, et al., 1980). Nodes (or spins in statistical physics terms) in the Ising model can be either in the state '-1' or '1.' The collection of all nodes' states is called the configuration of an Ising model. For example, the configuration for a five-node Ising model could take the form of {-1, -1, 1, 1, 1}. The probability of the different nodes assuming a certain configuration depends on two factors. First, the probability of a configuration is high when this configuration has low *energy*. Second, the influence of energy on probability is moderated by the *temperature* of the Ising model. Low temperature leads to a stronger correspondence between energy and probability: zero temperature implies that the system can only be in the lowest energy state, while infinitely high temperature implies that all configurations are equally likely no matter the energy. Temperature thus determines how randomly or deterministic a system behaves.

Temperatures between 0 and ∞ describe systems that are neither fully deterministic nor completely random (e.g., the system generally gravitates toward low energy, but can also show instances where it moves to higher energy states). Lower temperature results in a relatively more ordered system, while higher temperature results in a relatively more random system. For a technical explanation of calculating probabilities from the Ising model, see Technical Box 13.1.

The energy of an Ising model is affected by two classes of parameters. The first class of parameters contains couplings that describe the interactions between the nodes. These couplings can range from −∞ to ∞, with zero indicating the absence of a coupling

---

The probability of a configuration in the Ising model can be calculated using Equation 13.1:

$$P(x) = \frac{e^{-\beta H(x)}}{Z}, \tag{13.1}$$

where $H(x)$ represents the energy of a given configuration, β represents the inverse temperature of the system, and Z is the sum of all configurations' energies. As can be seen in Equation 13.1, temperature determines the extent to which differences in energy translate to differences in probability.

The energy $H(x)$ of a configuration can be calculated using Equation 13.2:

$$H(x) = -\sum_{<i,j>} \omega_{ij} x_i x_j - \sum_i \tau_i x_i, \tag{13.2}$$

where $H(x)$ represents the energy of a given configuration of the system of n distinct nodes $1, \ldots, i, j, \ldots, n$ that are in state x. ω represents the coupling between nodes and τ represents the external field of the nodes.

To run dynamical simulations on the Ising model, we can adapt Equation 13.2 in the following way:

$$H(x_i) = -\sum_j \omega_{ij} x_i x_j - \tau_i x_i,$$

where $H(x_i)$ represents the energy of a given node x_i, ω_{ij} represents the coupling of this node with a different node x_j, and τ_i represents the external field of the node. The advantage of adapting Equation 13.2 in this way is that we now can calculate the energy of each node separately. To run a dynamical simulation on the Ising model, in each iteration one node is randomly picked. Then the energy of this node is calculated and compared to the energy of the node if it were in its opposite state. The node then flips with this probability:

$$P(x_i \rightarrow x_i') = 1/(1 + e^{\beta \Delta H(x_i x_i')}),$$

where $P(x_i \rightarrow x_i')$ represents the probability that the node flips its state, x_i' represents the opposite state of the node, and $\Delta H(x_i x_i')$ represents the difference in energy between the current state of the node and its opposite state. This setup of dynamically simulating the Ising model is called Glauber dynamics (Glauber, 1963).

Technical Box 13.1. Calculating probabilities of the Ising model.

between two nodes. The energy of two nodes connected by a positive coupling is lower and probability therefore higher when the nodes are in the same state than when they are in different states, while the energy of two nodes connected by a negative coupling is lower when the nodes are in different states than when they are in the same state. The magnitude of the couplings determines how high the difference in energy and probability is between nodes that are in consistent states with the couplings and nodes that are in inconsistent states with the couplings. The second class of parameters is an external field that describes the disposition of the nodes to be in a given state. This external field can also range from $-\infty$ to ∞, with zero indicating that a node considered on its own has no disposition to be in a given state. The energy of a node with a positive external field is lower when the node is in the '1' state than when it is in the '-1' state. A node with a positive external field therefore has higher probability to be in the '1' state. In contrast, the energy of a node with a negative external field is lower when the node is in the '-1' state than when it is in the '1' state. A node with a negative external field therefore has higher probability to be in the '-1' state. The magnitude of the external field determines how high the difference in energy and probability is between nodes that are in a consistent state with their external field and nodes that are in an inconsistent state with their external field.

13.3   Idealized simulations of attitude dynamics

In this section, we illustrate some important dynamics of the Ising model using attitude networks as an example. In the network theory of attitudes (Dalege et al., 2016; Dalege et al., 2018), attitudes (the liking or disliking of an attitude object) are treated as higher level properties emerging from lower level beliefs, feelings, and behaviors. For example, a positive attitude towards a person might emerge from beliefs like judging the person to be kind and honest, feelings like affection and sympathy, and behaviors like spending a lot of time with this person. These lower level attitude elements can be represented as nodes in an Ising model, with the state of the nodes indicating whether these beliefs, feelings, and behaviors are present or absent. For example, judging a person as honest can be represented as the '1' state of the corresponding node, while not judging a person as honest can be represented as the '-1' state. The overall attitude is then the sum score of all nodes (e.g., judging the person as kind and honest, feelings of affection and sympathy, and spending a lot of time with this person). Couplings between attitude elements represent direct interactions between attitude elements that are of inferential nature and that increase the consistency of the attitude network. Different attitude elements that are similar to each other provide information on each other, which makes it more likely that if you endorse one belief you will also endorse a similar belief of the same valence. For example, one might infer that a person is honest, because one has observed this person to act in caring manner. Conversely, if attitude elements are similar but of different valence, they inhibit each other. For example, one might infer that a person is not honest, because one has observed this person to act in a egoistic way. The external field represents information that is external to the network. This external information can stem from outside the person (e.g., observing a person to be honest increases the external field of this attitude element) or from internal dispositions of the person (e.g., a person who is very trusting in general has a positive external field for judging a new acquaintance as honest). The (inverse) temperature of the attitude network subsumes several processes that increase consistency of attitudes, such as directing attention to the attitude object or importance of the attitude object. Low temperature indicates that the attitude object is of high personal importance, while high temperature indicates that one pays little attention to the attitude object. This simple setup is surprisingly successful in explaining several effects in the attitude literature. In the remainder of this section, we first illustrate how the Ising model can be used to model polarization. We then introduce the concept of hysteresis and provide a simple illustration of this phenomenon.

Polarization in the attitude literature refers to the phenomenon that attitudes become more extreme, with both the number of very negative and very positive attitudes increasing. Typical determinants of attitude polarization are the amount of thought directed at the attitude object (Tesser, 1978) and heightened subjective importance of the attitude object (Howe & Krosnick, 2017). These determinants can be straightforwardly modeled by decreasing the temperature of an Ising model. The reason to use temperature as an analogue of what happens when an individual thinks about an attitude object is that decreasing temperature increases the inferences between attitude elements. We assume that making such inferences requires attention. As can be seen in Figure 13.2 (top panels), decreasing the temperature in an Ising model indeed makes it more likely to find the system in polarized configurations, an individual is more likely to have a polarized attitude if they direct much attention to the attitude. However, the simulation we used here is static—there are no time dynamics and the distributions shown in the top panels of Figure 13.2 represent equilibrium distributions. For the next simulations, we will use a dynamic version of the Ising model, see Technical Box 13.1.

Using the dynamic simulator introduced in Technical Box 13.1, we can also model the process by which an individual transitions from a neutral attitude to a polarized attitude. To do so, we first run several iterations on the dynamic simulator with high temperature (representing that an individual pays little attention to an attitude object) and then decrease the temperature (representing that the individual thinks about the attitude object). As can be seen in Figure 13.2 (bottom panels), the dynamical simulation mirrors the results of the equilibrium distributions: under high temperature, we see a normal distribution around the sum score of 0 for the equilibrium distribution and the dynamical simulation shows a network fluctuating around the sum score of 0. Under low temperature, we see a bimodal distribution for the equilibrium distribution and the dynamical simulation shows a network transitioning between the extreme sum scores of -10 and 10. This also illustrates an important aspect of the Ising model: The processes modeled by the Ising model are egordic. Ergodicity implies that the results of taking an infinite number of single samples of identical systems are indistinguishable from the results of letting one of these systems run indefinitely.

Using the dynamic simulator for the Ising model, we now turn to a simulation of hysteresis. Hysteresis is one of the central characteristics of a dynamical system and in essence means that the current state of the system is not only dependent on the forces acting on the system momentarily but also on the history of the system. In the case of attitudes, hysteresis implies that the attitude someone holds does not only depend on the information

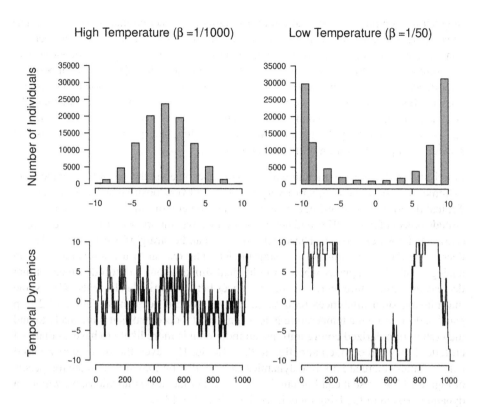

Figure 13.2. Illustration of modeling polarization using a ten-node Ising model. The upper plots show distributions of sum scores for equilibrium distributions for 10,000 networks under high (left) and low (right) temperature. The lower plots show sum scores for 1,000 time points of a network under high (left) and low (right) temperature.

someone receives, but also on the order that one receives the information (van der Maas et al., 2003). For example, if one meets a person and the first few interactions are positive, it requires a disproportionate amount of negative interactions to change one's mind. In contrast, if one had first experienced the negative interactions, one's attitude would be considerably more negative.

To model hysteresis, we again make use of our dynamic simulator. We start the simulation either with a negative or positive field acting on all nodes (implying that a person first had mostly negative or positive interactions with another person) and then increasingly shift the external field to the opposite value. We do this for different values of temperature. As can be seen in Figure 13.3, we observe hysteresis only if the temperature is sufficiently low. This implies that only attitudes of sufficiently high importance show hysteresis. If we don't care about an attitude object, we shift our attitudes in accordance with the information that we receive. In contrast, if the attitude object is important to us, it takes a disproportionate amount of information to change our attitudes. If a subjectively important attitude changes, however, the change is extreme. For example, an ardent supporter of a politician will not simply become indifferent if they receive negative information about that politician, but will change to a fierce opponent if the negative information cannot be discarded anymore.

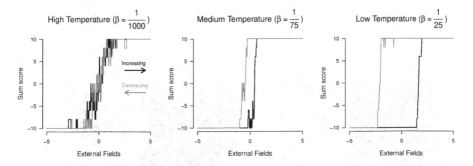

Figure 13.3. Illustration of modeling hysteresis using a ten-node Ising model. The left plot shows the dynamics of a high-temperature Ising model, the middle plot shows the dynamics of a moderate-temperature Ising model, the right plot shows the dynamics of a low-temperature Ising model. Dark grey lines show dynamics where the external fields changed from negative to positive and light grey lines show dynamics where the external fields changed from positive to negative. Larger gaps between the lines indicate stronger hysteresis effects.

13.4 Modeling cross-sectional phenomena in intelligence research

So far, we focused on how the Ising model can be used as a model of time-dependent dynamics. Many phenomena in psychology, however, are concerned with patterns in cross-sectional (single measurement) data rather than with patterns that develop over time. In this section, we discuss how the Ising model can be used to model such cross-sectional phenomena. Many prominent psychological phenomena were discovered by analysing cross-sectional data. For example, general intelligence is studied by analyzing the cognitive test scores (e.g., IQ tests) across individuals. The empirical phenomena gleaned from these cross-sectional analyses inspired the classic g-factor theory of general intelligence (Spearman, 1904, 1927). A prominent example is the pattern of exclusively positive correlations between cognitive test scores known as the positive manifold (Spearman, 1904). Another important example is the block structure in observed correlation matrices (Carroll, 1993). A well-known example of a block structure in correlation matrices is the finding that common personality tests result in five blocks with high correlations within and lower correlations between blocks. This finding underlies the Big-Five theory of personality, which holds that these blocks of high correlations represent fundamental traits of personality (e.g., extraversion). Latent trait theories such as the g-factor theory of general intelligence and the Big-Five theory of personality have a long history in psychometrics. However, recent work revealed that the phenomena that inspired latent trait theories could also be studied using networks such as the Ising model.

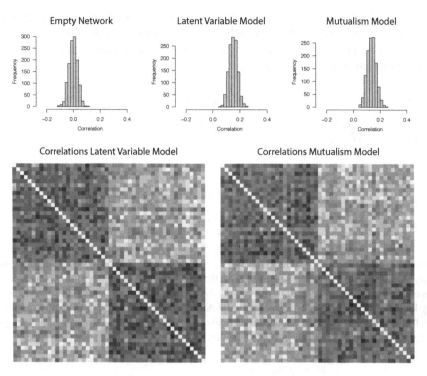

Figure 13.4. Illustration of the positive manifold and block structures emerging from latent variable models and the Ising model. The upper plots show histograms for the correlations between nodes for an empty network (left), a latent variable model where the external fields are correlated (middle), and the mutualism model where nodes are connected by couplings (right). The lower plots show heatmaps of the correlations for a latent variable model with two latent factors (left) and for a mutualism model with two distinct clusters (right).

In contrast to latent-trait theories, the mutualistic theory of general intelligence gives a dynamic account of phenomena such as the positive manifold (van der Maas et al., 2006) and revolves around the Lotka-Volterra mutualism model (Murray, 2002). We provide a rough translation of mutualism theory using the Ising model to explore with our dynamic simulator introduced in Technical Box 13.1. Mutualism theory starts with a conceptual network of low-level processes, abilities, and skills as nodes (spins in the Ising model). The network's couplings reflect mutual relations between the processes, abilities, and skills, and the external fields govern their activation. For example, a child's vocabulary acquisition feeds of improvements in short-term memory, which facilitates breaking down complex problems into manageable mental chunks. In the mutualism model, an increasing external field models a skill's growth. These external fields are random variables (vary across persons), but the couplings are fixed parameters. Van der Maas et al. (2006) start with a situation in which there are no couplings between the network's skills and uncorrelated external fields. This setup would imply that there are no interactions between skills, and that dispositions of skills are also independent from each other (e.g., an individual who has a high disposition for reading skills is not more likely to have a high disposition for mathematical skills than an individual who has a low disposition for reading skills). Fixing the external fields to zero (or another reasonable value) and running our dynamic simulation on this network set-up will generate data that lack any structural relations between processes, abilities, and skills (c.f., the correlation in the upper left plot of Figure 13.4). Thus, there is no positive manifold. Van der Maas et al. (2006) then discuss two different scenarios that generate the positive manifold. Note that in all simulations in this section, temperature is set to 1.

The second scenario correlates the thresholds. Correlating the thresholds models a scenario in which individuals who have high disposition for a given skill are also more likely to have a high disposition for a different skill. Basically, some individuals are just more intelligent than other individuals across the board. See Technical Box 13.2 for the technical details of the simulations in this section. If the couplings are absent (i.e., are all equal to zero) in the presence of correlated thresholds, this set-up is consistent with a latent variable model known as the Rasch model (Rasch, 1960). In other words, running our dynamic simulation on this network set-up will generate data that are consistent with the positive manifold. The upper middle plot of Figure 13.4 confirms that this is the case.

Things become more interesting with the third scenario of van der Maas et al. (2006). Here the thresholds are again uncorrelated (i.e., fixed), but the couplings ω_{ij} are set to a positive value. This scenario reflects the core idea of mutualism theory that "…cognitive processes have mutual beneficial or facilitating relations" (van der Maas et al., 2006, p. 845). Remarkably, running our dynamic simulation on this network set-up generates

---

Here we provide the technical details of the simulations on the positive manifold. Thresholds were correlated using the following equation:

$$\tau_{ip} = g_p + \mu_i.$$

This equation decomposes the threshold in a person effect g_p that offers a constant contribution to all skills of person p and an effect μ_i that is specific to the particular skill i.

We use the following model for two separate external fields:

$$\tau_{ip} = \begin{cases} g_p + l_p + \mu_i & \text{if skill } i \text{ is in the language domain.} \\ g_p + m_p + \mu_i & \text{if skill } i \text{ is in the mathematics domain.} \end{cases}$$

To model two different clusters, we use two types of couplings, the within domain coupling ω^W and the between domain coupling ω^B with $\omega^W > \omega^B$, such that

$$\omega_{ij} = \begin{cases} \omega^W & \text{if skills } i \text{ and } j \text{ belong to the same domain.} \\ \omega^B & \text{if skills } i \text{ and } j \text{ belong to different domains.} \end{cases}$$

Technical Box 13.2. Modeling the positive manifold with the Ising model.

data that also show the positive manifold (c.f., upper right plot in Figure 13.4). Thus, we have shown that a phenomenon like the positive manifold can emerge from the positively reinforcing relations between processes in the network. Our simple dynamic simulator offers an alternative explanation of the positive manifold that does not require the latent g-factor. Recent work established a formal mathematical relation between the two scenarios (Epskamp et al., 2018; Marsman et al., 2018).

We now turn to the situation that some cognitive domains form clusters. The typical block structure in correlation matrices of intelligence tests reflects this phenomenon. In the latent trait scenario—Scenario two—we explain the phenomenon by introducing an additional latent trait for each cognitive domain. Suppose that there are two cognitive domains: language and mathematics. We model these two latent traits by having separate external fields for the traits. In the absence of couplings, this set-up would be consistent with a latent variable model known as the multidimensional item response theory model. Running our dynamic simulator on this network set-up generates data that reflect the block pattern in the correlation matrix (c.f., lower left plot in Figure 13.4).

In the network scenario—Scenario three—the block pattern in the observed correlation matrix reflects a community structure in the network. A community is a collection of nodes that share high couplings (i.e., have stronger mutual relations). Here, the cognitive domains form the communities, and we differentiate the couplings between skills of the same domain from the couplings between skills of different domains. Running the dynamic simulation on the network in this third set-up will generate data with a block pattern in observed correlations (c.f., lower right plot in Figure 13.4). Again, we needed no latent traits to generate data consistent with the phenomenon.

With our rough translation of the mutualism model to the Ising model and our simple dynamic simulator, we can generate established cross-sectional phenomena of general intelligence. Even though this offers an alternative to the classic theory for these phenomena, the model is overly simplistic. For example, why is the network's structure the same for each individual? Given our idiosyncratic developmental trajectories, that does not automatically make sense. And what about developmental phenomena? The ideas above culminated in a novel network theory of general intelligence that builds on mutualism theory and addresses these concerns (Savi et al., 2019). This theory consists of two parts. The first part, wired intelligence, uses a specific formulation of the Ising model to account for heterogeneity (Marsman & Huth, 2021). Specifically, it uses a set-up in which the network's topology is random (varies across persons) while ensuring that we have a single Ising model cross-sectionally. That is, the particular Ising model is itself an emergent property. In this way, we can model individual networks while retaining consistency with cross-sectional phenomena. In the second part, wiring intelligence, the individual's network is grown so that developmental phenomena emerge. Savi et al. (2019) discuss two developmental phenomena. The age de-differentiation hypothesis or increasing positive manifold reflects the gradual increase of a common structure in intelligence across individuals; correlations between skills increase with age. In Savi et al. (2019), this property emerges from simply growing the individual networks. Furthermore, the authors show that we could use particular growth strategies to generate data consistent with a second developmental phenomenon. The Matthew effect reflects accumulating individual differences due to minor differences in early success in, for instance, reading. However, more research is needed to establish exactly if and how such phenomena emerge in our cognitive development.

13.5 Conclusion

In this chapter, we discussed the Ising model as an idealized data-generating model for psychological networks. We first showed how the Ising model can be used to model emergent dynamics of networks. Using attitude networks, we illustrated that simple Ising models can reproduce phenomena like polarization and hysteresis. A central theme in these illustrations is that the temperature of an Ising model has fundamental implications for the emergent behavior of Ising models. Low temperature results in networks becoming more deterministic, which in turn results in the emergence of polarization and hysteresis. High temperature, in contrast, results in networks behaving more randomly and their emergent dynamics are more simple than the dynamics of low temperature networks. We then showed that the Ising model can also be utilized to model cross-sectional phenomena. Using the example of general intelligence, we showed that Ising models can reproduce positive manifolds. Additionally, introducing communities in an Ising model results in block structures in correlation matrices. The simulations in this chapter are deliberately simple, but more complex models can be built using simple models like the Ising model as a starting point. For example, nested Ising models can be developed for the study of attitude networks in which individual attitude networks are embedded in a social network (Galesic et al., 2021; van der Maas et al., 2020). We hope that our introduction of the Ising model as an idealized data-generating model for psychological networks will inspire further investigations into the formalization of psychological theories. Such efforts can improve the testability and applicability of psychological theories—ultimately contributing to transform psychological science to a more mature science.

13.6 Exercises

Conceptual

13.1. Think of a research area within psychology not covered in this chapter and investigate whether the Ising model could be used as an idealized model for this area. What would the spins, couplings, external field, and temperature represent? Do you think the Ising model might be a promising model for this area? What are reasons that speak for the Ising model and what are reasons that speak against the Ising model in this area?

13.2. Choosing either the example of attitudes or general intelligence, provide three reasons why the Ising model is *not* a good model for this example.

13.3. Think of a finding within psychology that could be related to hysteresis. Discuss why the Ising model might or might not be suited to model this finding.

13.4. Think of a research area within psychology other than intelligence where a positive manifold has been observed as well. Discuss whether a latent trait theory or a network theory might be best suited to explain this positive manifold.

13.5. Search the literature for the phenomenon of 'critical slowing down.' Do you think this phenomenon could be modeled with an Ising model?

True or false

13.6. When temperature of an Ising model is low, the correlations between nodes are high.

13.7. Ising models always show hysteresis.

13.8. Highly important attitudes (modeled as low temperature Ising models) are more stable than unimportant attitudes (modeled as high temperature Ising models).

13.9. The Ising model can only be used to model within-person processes.

13.10. A network theory of intelligence is better suited to explain the positive manifold found for intelligence tests than a latent trait theory.

References

Carroll, J. B. (1993). *Human cognitive abilities: A survey of factor-analytic studies.* Cambridge University Press.

Dalege, J., Borsboom, D., van Harreveld, F., van den Berg, H., Conner, M., & van der Maas, H. L. J. (2016). Toward a formalized account of attitudes: The causal attitude network (CAN) model. *Psychological Review, 123*(1), 2–22.

Dalege, J., Borsboom, D., van Harreveld, F., & van der Maas, H. L. J. (2018). The attitudinal entropy (AE) framework as a general theory of individual attitudes. *Psychological Inquiry, 29*(4), 175–193.

Epskamp, S., Maris, G. K. J., Waldorp, L. J., & Borsboom, D. (2018). Network psychometrics. In P. Irwing, D. Hughes, & T. Booth (Eds.), *The wiley handbook of psychometric testing* (pp. 953–986). John Wiley & Sons, Ltd.

Fraiman, D., Balenzuela, P., Foss, J., & Chialvo, D. R. (2009). Ising-like dynamics in large-scale functional brain networks. *Physical Review E, 79*(6), 061922.

Galam, S., Gefen, Y., & Shapir, Y. (1982). Sociophysics: A new approach of sociological collective behaviour. I. mean-behaviour description of a strike. *Journal of Mathematical Sociology, 9*(1), 1–13.

Galesic, M., Olsson, H., Dalege, J., van der Does, T., & Stein, D. L. (2021). Integrating social and cognitive aspects of belief dynamics: Towards a unifying framework. *Journal of the Royal Society Interface, 18*(176), 20200857.

Glauber, R. J. (1963). Time-dependent statistics of the Ising model. *Journal of Mathematical Physics, 4*(2), 294–307.

Howe, L. C., & Krosnick, J. A. (2017). Attitude strength. *Annual Review of Psychology, 68*(1), 327–351.

Ising, E. (1925). Beitrag zur theorie des ferromagnetismus. *Zeitschrift für Physik A Hadrons and Nuclei, 31*(1), 253–258.

Kim, B. J., Liu, J., Um, J., & Lee, S.-I. (2005). Instability of defensive alliances in the predator-prey model on complex networks. *Physical Review E, 72*(4), 041906.

Kindermann, R., Snell, J. L. et al. (1980). *Markov random fields and their applications.* American Mathematical Society.

Marsman, M., & Huth, K. (2021). Idiographic Ising and divide and color models: Encompassing networks for heterogeneous binary data. *PsyArXiv.* https://doi.org/10.31234/osf.io/h3ka5

Marsman, M., Borsboom, D., Kruis, J., Epskamp, S., van Bork, R., Waldorp, L., Maas, H., Maris, G., Bork, V., Waldorp, L., van der Maas, H. L. J., Maris, G., & Marsman, M. (2018). An introduction to network psychometrics: Relating ising network models to item response theory models. *Multivariate Behavioral Research, 53*(1), 15–35.

Murray, D. D. (2002). *Mathematical biology: I. An introduction* (3rd ed.). Springer Verlag.

Rasch, G. (1960). *Probabilistic models for some intelligence and attainment tests.* Danish Institute for Educational Research.

Savi, A. O., Marsman, M., van der Maas, H. L. J., & Maris, G. K. J. (2019). The wiring of intelligence. *Perspectives on Psychological Science, 16*(6), 1034–1061.

Spearman, C. (1904). ''General intelligence,'' objectively determined and measured. *The American Journal of Psychology, 15*(2), 201–292.

Spearman, C. (1927). *The abilities of man: Their nature and measurement.* Macmillan.

Tesser, A. (1978). Self-generated attitude change. *Advances in Experimental Social Psychology, 11*, 289–338.

van der Maas, H. L. J., Dalege, J., & Waldorp, L. (2020). The polarization within and across individuals: The hierarchical Ising opinion model. *Journal of Complex Networks, 8*(2), cnaa010.

van der Maas, H. L. J., Dolan, C. V., Grasman, R. P., Wicherts, J. M., Huizenga, H. M., & Raijmakers, M. E. (2006). A dynamical model of general intelligence: The positive manifold of intelligence by mutualism. *Psychological Review, 113*(4), 842–861.

van der Maas, H. L. J., Kolstein, R., & van der Pligt, J. (2003). Sudden transitions in attitudes. *Sociological Methods & Research, 32*(2), 125–152.

Vazquez, F., Krapivsky, P. L., & Redner, S. (2003). Constrained opinion dynamics: Freezing and slow evolution. *Journal of Physics A: Mathematical and General, 36*(3), L61.

Index